Eccentric
Chuck with
the
Rose Engine.

Oval Chuck
with the
Rose Engine

Each Specimen on the other side is the result of a different Apparatus.

This page shows the effect of the same Apparatus, when employed in conjunction with the Rose Engine.

Although only one Specimen of each individual Apparatus is given, yet the Patterns, which may be considered almost endless, depend on the skill and taste of the Operator.

Geometric Chuck combined with the Rose Engine

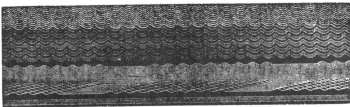

Straight Line Chuck combined with the Rose Engine.

Two
Eccentric
Movements.

One Oval
and one
Eccentric
Movement.

HOLTZAPFFEL & Co.'s *Compound Oval and Eccentric Chuck with the Rose Engine.*

TURNING

AND

MECHANICAL MANIPULATION.

INTENDED AS

A WORK OF GENERAL REFERENCE AND PRACTICAL INSTRUCTIO[N]

ON THE LATHE,

AND THE VARIOUS MECHANICAL PURSUITS

FOLLOWED BY AMATEURS.

———◆———

BY THE LATE

CHARLES HOLTZAPFFEL,

ASSOCIATE OF THE INSTITUTION OF CIVIL ENGINEERS, LONDON ;

HONORARY MEMBER OF THE ROYAL SCOTTISH SOCIETY OF ARTS, EDINBURGH ;

CORRESPONDING MEMBER OF THE AMERICAN INSTITUTE OF NEW YORK ;

ALSO OF THE FRANKLIN INSTITUTE, PHILADELPHIA,

ETC., ETC.

———

TO BE COMPRISED IN SIX VOLUMES.

———

VOL. III.

ABRASIVE AND MISCELLANEOUS PROCESSES, WHICH CANNOT BE
ACCOMPLISHED WITH CUTTING TOOLS.

Illustrated by upwards of One Hundred and Eighty Wood Cuts.

TEE Publishing
Warwickshire
England

Published in England by
TEE Publishing
The Fosse,
Fosse Way,
Radford Semele,
Warwickshire, CV31 1XE

First published 1850
Reprinted 1993

ISBN 1-85761-033-4

© TEE Publishing

Printed and bound in England by WBC Ltd., Bridgend.

GENERAL SKETCH

OF THE

CONTENTS OF THE WORK.

VOL. I.

MATERIALS, THEIR DIFFERENCES, CHOICE, AND PREPARATION; VARIOUS MODES OF WORKING THEM, GENERALLY WITHOUT CUTTING TOOLS.

Introduction—Materials from the Vegetable, the Animal, and the Mineral Kingdoms.—Their uses in the Mechanical Arts depend on their structural differences, and physical characters. The modes of severally preparing, working, and joining the materials, with the practical description of a variety of Processes, which do not, generally, require the use of Tools with cutting edges.

VOL. II.

THE PRINCIPLES OF CONSTRUCTION, ACTION, AND APPLICATION, OF CUTTING TOOLS USED BY HAND; AND ALSO OF MACHINES DERIVED FROM THE HAND TOOLS.

The principles and descriptions of Cutting Tools generally—namely, Chisels and Planes, Turning Tools, Boring Tools, Screw-cutting Tools, Saws, Files, Shears, and Punches. The hand tools and their modes of use are first described; and subsequently various machines in which the hand processes are more or less closely followed.

VOL. III.

ABRASIVE AND MISCELLANEOUS PROCESSES, WHICH CANNOT BE ACCOMPLISHED WITH CUTTING TOOLS.

Grinding and Polishing, viewed as extremes of the same process, and as applied both to the production of form, and the embellishment of surface, in numerous cases to which, from the nature of the materials operated upon, and other causes, Cutting Tools are altogether inapplicable. Preparation and Application of Varnishes, Lackers, &c.

VOL. IV.

THE PRINCIPLES AND PRACTICE OF HAND OR SIMPLE TURNING.

Descriptions of various Lathes;—applications of numerous Chucks, or apparatus for fixing works in the Lathe. Elementary instructions in turning the soft and hard woods, ivory and metals, and also in Screw-cutting. With numerous Practical Examples, some plain and simple, others difficult and complex, to show how much may be done with hand tools alone.

VOL. V.

THE PRINCIPLES AND PRACTICE OF ORNAMENTAL OR COMPLEX TURNING.

Sliding Rest with Fixed Tools—Revolving Cutters, used in the Sliding Rest with the Division Plate and Overhead Motion. Various kinds of Eccentric, Oval, Spherical, Right-line and other Chucks. Ibbetson's Geometric Chuck. The Rose Engine, and analogous contrivances, &c. With numerous Practical Examples.

VOL. VI.

THE PRINCIPLES AND PRACTICE OF AMATEUR MECHANICAL ENGINEERING.

Lathes with Sliding Rests for metal turning, Self-acting and Screw-cutting Lathes—Drilling Machines—Planing Engines—Key-groove, Slotting and Paring Machines—Wheel-cutting and Shaping Engines, &c. With numerous Practical Examples.

⁎ *The First, Second, and Third Volumes of this work, are written as accompanying books, and have one Index in common, so as to constitute a general and preliminary work, the addition to which of any of the other volumes, will render the subject complete for the three classes of Amateurs referred to in the Introductory Chapter.*

A few additional copies of the Index have been printed for the convenience of those who may desire to bind the Index with Vols. I. and II.

ADDRESS.

It is a source of extreme gratification to H. & Co., to notice the extent to which the Mechanical Arts, and more particularly that of Turning, are pursued; the Turning Lathe, in its various modifications, assisted by its appendages of mechanism, being at present absolutely essential to some stage of every manufacture.

The cultivation of Mechanics by Gentlemen who have the advantages of general acquirements and of leisure, has given rise to many ideas and suggestions on their part, which have led to valuable practical improvements. H. & Co. have a large share of these obligations to acknowledge, but it would obviously be extremely difficult to particularise them, as the ultimate form of any successful piece of mechanism is commonly the result of *many* successive modifications.

In some cases H. & Co. have been furnished by Gentlemen with the theoretical and general sketch of machines, the details of construction being entrusted partially, or wholly, to themselves; and in others they have merely carried into practical effect the finished designs.

To each of the Gentlemen by whom they have been favoured with communications, as well as to those whose names appear in this Catalogue, they beg to return their most sincere thanks, with the assurance that it would give them great pleasure to make further additions to this list under similar circumstances.

The public is respectfully invited to inspect H. & Co.'s ware-rooms, where may be seen the principal part of the tools and machines specified in this list; but of these numerous apparatus, some few are only made to order, and others cannot be always in readiness; consequently, drawings of nearly the whole are in preparation, to supply this inevitable deficiency. The drawings are often found to assist foreign Gentlemen, and others, who experience inconvenience from being unacquainted with the technical names of the various apparatus.

Amateurs who desire to receive instruction in Turning or Mechanical Manipulation generally, can receive lessons from H. & Co.'s experienced workmen, either in rooms fitted up for the purpose at Charing Cross, or at their private residences, in town or country.

No. 64, Charing Cross,
October, 1844.

PREFACE TO THE THIRD VOLUME.

In offering to the public the third volume of the late Mr. Charles Holtzapffel's work on Turning and Mechanical Manipulation, some explanation is required of the circumstances under which the work has been continued. On the premature and lamented death of the highly talented author, it became necessary either to abandon the work, or to endeavour to realize the views with which it had been undertaken. In deciding on the latter course, Holtzapffel & Co. were influenced partly by the circumstance, mentioned in the preface to the first volume, of the absence of any general treatise in the English language for the guidance of amateurs of mechanical pursuits, but principally by the desire of fulfilling the intentions of the author, and of preventing disappointment to his kind and numerous patrons, who have most strenuously urged the importance of completing the work, more especially as the first two volumes had been so favourably received by the public.

The arrangement of the subjects to be treated on in the present and succeeding volumes had been determined on by the late author, many notes had been written, and considerable progress made in the advancement of the work. The third volume being now completed, it is respectfully submitted to the public, with humble confidence that it will be received with leniency.

In compiling the present volume every endeavour has been made to follow, as closely as possible, the course indicated by the late Mr. C. Holtzapffel, and it is trusted that these efforts have been in great measure successful; but notwithstanding that every care has been taken to render this part of the work as complete and correct as possible, imperfections, omissions, and errors, have doubtless arisen; it is hoped that these defects will be viewed with liberal kindness, and pointed out for future correction.

In conclusion, it may be permitted to mention that the delay in the completion of the present volume has been considerably increased by the interruptions of ordinary business, and other circumstances wholly unavoidable. It is, however, fully expected that the fourth volume will be published within a much more limited period, as the late author's notes on its subjects are more complete, and upwards of one hundred and fifty pages had been printed under his personal superintendence.

CHARING CROSS, LONDON,
December 5, 1850.

TABLE OF CONTENTS OF THE THIRD VOLUME.

CHAP. XXXII.—GRINDING AND SHARPENING CUTTING TOOLS.

CHAP. XXXIII.—THE FIGURATION OF MATERIALS BY ABRASION.

CHAP. XXXIV.—LAPIDARY WORK.

CHAP. XXXV.—GEM AND GLASS ENGRAVING.

CHAP. XXXVI.—VARNISHING AND LACKERING.

ERRATA.

TURNING

AND

MECHANICAL MANIPULATION.

VOL. III.

ABRASIVE AND MISCELLANEOUS PROCESSES, WHICH CANNOT BE ACCOMPLISHED WITH CUTTING TOOLS.

CHAPTER XXXI.

GENERAL REMARKS UPON ABRASIVE PROCESSES.

INTRODUCTION.

THE third volume, which is now to be commenced, refers to a class of operations entirely dissimilar to those which have been described in the foregoing pages; as the former descriptions and instructions have referred alone to the treatment of such materials as admit of being cut with steel tools. In page 12 of the Introduction to the first volume of this work, it is stated that—

" The third volume will be devoted to the explanation of abrasive processes; namely, those for restoring or sharpening the edges of cutting tools; those for working upon substances to which, from their hardness or crystalline structure, the cutting tools, (made of hardened and tempered steel,) are quite inapplicable; and also to the modes of polishing, which may be viewed as a delicate and extreme application of the abrasive process, and the final operation after the cutting tools, and lastly, to the ordinary modes of staining, lackering, varnishing, and other miscellaneous subjects."

In addition to the broad distinction between the processes which have been hitherto described, and that *are* performed with cutting tools of steel, there is another conspicuous difference, namely, that in works executed by cutting, the material is mostly removed in chips and fragments, which in the case of woods may be burned as fuel, or in metals usually admit of being reunited by fusion, and again converted into ingots, bars, or sheets, for subsequent use in the arts,—whereas in the second class of effects now to be considered, or those of abrasion by various frictional processes, the removed materials are ground to powder, and are mostly unsuited to further use.

On examination of the various abrasive processes, and of which grinding for the production of form, and polishing for the production of surface, may be considered as the extremes, it will be seen there are in every case of abrasion three distinct points to be considered.

First, the substances that are to be ground or polished.

Secondly, the materials or abrasive powders by the successive employment of which different substances are polished.

Thirdly, the tools or apparatus by the agency of which abrasive substances are applied to the objects to be ground or polished.

Much variety necessarily exists under all three of these heads, and sometimes the very same substance may be referred to all of them ; for example—glass is frequently polished, as in plate glass, cut glass, and lenses.—Glass is frequently used as a polishing material when pulverized and glued upon paper.—And glass is also frequently used by watchmakers and some other artizans, as a tool or rubber through the medium of which, some of the polishing powders are applied to metal works in the act of polishing them.

The same thing may be observed of iron.—This metal in its various metallic forms is continually ground and polished.—An iron disk is used with diamond powder under the name of a *skive*, as the lap whereby diamonds for jewellery are polished,— and iron when reduced to the form of the peroxide or crocus, is used for very many purposes in the arts, and amongst others for polishing the specula of reflecting telescopes.

By way of condensing the numerous particulars that are to be offered under these several heads and rendering them easy of access and comparison, they will be arranged in alphabetical form in a " Descriptive Catalogue of the Apparatus Materials and Processes for Grinding and Polishing, commonly employed in the Mechanical and Useful arts."

The catalogue will be found to contain much general information upon, and many practical examples of abrasive processes, and will be followed by one chapter on the grinding and sharpening of tools of various kinds;—one chapter on the figuration of materials by abrasion,—in which will be described under distinct sections, some of the modes of producing plane surfaces, cylindrical and conical surfaces, spheres and spherical surfaces, and various mixed and arbitrary forms. After which, two other chapters will relate respectively to the art of the lapidary, and those of the engravers on glass and gems,—which several chapters will be materially assisted by the matter contained in the alphabetical catalogue,—before proceeding to which it is proposed to add a few explanatory remarks on the three classes of information contained in the catalogue.

SECT. I.—PRELIMINARY OBSERVATIONS ON GRINDING AND POLISHING.

First, on the substances that are to be ground and polished.

The objects or substances the grinding and polishing of which are described, will be found to include nearly all those materials from the vegetable, animal, and mineral kingdoms, which are commonly used in the mechanical arts; those especially of which mention has been made in the first volume of this work in reference to their preparation and figuration by means of cutting tools, so far as regards the substances which admit of being subsequently polished. To these will be added the cutting, grinding and polishing of various hard and crystalline bodies on which cutting tools are ineffective.

Part of these materials such as the woods, ivory, and some of the metals and alloys, marble, glass, &c., receive dissimilar treatment from different classes of artizans, the principal variations of practice will be respectively noticed and contrasted under their respective heads: but it will be readily imagined that many unimportant variations are made, that are based rather on prejudice than necessity, and the insertion of which would tend perhaps to confuse rather than assist, and therefore the ordinary routines will be alone adverted to.

Secondly, on the materials or abrasive powders, by the successive employment of which different substances are polished.

The grinding and polishing materials used in the arts will be found principally to consist of carbon, alumina, and silex, in various degrees of crystallization and admixture, and usually combined with the oxide of iron and some other substances as may be seen by their comparative analyses given in the annexed table.

TABLE OF THE ANALYSES OF POLISHING MATERIALS.

	Carbon.	Alumine.	Silex.	Lime.	Iron.	Authorities, &c.
(1) Diamond . .	100·					
(2) Sapphire . . .	...	98·5	...	0·5	1·0	Klaproth.
Ruby	...	90·0	7·0	...	1·2	Chenevix.
Corundum . .	...	86·5	7·0	...	4·0	Chenevix.
Emery of Naxos	...	86·5	3·0	...	4·0	Tennant.
Emery of Jersey	...	53·83	12·66	1·66	24·66	Vauquelin.
Rottenstone . .	10·0	86·0	4·0	...	...	R. Phillips.
(3) Flint	...	0·25	98·0	0·5	0·25	Water 1·0. Klaproth.
Tripoli . . .	...	10·0	90·0	...	...	Trace of Iron and Lime.
Tripoli . . .	...	1·5	81·0	...	8·0	{ Water & Sulp. Acid 8·5. { Bucholz.
Polishing Slate .	...	4·0	83·5	8·5	1·6	Water 9·0. Bucholz.
Polishing Slate .	...	7·0	66·5	1·25	2·5	{ Water 19. Magnesia 1·5. { Klaproth.
Bohemian Stone	...	1·0	79·0	1·0	4·0	Water 14·0 Bucholz.
Turkey Hone .	...	3·33	72·0	13·33	...	Carbonic Acid 10·33. Holme.
Pumice Stone .	...	16·0	70·0	2·5	0·5	{ Potash 6·5, Water 3·0. { Berthier.
(4) Oxide of Iron .	...	...	...	...	69·22	Oxygen 30·78. Berzelius.
Oxide of Tin .	...	...	..	...	...	{ Tin 78·34. Oxygen 21·66. { J. Davy.
Chalk	...	...	...	56·5	...	{ Carbonic Acid 43·0. { Water 0·5. Bucholz.

Carbon in its purest and most crystalline form constitutes the diamond, the hardest substance in nature, and which in the pulverized state is variously employed, as, for example, in the polishing of diamonds for jewellery; in the configuration of the rubies and sapphires used for the pivot holes of watches and chronometers; diamond powder is also used by the lapidary in slitting all stones, of course including even those which admit of being polished by abrasive powders of inferior hardness to the diamond. Carbon, in another of its conditions, also constitutes charcoal, and which, probably from the minute particles of silex disseminated throughout its substance, is employed in polishing copper and others of the softer metals.

Alumina when highly crystallized is the basis of the ruby, sapphire, and other gems which are next in hardness to the diamond. This earth, with the addition of a little silex and iron, constitutes the principal part of corundum, emery, and rotten-stone; abrasive materials that are largely employed in grinding and polishing the harder metals and mineral substances. Alumina, when decomposed, is the basis of most of the clays and loams, some of which, under different names, are likewise used in abrasive processes. It is fortunate for the mechanical arts, that emery, which is nearly the hardest and most useful of all abrasive substances, is also found in sufficient abundance to serve for every required application.

Silex, in its crystalline form, and variously coloured, assumes the names of quartz, amethyst, rock crystal, flint, agate, and when in a disentegrated state, that of sand. Silex, with the addition of a little alumina and foreign matters, constitutes also the major part of the abrasive materials known as grit or grind-stones, rubstones, hones and slaty stones, pumice stone, tripoli, and some others, all of which are softer than those mineral substances which are composed principally of alumina.

Of the siliceous abrasives, the gritty and slaty stones are very largely employed in the formation and sharpening of tools; pumice-stone, tripoli, and others for polishing metallic and other substances, softer than those which, from their superior hardness, require the employment of emery and rottenstone, abrasives that have alumina for their common base.

To those abrasive materials of which carbon, alumina, and silex form the base, may be added the oxide of iron used under the names of crocus and rouge, and the oxides of tin and lead, or putty powders, these are artificially prepared; and a few mineral substances of no great importance as abrasives are used without any preparation, such as lime and chalk.

Thirdly, on the tools or apparatus, by the agency of which abrasive substances are applied to the objects to be ground or polished.

Some of the abrasive substances are employed in the solid forms in which they are first obtained, as the grindstone, oil-stone, hones, charcoal, Dutch rush, and fish skin; a few are pulverized and mixed with various cements, thus the effective grindstone and razor hone of the Hindoo are corundum mixed with melted gum lac, and moulded into form; wax and crocus similarly mixed are used in optical works amongst ourselves; and of late years emery has been reunited into factitious stones. But metal, wood, paper, leather, cloth, or bristles, are the more common implements or vehicles, by aid of which the several powders are applied in a variety of ways, after the powders have been carefully separated into grains of similar magnitude, the sizes of which must be proportioned to the perfection of the surface to be produced, and with a gradual transition from coarse to fine. This succession is adopted upon the same principle as that in filing a coarse file is *first* used, because it may be made to act rapidly; but as the form of the work becomes gradually developed, a second cut file, a smooth, and lastly, a superfine file is used, and which *progressive* mode of action is in no case more distinctly seen in works of polishing, than in the manufacture of a highly finished razor, which is described under the head Cutlery in the following Catalogue.

The grinding powder is of course always harder than the substance to be ground, whereas the implement or grinding tool is softer, and generally agrees in form with the analogous cutting or moulding tools used for producing work of corresponding shapes in other substances, as practised in different branches of the mechanical arts. Thus turned works are often polished with blunt factitious turning tools of wood supplied with the powders; flat works require artificial saws, files, and planes; a convex surface requires a concave grinding tool, and so on.

Cleanliness should be most scrupulously observed in polishing. This remark may appear misemployed as regards a process in which various dark-coloured powders, &c. are mingled with oil or water somewhat like the pigments used by artists, and are so employed, that the hands must almost inevitably become more or less soiled; but that degree of care and order must at any rate be adhered to, which will entirely avoid the different powders and materials becoming mixed. The finest powder, if mingled with the coarse, would be comparatively inert and harmless, but a grain or two of the coarse powders, if accidentally present along with the fine, would inflict deep scratches, and completely nullify the efforts at obtaining a highly polished surface.

On this account it is desirable not only to keep the various polishing tools and powders carefully separated in boxes or bottles, but also before proceeding to each finer stage of the process, carefully to wipe or even to rinse the work in water, for the entire removal of all the previous materials employed in the earlier stages of polishing.

Having advanced these preliminary and general remarks, we shall at once proceed to the descriptive and general Catalogue, deferring until the subsequent chapters a variety of additional matters of a more specific character.

DESCRIPTIVE CATALOGUE

OF THE

APPARATUS, MATERIALS, AND PROCESSES

FOR

GRINDING AND POLISHING,

COMMONLY EMPLOYED

IN THE

MECHANICAL AND USEFUL ARTS.

N.B.—The descriptions of the Mineral Substances, are for the most part extracted or modified from those given in Wm. Phillips's Mineralogy, 3rd edition, London, 1823.

AGATE. Some of the uses of Agate in the mechanical and useful arts are described in Vol. i. page 173, and this substance although much harder than Carnelian is cut and polished precisely after the same manner, and which process is fully described under the head CARNELIAN in this Catalogue.

ALABASTER. The general modes of working Alabaster with saws, chisels, files, and turning tools, as regards its configuration, are described in pages 164-5 of the first volume, but this substance is polished quite differently by the sculptor in chiselled or carved works, by the marble worker in turned works, and by the lapidary in small objects of bijouterie and vertu ; it is therefore proposed briefly to describe these three several modes.

1.—ALABASTER.—CHISELLED OR SCULPTURED WORKS. The dull or dead parts of sculpture, after having been carved with chisels, as more fully described under the head marble, are, 1st, smoothed with bent rasps and files, known as rifflers, and, 2ndly, are afterwards scraped with a triangular scraper. 3rdly, they are additionally smoothed with fish skin or glass paper, and, 4thly, with Dutch rush used with water.

In some few instances carved works are polished, or else the ground alone from which the figures are relieved is polished by way of contrast, in such cases after the four previous stages, the parts to be polished are wrought with the end of a stick of deal or other soft wood, supplied with Trent sand

and water, and used as a pencil or brush with small circular strokes, and afterwards with a stick and putty powder with water, just the same as in corresponding works of marble, which are fully treated under that head in this Catalogue.

2.—ALABASTER.—TURNED AND POLISHED WORKS. Mr. Hall of Derby has kindly furnished the author with the following outline of his usual practice. " When the article is finished with the turning tool, take, 1st, a piece of very fine soft sandstone, (found in Derbyshire in thin beds in the red marl formation,) and apply it with water to the work, whilst it is in quick revolution moving the stone all over until there is worked up a body of mud ; 2ndly, take a wet rag and work this sludge well on the alabaster, then wash the work clean ; and 3rdly, apply a rag charged with putty powder and water, until there is a gloss upon the work. 4thly and lastly, apply another rag charged with a mixture of putty powder, and soap and water, for a short time and wipe the alabaster dry which completes the polish."

3.—ALABASTER AS TREATED BY THE LAPIDARY. Alabaster is far less frequently wrought by the lapidary than the sculptor, but as it is treated by the former in a manner somewhat different from the harder stones, it is made one of the three general examples of the lapidary's art, introduced into this cata-logue, namely, the working of Alabaster ; the working of Carnelian ; and the working of Sapphire ; which substances differ greatly in hardness. To these three descriptions are appended lists of the principal stones and other substances that are similarly treated, by Mr. Ward and other lapidaries, whom the author has consulted. In the Chapter on Lapidary Work these outlines will be filled up, and the general practice of this curious and interesting art will be considered somewhat more at length.

In working Alabaster to the required forms the lapidary first employs as usual the slitting mill, which is a thin plate of iron fixed on a vertical spindle, and made to revolve with moderate velocity, the edge of the slicer is charged with diamond powder, and lubricated with the Oil of Brick. This instru-ment which may be considered as the circular saw for small stones, is used with light pressure and plenty of brick oil.

Secondly the alabaster is *roughed*, or roughly ground on what the lapidary terms a *roughing* or *lead mill*, namely a flat circular plate of lead, fixed on a spindle similar to that of the slicer, the mill or lap therefore travels in a horizontal plane, and is abundantly supplied with coarse emery and water by means of a brush. The stone is moved to and from the center of the rapidly revolving lap, until all the marks from the slitting mill are removed, and the stone is reduced to a flat surface.

Thirdly the alabaster is *smoothed* on the same lead mill with flour emery, but prior to smoothing the stone, the grains of the coarse emery previously used, and that remain on the lap, are rubbed down fine with a smooth lump of emery stone. It would apparently be a better practice to use two different laps, and together with them emery of two different sizes ; as in the first place, the operation of smoothing the mill, is tedious, it also tends to wear away the lap towards the edge, thus degenerating the plane or flat surface into an irregularly coned surface, with which it is impossible to grind works accurately flat ; and moreover if any coarse grains of emery are left in the lap, they greatly retard the smoothing, and consequently the polishing also. Indeed it will be found a most erroneous practice, to hurry over any one process with the intention of making up for it in the next, for as each stage of the work requires successively finer polishing powders, the various steps should be continued the proportional times, or ultimate success will be more tediously, if at all attained.

As it is difficult to polish alabaster and substances equally soft on the inelastic lead lap with rottenstone, (the means usually employed for harder stones,) the following is the course ordinarily followed. After the roughing mill has been used, the stone is smoothed on a *wood mill* or a disk of mahogany used with flour emery and water ; on account of the greater elasticity of the wood mill, and the slight roughness of its face from the rubbing up of the fibres, it acts more quickly and satisfactorily than the metal tool.

Fourthly the earlier stage of the polishing is accomplished on a *list mill* with pumice-stone and water, but as the list which is wound on spirally is very elastic, flat works must be lightly applied, or they will sink into the soft face of the list mill and become rounded at the edges.

Fifthly the polishing is completed on a leather lap, or a thick piece of buff leather pasted securely on a wooden disk, and supplied with fine putty powder and water. Sometimes indeed the naked hand, and a little moistened putty powder are finally used for the last polish.

These several mills or laps are more particularly described under the article WHEELS in this Catalogue.

The following substances are worked by the lapidary in nearly or exactly the same manner as Alabaster, and descriptive articles are severally introduced in the Catalogue upon these particular substances, pointing out also any peculiarities of method pursued either by the lapidary or other artizan, as the case may be, in working them.

(Substances treated by the Lapidary like Alabaster.)

Amber.	Jet.	Opal.
Cannel Coal.	Lava.	Potstone.
Coral.	Malachite.	Satinstone.
Enamels.	Mother of Pearl.	Steatite.
Glass.	Nacreous Shells.	Turquoise.

4.—CLEANING ALABASTER.—Ornamental works in alabaster that have become soiled are sometimes cleaned in the following simple manner :—The object is first immersed in plain spring water for four or five days, the water is then changed and a small quantity of lime is added, the alabaster is allowed to remain in this solution for a further period of four or five days, after which it is only necessary to thoroughly rinse the object, which is allowed to dry gradually in the open air, and the process of cleaning is completed. Should the alabaster have been very much soiled, a single course of the above treatment may fail to restore the original whiteness ; in this case the process is repeated, and in extreme instances a third application is sometimes necessary. Earthenware pans are the most suitable vessels to be employed, as wooden tubs, especially those of oak, are almost certain to stain the alabaster.

Objects that consist of several pieces will be separated by the above process ; they are, therefore, lastly, reunited with plaster of Paris, all the parts to which the plaster is to be applied being first moistened with water to ensure the adhesion of the plaster.

In the original working and finishing of the alabaster, all the pores or grain of the stone become filled with the fine powder produced in polishing, and which gives the alabaster a more compact surface than it would otherwise present. This powder is removed by the above treatment, and the alabaster then exhibits its natural granular and sparkling appearance : should this be objected to, the polish may be renewed by the employment of putty powder, applied upon a rag or stick as described in article 1.

ALBATA or BRITISH PLATE of the best kind is treated almost like silver work. In polishing spoons made of the inferior kinds of Albata, the 1st operation, which is called *roughing*, is done upon bobs (see WHEELS, article 51,) covered with sea-horse hide with a plentiful supply of Trent sand and oil ; 2ndly, rottenstone and oil is used ; and 3dly, the finishing is done upon bobs with oil and very finely powdered lime, materials that are of the cheapest kind, and require little or no preparation.

ALBATA or GERMAN SILVER is polished by the mathematical instrument makers the same as BRASS. See that article, paragraph 4.

ALUMINA, in a compact or crystalline form is the base of some very hard mineral substances used in the arts, namely, emery, corundum, sapphire and ruby, of which it constitutes from 86½ to 98 per cent.: these are only exceeded in hardness by the diamond. See the table, page 1029.

AMBER after having been filed, may be polished 1st with Trent sand, or scraped Flanders brick on flannel with water ; 2ndly, rottenstone with oil on flannel ; 3rdly, rottenstone dry on the hand.

Turned works are generally polished first with glass paper, and then with rottenstone and oil.

The lapidary works amber just after the mode described under Alabaster, article 3, but necklaces and other ornaments in amber that are cut into facets, are more usually and better executed by the gold cutters, or those artizans who cut and polish facetted works, and by the same routine as that described in the article 3, under the head GOLD.

AMETHYST or violet quartz is cut and polished by the lapidary like CARNELIAN, which see.

AQUAMARINE, called also BERYL, and ANCIENT BERYL, is of various shades of pale yellow, green and blue, it was so named from its resemblance to sea water, and is worked like CARNELIAN.

ASTERIA. See SAPPHIRE.

AVANTURINE, a mineral which is found variously coloured and always enclosing particles of mica ; the most common colour of the base is brown or reddish brown. It is worked by the lapidary like Carnelian, but does not admit of so good a polish as the imitation.

  2.—FACTITIOUS AVANTURINE, which is glass or paste enclosing particles of metal is generally more close and brilliant than the real stone, and was much used in common jewellery, the imitation avanturine is cut and polished like other pastes, as described under the head ALABASTER, article 3. The method of making this artificial avanturine which is now lost, is considered to have originated with the Italian artists, this substance is now very scarce and much valued.

  3.—ARTIFICIAL AVANTURINE which is more brilliant than the last, and used as a microscopic object, is prepared from blue glass coloured by the oxide of copper, which is stirred with an iron rod. The oxygen from its superior affinity for the latter metal quits the copper, and unites itself to the iron, and in the act of resuming the metallic form, the copper partially crystallizes, and becomes entangled in the glass. From the striated condition the glass assumes on being stirred, the bright and metallic picture is irregular, and appears full of hills and dales, occasionally clouded with the dark coloured glass in which no copper is visible. The crystallization may be distinctly seen with a common lens of half an inch focus.

BERYL, a term that designates amongst lapidaries and virtuosi a very rich deep brown diaphanous carnelian ; it is frequently engraved into intaglios, just after the manner of carnelian generally.

BETEL-NUTS, when turned, are in general polished only with fine glass paper, and a few of their own shavings ; whiting and water may be used as for Ivory.

" BLOODSTONE is a very hard, compact variety of hœmatite iron ore, which when reduced to a suitable form, fixed into a handle, and well polished, forms the best description of burnisher for producing a higher lustre on gilt coat-buttons, which is performed in the turning lathe by the Birmingham manu-facturers. The gold on china ware is burnished by its means. Burnishers are likewise formed of agate and flint ; the former substance is preferred by bookbinders, and the latter for gilding on wood, as picture-frames, &c."—*Knight.*

  BLOODSTONE, the appellation sometimes employed by the lapidary and jeweller, to distinguish a dark green stone usually containing red spots, whence its popular name of bloodstone ; it is mineralogically known as the Heliotrope, and is considered as a variety of chalcedony : this stone is worked exactly like CARNELIAN, but is much harder and takes longer to polish.

BOB, a familiar name used at Birmingham, for small leather polishing wheels, with rounded edges, each made entirely of a thick piece of *bull-neck,* or sea-cow leather, perforated to receive the spindle, and used in polishing the_insides of the bowls of spoons and other articles. See WHEELS, article 52.

BONE.—After the turning tool or scraper has been used, bone is polished, 1st, with glass paper, 2ndly, with Trent sand or Flanders' brick with water on flannel ; 3rdly, whiting and water on woollen rag ; 4thly, a small quantity of white wax is rubbed on the work with a very quick motion, the wax fills the minute pores, but only a very small quantity should be allowed to remain on the work. Common bone works, such as nail and tooth-brushes, are frequently polished only with slaked lime used wet on flannel or woollen cloth.

BOULDERING STONE.—This name is applied by the Sheffield cutlers to the smooth translucent flint pebbles, found in gravel pits, with which they smooth down the faces of buff and wooden wheels, by abrading any large grains of emery, or other powder contained on their surfaces. See WHEELS, articles 43 and 44. The bouldering stones are usually selected of about the size of a hen's or pigeon's egg, and of a flattened form ; and the flat side becomes gradually worn down and smooth from its continual application. The term appears to be derived from the provincial use of the word *boulder,* to denote the round stones used in paving ; whence, also, boulder-setter or pavior.

Metal laps are "*bouldered down ;*" first, they are supplied with a little emery and oil, which is spread with the fingers, and then pressed into the metal and worn down fine and smooth with the *bouldering stone,* and wood laps are first anointed with flour emery or fine flour emery ; they are then well *bouldered,* and are lastly waxed by holding a small piece of wax against the revolving wheel ; these processes greatly reduce the cut of the powders ; and unless the bouldering stone is plentifully applied the *colour* or high gloss cannot be produced on the works.

BRASS is finished by different classes of artizans, by methods that are widely dissimilar, many of which are described ; and it may be considered that the same modes are also suited to the other alloys, consisting principally of copper, such as gun metal, electrum, or German silver, &c., particularly as regards parts of machinery and mathematical instruments.

1.—TURNED WORKS IN BRASS are frequently polished with emery paper alone, two sizes of which are mostly used with a little oil. For plane and cylindrical surfaces, the emery paper is wrapped around a parallel piece of stick, and for internal plane surfaces it is applied by means of a small cubical block of wood ; these methods tend to preserve the external angles from being rounded. An additional lustre is given, if required, by woollen cloths with oil and rottenstone. When the work is not to be varnished, a minute quantity of the polishing oil is left on, which somewhat prevents tarnishing.

The sliding tubes of telescopes, after having been cleaned off with fine emery paper, are brushed with a revolving or wheel brush, with fine crocus and oil, and are finished with a woollen rag and rottenstone, nearly free from oil, and rubbed lengthways, the lathe being for the time at rest.

2.—COMMON FLAT WORKS, after they have been filed up, are frequently finished first with coarse and then with fine emery paper, which is often used dry or without oil, and wrapped around a file or wooden rubber. The grain is usually laid straight, or in one direction ; at other times the works are coarsely curled by a circulating motion of the hand.

3.—SUPERIOR FLAT WORKS.—The brass plates for the mechanism of harps are perhaps more carefully treated than any of this kind. The plates of the harp machinery are planed and scraped, the mechanism is then fitted, and the second axes or arbors are ground into their respective pivot-holes with fine oilstone powder. The plates are again carefully scraped, after which they are polished, 1st, with charcoal in the stick, to remove all the marks made with the scraper and file. 2ndly, flour emery is dusted over the plate from a muslin bag, and rubbed with a piece of wood three or four inches square, covered with baize nailed around the edges, to serve as a rubber. 3rdly, rottenstone is similarly employed upon a rubber covered with two or three thicknesses of fine woollen cloth ; the plate is then washed quite clean and dried. 4thly, it is finished with a dry buff rubber and rottenstone ; the holes are then cleaned out with a feather slightly coated with dry whiting, and finally the plate is varnished. In all the processes it is necessary to follow the curvature of the plate, in order to lay the grain in accordance therewith.

Brass door-plates of the best kind are treated with nearly the same care, although immaterial variations are often made in the routine.

4.—FLAT WORKS IN MATHEMATICAL INSTRUMENTS.—Such of these as are in brass and gun metal, when left from a very smooth file are prepared first with a stick of water of ayr stone ; and are afterwards finished with water of ayr stone scraped to a fine powder, mixed with a little oil to the consistence of treacle, and applied with a smooth piece of white deal. If the work present lines from the grain of the wood, it is rubbed with the clean finger, or a buff stick smeared with oil, the polishing stuff that remains on the work being sufficient for the concluding step.

The edges of work, after having been drawfiled, are scraped with a sharp triangular scraper, applied almost without pressure, in order to avoid utters or indentations ; oilstone powder with oil is next used on a piece of mahogany, then scraped water of ayr stone, as above, and lastly, a buff stick with dry rottenstone.

5.—FLAT WORKS CURLED.—These are filed, scraped, and stoned, as by the mathematical instrument makers. The work is then clouded with a piece of charcoal and water, by means of which the entire surface is covered with large curly marks, which form the ground. The curls resemble an irregular cycloidal pattern, with loops of from one quarter to one inch diameter, according to the magnitude of the work. Similar, but much smaller marks are then made with a piece of snake-stone, blue-stone, or even common slate pencil, filed to a blunt point. The general effect of the work much depends upon the entire surface being uniformly covered, with which view the curls should be first regularly continued around the margin, the central parts are then filled in ; after which the work is ready to be varnished.

The curled surfaces are desirable, in so much as any little accidental injuries or rubbing, arising from the continued use of the articles, are less observable upon curled surfaces than upon similar pieces laid with an even grain ; and the curled parts mixed with the bright edges have a good effect. The mode was introduced by the author's father.

6.—WATCHWORK IN BRASS.—Flat works of medium character, after having been filed, are polished, 1st, with a stick of blue stone and water, and 2ndly, with a slip of box wood, with the unguent obtained by rubbing two pieces of blue-stone together with oil. The best and flattest watch works, after 1st, the blue-stone, are polished 2ndly with pewter and red stuff or crocus, and 3rdly with a piece of tortoiseshell, horn, or ivory, supplied with very fine red stuff and oil.

Tortoiseshell is preferred for the polisher, as it may be used nearly dry and leaves the fewest streaks or shades in the work ; horn is next in estimation, and ivory the least of the three ; each of which materials, and also pewter, glass, &c., are used in flat pieces from one to two inches square, which are smeared with the powders mixed with oil ; the work is then rubbed on the surface with the fingers, as if it were the muller used in grinding paint ; this produces very flat surfaces. The burnisher is sometimes used after the powders.

Most of the brass work of watches is gilt by water gilding, to prevent it tarnishing from the effect of the atmosphere. The polishing of the steel part of watchwork is described under the head MACHINERY in iron and steel in this catalogue, article 13.

7.—BRAZIERS WORKS.—The coppersmiths and braziers adopt nearly the same treatment for brass as for copper. Subsequently to the brass work having been annealed for the last time, and before it is planished with the hammer, it is generally pickled with nitrous acid diluted with very little water, and then scoured with coarse red tripoli and water to remove the oxidation caused by the fire. The work when planished is cleaned 1st with crocus and oil ; 2ndly, the oil is rubbed off with whiting ; and 3rdly, the final polish is given with dry rottenstone usually applied on an old worsted stocking.

8.—STAMPED WORKS IN BRASS, for house furniture, such as finger plates for doors, and numerous other objects stamped out of sheet brass, are treated in a manner entirely different from all the preceding, as the sheet brass when carefully rolled is left very smooth and only requires to be made bright. The stamped works are 1st cut out, 2ndly figured between dies, in a fly press, or under a stamp hammer usually called a force, 3rdly they are annealed, 4thly coloured by immersion in an acid preparation, 5thly washed and dried in saw-dust. The entire surface is now of a rich yellow or gold colour but dead or dull, 6thly the parts desired to be bright are burnished with a steel burnisher which is lubricated with water alone, or with water having a trifling admixture of vinegar or beer, and 7thly the work is varnished. The methods of colouring, bronzing, and varnishing, stamped works and others of the same character, will be hereafter detailed.

9.—CAST WORKS IN BRASS FOR HOUSE FURNITURE, including lamp and gas fittings. These works receive little or no polishing by the ordinary methods of abrasion with powders, which would be too tedious and expensive a process. The smallest and commonest of the castings, after having been cleaned by the brass founder, in the rumble, are coarsely filed and then scraped; those pieces which are more carefully moulded, as described under *fine casting*, (vol. i. p. 341,) require only the removal of the rough edges or burrs, and the tubes employed in gas works, &c., are left sufficiently smooth from the draw-plate. The several parts after having been adapted together, by aid of the file, turning tool, screws or solder, are almost exclusively decorated by the processes of dipping, bronzing, burnishing and varnishing; part of which processes, as noticed in the last article, will be treated of towards the end of this volume.

BRITANNIA METAL works, like those in hard pewter, which this alloy considerably resembles, after having been turned are in great measure finished by the steel burnisher with an abundance of oil; the final lustre is usually given with rottenstone and oil on woollen rag. Frequently a very minute coat of oil is left as a defence to retard the action of the atmosphere, at other times the surfaces are thoroughly brightened with dry whiting, applied on wash leather.

Many workmen polish Britannia metal with Trent sand and oil, to the exclusion of all other applications. This sand is probably unequalled as to fineness.

BRONZE.—The Bronze metal, (copper and tin,) is now usually called gun-metal, or bell metal, according to its proportions, and is polished after the manner of BRASS, which see articles 1 to 5.

The colours of bronzes, imitative of those tints which occur on the metal from long exposure to the atmosphere, are sometimes produced chemically in the modes to be subsequently described.

BRUSH WHEELS, circular revolving brushes are used with various polishing materials, see WHEELS articles 65 and 66. Hand polishing brushes are also used, which are made almost like nail brushes, but many of them are longer, narrower, and also softer, especially such as are used by watchmakers, jewellers, and others.

BUFF LEATHER is used in various ways for polishing ; thus it is glued on the circular edges or plane surfaces of wooden polishing wheels, and used with coarse emery, crocus, rottenstone, and other powders, see WHEELS, article 5.

BUFF STICKS are parallel rods of deal upon which strips of buff leather are fixed, either by means of glue, or by folding the leather around the ends, and securing it by iron tacks. The buff sticks are principally used with crocus and rottenstone, both with or without oil, and for most of the metals as well as various other substances ; in some few cases the buff stick is moistened with water, see TORTOISESHELL.

BUFF WHEELS are described under the head WHEELS, articles 51 to 53.

BURNISHER.—This valuable instrument is in general a piece of hardened steel very highly polished, and when judiciously applied to the smooth surfaces of metals, it imparts to them, by means of friction, or intimate contact, a polish nearly equal to that which the burnisher itself possesses.

2.—THE ACTION OF THE BURNISHER appears to depend upon two circumstances ; first, that the harder the material to be polished the greater lustre it will receive, and the burnisher is commonly made of *hardened steel,* which exceeds in hardness nearly every metallic body. And secondly, its action depends on the intimacy of the contact, betwixt the burnisher and the work ; and the pressure of the brightened burnisher being, in reality, from its rounded or elliptical section, exerted upon only one mathematical line or point of the work at a time, it acts with great pressure and in a manner distantly analogous to the steel die used in making coin ; in which latter case, the dull but smooth blank, becomes instantly the bright and lustrous coin, in virtue of the intimate contact produced in the coining press, between the entire surface of the blank and that of the highly polished die.

It by no means follows however that the burnisher will produce highly finished surfaces, unless they have been previously rendered smooth, and proper for the application of this instrument ; as a rough surface having any file marks or scratches, will exhibit the original defects, notwithstanding that they may be glossed over with the burnisher which follows every irregularity ; and excessive pressure, which might be expected to correct the evil as in coining, only fills the work with furrows, or produces an irregular indented surface, which by workmen is said to be *full of utters.*

Therefore, the greater the degree of excellence that is required in burnished works, the more carefully should they be smoothed before the application of the burnisher, and which should be cleaned on a buff stick with crocus immediately before use ; and it should in general be applied with the least degree of friction that will suffice. Cutlers mostly consider that burnishers for steel are best rubbed on a buff stick with the finest flour emery; for silver however they polish the burnisher with crocus as usual. Most of the metals previously to their being burnished are rubbed with oil to lessen the risk of tearing or scratching them, but for gold and silver, the burnisher is commonly used dry, unless soap and water or skimmed milk are employed; and for brass furniture, water with or without a little vinegar, or else beer is preferred for lubricating the burnisher.

3.—THE MOST GENERAL FORMS OF BURNISHERS.—The burnisher used by mechanicians generally, resembles in form a file of elliptical section without teeth; it is made particularly hard and well polished. For engravers in line and mezzotint, the burnishers are sometimes crooked like the horn of a cow; for watchmakers and others, they are flat so as to apply to pivots, and other burnishers for these artizans are nearly cylindrical for the interior surfaces of pivot holes, and which are applied as in using a polygonal broach. For ironmongery a narrow piece of steel is inlaid in a cross handle of wood, that is used almost like a spoke-shave, and the pressure is increased by a leather strap or bridle attached on both sides of the burnisher, in the bend of which the workman places his foot, to give the pressure. The same form of burnisher is employed in Sheffield for the springs of pocket knives, but the strap is generally omitted.

The burnisher is sometimes also fitted up with a handle at one end and a hook and staple at the other, somewhat like the paring knife used by clog makers and others (see fig. 18, vol. 1, page 26). This kind, which is called the *clog burnisher*, is much used at Sheffield, for the backs and squares of knife blades, which, after they have been made quite smooth, are moistened with the tongue and burnished with the clog burnisher, then the work and tool are wiped quite dry with a clean linen cloth, and a very gentle dry burnishing completes the work.

Fender makers and others have the burnisher at the bottom end of a pole suspended from the ceiling, or rather from a long and strong spring like that of the pole lathe, or a straight coach spring; this enables them to take a very long and equal stroke. The same contrivance, (which is also used in calendering cloth by hand,) is nearly copied, but with a piece of leather and emery, for laying a straight and dull grain on long works.

Burnishers made of flint, agate, and bloodstone are used by bookbinders and picture frame makers, also by silversmiths and jewellers, and other artizans, see BLOODSTONE.

CANNEL COAL.—In polishing flat works of this material, such as inkstands, water of ayr stone in the stick is 1st used with water; 2ndly, charcoal dust and soft soap on a flannel; and although 3rdly, for fine works rottenstone on the hand or flannel have been used, it is better to continue the second process until the completion, adding only additional soft soap with water as a lubricator. For the working of cannel coal, see vol. 1, p. 162.

For objects turned in the lathe, the water of ayr stone is superseded by emery paper.

The Lapidary works Cannel Coal just as he would Alabaster; see Article 3 under that head.

CAP.—A term used by many of the Sheffield Cutlers to designate wooden wheels, *capped* or surrounded with a ring of metal to constitute laps, the edges only of which are used, see WHEELS, articles 37 to 47, where their construction and application are described.

CARBON, when highly crystallized, as in the diamond, is the hardest substance in nature, and cuts all others. Next in hardness to the diamond are those mineral substances having for their bases alumina, silex, and the metallic oxides of iron and tin. See also the articles on DIAMOND and CHARCOAL.

CARBUNCLE.—The stone that is considered to have obtained this name, in ancient as well as in modern times, is the Almandine, or Precious Garnet of mineralogy; it is usually polished *en cabochon*, or with a rounded surface without facets, after the general manner of oriental jewellery, and is worked like CARNELIAN, as described in the following article.

CARNELIAN is the substance that has been selected as the example of the mode of cutting and polishing stones of a medium degree of hardness, the two other examples being Alabaster for the softest stones, and Sapphire for the hardest, excepting alone the diamond, which last is worked in a manner peculiar to itself, and is separately considered. As already observed, some of these subjects will be resumed more at length in Chapter XXXIV. on Lapidary work.

1.—CARNELIAN when operated upon by the Lapidary, is, 1st, slit with the thin iron slicer fed with diamond dust and moistened with brick oil; 2ndly, it is rough ground on the lead mill with coarse emery and water; and, 3rdly, it is smoothed either on the same lap rubbed down fine, or with a similar lap used with finer emery; thus far the steps are precisely as explained with regard to Alabaster.

4thly. Carnelian and stones of similar or superior hardness, and which are not smaller than about one third of an inch in diameter, are in almost all cases polished on a lead mill plentifully supplied with rottenstone and water; but this fine powder will scarcely adhere after the manner of the coarser and granular emery, or by simple pressure, and therefore to expedite the process the face of the polishing lap is *hacked*, or *jarred*, although in a manner quite different from that pursued by the cutler.

The Lapidary employs the blade of an old table knife which he holds slenderly between the thumb and finger, placed near the middle of the blade, while the front part of the edge rests on the lap, not perpendicularly, but slanted a little forwards, so as to meet the lap edge foremost during its revolution: the unstable position of the knife causes it to jump, vibrate, or chatter on the lap, and at each jump it makes a very slight furrow; these fill the face of the mill with minute lines or grooves, that serve for the lodgement of the finely powdered rottenstone. It is however to be observed that the wheel should be made first to revolve in the one direction, and then in the opposite, that the marks of the hacking-knife may cross each other.

2.—Smaller and harder stones are more commonly polished on a pewter than a lead lap, and for the smallest and hardest stones a copper lap is preferred ; but all the polishing tools, of what metal soever they may be made, are hacked as above described, and used with rottenstone and water.

3.—ROUNDED OR CONVEX STONES, or those said to be cut *en cabochon*, whether of Carnelian or even several of the harder stones, are in many cases successively wrought by means of the wood mill with fine emery, the list mill with pumice-stone, and leather lap with putty powder, precisely as described under the head Alabaster. This is done on account of the greater elasticity of these apparatus, which enables them to ply more conveniently to the globular forms of the works to be polished, and avoid wearing them in ridges or flat places.

4.—FACETTED WORKS on all stones and hard substances, are for the most part cut by the Lapidary after one of three different modes. First, for pastes or artificial stones, and many soft stones, as amber, carnelian, jet, &c., the facets are usually cut on a lead wheel with emery, and polished on pewter with rottenstone.—Secondly, for some of a harder kind but inferior in hardness to sapphires, the succession of tools is a pewter lap and fine emery for the cutting, and a copper lap with rottenstone for the polishing.—Thirdly, for sapphires, the chrysoberyl, and rarely for some few others likewise, a copper lap with diamond powder is used for cutting the facets, and a copper lap with rottenstone for polishing them.—And fourthly, with the diamond, two stones are rubbed in a peculiar manner the one against the other to cut the facets, and they are polished by means of the *dop*, and an *iron* lap or *skive* fed with diamond powder ; this process is more fully described in vol. 1, page 176.

5.—From the comparatively small size of the stones and gems that are cut into facets, they cannot generally be held unassistedly in the fingers, the stone is consequently cemented centrally upon the end of a round stick of wood, nearly like a drawing pencil. The stick when held *vertically*, gives the position for grinding the central facet or *table* of the stone, the stick is inclined to a certain angle for the eight, twelve, or more facets, contiguous to the table ; of which facets, two, three, or four series are commonly required at different inclinations, and, lastly, the *horizontal* position of the stick serves in cutting the girdle or central band around the exterior edge of the stones.

The several inclinations of the stick on which the stone is cemented, are easily determined by placing the upper end of the stick into one of several holes in a vertical post, fixed alongside the lap, and this retains the inclination very accurately and simply, but all these matters will be further elucidated in the 34th chapter on Lapidary Work generally.

6.—The following substances are worked by the lapidary in nearly or exactly the same manner as carnelian, and descriptive articles are introduced in the catalogue upon each of these particular substances, pointing out their principal external features, and also any peculiarities of method, pursued either by the lapidary or other artizan, as the case may be, in working them.

(SUBSTANCES TREATED BY THE LAPIDARY LIKE CARNELIAN.)

Agate	Elvans	Mina Nova
Amethyst	Emerald	Onyx
Aquamarine	Felspar	Opal
Beryl	Flint	Pastes
Bloodstone	Fluor Spar	Peridot
Brazilian Topaz	Garnet	Plasma
Carbuncle	Granite	Porphyry
Cat's-eye	Heliotrope	Quartz
Chalcedony	Jade	Sard
Chrysolite	Jasper	Sardonyx
Chrysoprase	Lapis Lazuli	Serpentine
Crystal	Marble	Topazes.

CAST-IRON.—When the parts of machinery that are made in cast-iron are polished they are treated as described in this catalogue under the general article on MACHINERY made of iron and steel.

THE FRONT OF STOVES, and similar bright works in cast iron, are first ground on large grindstones, and then buffed on large revolving buffs upon which a coating of emery has been fixed by glue. They are sometimes finished by a hand rubber used as a spokeshave having a piece of leather supplied with fine emery and oil, but the rubbers suspended from the ceiling at the end of a powerful spring, are also very judiciously employed in these large works. See the end of the article BURNISHER.

FIRE IRONS are often cast in iron that is afterwards rendered malleable ; which is a rapid way of producing beautiful form, combined with strength and a certain measure of flexibility, see vol. 1, page 259, the works are afterwards case-hardened, that they may admit of a better lustre, and which is generally given by grindstones, glazers, buffs and brushwheels, much the same as in cutlery but on a larger scale.

CAT'S-EYE, a mineral consisting of quartz enclosing amianthus or asbestos, and thence possessing the property emphatically described by the French as *chatoyant ;* the cat's-eye is polished just like AGATE or CARNELIAN.

CHALCEDONY, a name applied to many siliceous minerals including as varieties the onyx, sard, sardonyx, plasma, heliotrope, and chrysoprase : they are wrought like CARNELIAN, which see.

CHALK when simply scraped, or else crushed under the hammer, is occasionally used in polishing bone, ivory, and some few soft substances, it cuts much more quickly in its natural state as above, than when manufactured into the well known article Whiting.

2.—WHITING is made by grinding the chalk under a runner, washing it for the removal of sand and other impurities, sometimes met with in chalk, and then drying it in lumps. In the prepared state the particles of the chalk are so smooth, as hardly to abrade any but very soft materials, therefore the principal use of whiting when applied to the metals seems to be the absorption of the grease, from works previously polished by other means.

3.—CHALK PREPARED BY DOUBLE DECOMPOSITION.—A recent mode of preparing this polishing material, so as to obtain it perfectly free from silex, (which sometimes accompanies the ordinary kind and is a very active polishing material,) is as follows. Mix filtered and transparent solutions of the *muriate of lime*, and the *carbonate of soda*, when these are thrown in contact, the muriatic acid quits the lime and combines with the soda, making common table salt, and the carbonic acid and lime unite and fall down as an impalpable precipitate, which may be collected by filtration. The pure carbonate of lime thus prepared, polishes quickly and smoothly, and nevertheless wears away the material so little as not in any perceptible degree to injure its form or sharpness, it seems rather to burnish than abrade the work.

CHARCOAL.—Sticks of this material are very extensively used for polishing several of the metals, and the action seems to depend on the silex disseminated throughout the substance of the charcoal. Considerable discrimination is required in the selection of pieces, from the bulk of that which is prepared from small green wood for metallurgical and domestic purposes, as but few pieces possess the requisite cutting quality ; the workmen generally try it either on the teeth or finger nail.

The stick of charcoal is applied at an angle of about 40 or 50 degrees to the work, the position best suited to every piece being found by trial. Some pieces will cut rapidly and coarsely with water, others more slowly and smoothly with oil ; and pieces of good quality are very highly prized by workmen. Some artizans conceive that charcoal cuts more greedily when moistened with vinegar, but which fluid is objectionable as it stains the metals.

In the course of polishing, the charcoal picks up the abraded particles of metal, they sometimes enter its pores, and would scratch the work if allowed to remain on the charcoal, consequently two pieces are mostly used ; the one merely to clean the other by rubbing them together at their ends in the same manner that the painter rubs two lumps of pumice-stone together to clean their surfaces. In finishing delicate works, and laying the grain, abundance of oil or water should be used, so as to float off the minute particles of metal removed in the process.

The charcoal prepared from the wood of elder appears to have the decided preference especially for polishing the steel and copper plates used by engravers, both in their first preparation, and in the removal of the burrs thrown up by the graver. To ensure the possession of the true sort, it is recommended to obtain the waste pieces of elder from the rule maker, to cut them into short pieces, and then to burn them in a crucible filled with sand, in order to exclude the air, otherwise the entire substance of the wood may be burned to ashes; the kitchen or forge fire may be used, and the crucible should be allowed to cool in the embers.

The charcoal made from willow truncheons, is described as being much in esteem by the manufacturers of copper plates for engravers ; and elm wood is also stated by Mr. Thomas Gill as being suitable for making the charcoal for polishing. See Tech. Repos. vol. ii. p. 264.

CHARNLEY FOREST STONE, *See* HONE SLATES, article 2.

CHRYSOBERYL, a hard aluminous stone, of a green colour, and semi-transparent; it is chiefly procured in Brazil, and is worked like the SAPPHIRE.

CHRYSOLITE or PERIDOT, a yellow gem, sometimes tinged with green or brown, that is obtained principally from the Levant. It possesses a peculiarity, inasmuch as although it is slit and facetted just like Carnelian, it can scarcely be well polished, otherwise than by means of a copper lap with rottenstone, a few drops of *sulphuric acid* being used instead of water to moisten the rottenstone.

CHRYSOPRASE, a variety of CHALCEDONY, of an apple green colour, and semi-opaque, which is much prized by jewellers. It is cut and polished after the mode of Carnelian, and frequently of a convex form, or *en cabochon*.

CLAY, *see* LOAM.

CLOTH is extensively used as a vehicle for polishing powders of all kinds ; woollen and felted cloths are the most in requisition. Some of the felted cloths used for marble, glass, &c., and which are called *nap*, are upwards of half an inch thick. Thinner cloths, such as the stout cloths used for great coats and for the blankets of printing presses, are also employed, especially when discarded from their original purposes, and also ordinary woollen cloth, including the list, or selvedges, and so on.

Old worsted stockings are used in many trades ; linen and cotton cloths and rags are also employed, but, from being thinner, are less generally used than woollen cloths.

CLOTH WHEELS, *see* Wheels, articles 61 to 64.

COLCOTHAR OF VITRIOL, *see* OXIDE OF IRON.

CONES.—The principal modes of grinding cones will be explained in Chap. XXXIII., Sect. 3.

COPPERSMITH'S WORK, subsequently to its having been annealed for the last time, and before it is planished with the hammer, is generally pickled with sulphuric acid and water, in about equal parts, and scoured with coarse red tripoli and water, to remove the oxidation caused by the fire. The work when planished is cleaned, 1st, with crocus and oil, 2ndly, the oil is rubbed off with whiting, and 3rdly, the work is polished with dry crocus, the rubber being generally an old worsted stocking.

COQUILLA NUT receives a good natural polish by the following applications :— 1st, glass paper ; 2ndly, tripoli and oil on rag ; 3rdly, dry putty powder or rottenstone. This routine gives a more durable polish than hardwood lacker applied with friction, a mode of finish also employed.

Common turned and filed works are often finished with one or two coats of varnish, applied like paint with a brush, this gives them a coarse brightness.

Eccentric turned works in coquilla nut are polished very slightly with putty powder or rottenstone and oil on a brush ; but the tools should be very sharp, so as to leave but little or no necessity for polishing at all.

CORAL.—The red variety of this singular substance is somewhat used in jewellery, and admits of an excellent polish. When in rounded pieces, it is polished after the routine followed by the lapidary with ALABASTER ; when coral is cut in facets as for beads, &c., it is worked like CARNELIAN.

COROSOS or the vegetable ivory nut, *see* vol. 1, page 112, is polished just the same as the ivory of the elephant, and other animals ; but the vegetable ivory, apparently from its facility of absorbing moisture, alters sensibly in size and form during the process of polishing.

CORUNDUM includes very dissimilar minerals, all consisting almost entirely of highly crystalline alumina, namely,—Precious Corundum, or the Sapphire and Ruby,—Common Corundum—and Emery.—The last two are the common abrasives of the Asiatics and Europeans respectively ; and all are separately described under their respective heads in this catalogue.

1.—COMMON CORUNDUM, says Phillips, probably from its texture, has received the name of *imperfect* Corundum ; and from its hardness, and from its occasional pearly lustre, *Adamantine Spar:* it occurs everywhere from China to Bengal, and is met with of various colours, but more often of a greyish or greenish tint. Corundum is much used in India for Corundum Wheels and Rubbers, the methods of constructing which are described in the following articles :—

2.—CORUNDUM WHEEL.—" This kind of lapidaries' wheel is called in the *Tamul* language *Couroundum-sane*. It is composed of *corundum*, more or less finely powdered, cemented together by lac-resin : the proportions, by volume, consisting of two-thirds of powdered corundum, and one-third of lac-resin. The corundum powder is put into an earthen vessel, and heated over a clear fire ; and when of a sufficient heat, (which is ascertained by a small piece of the resin readily fusing,) the resin is added in portions, carefully stirring at the time, to form an intimate mixture. When made into a mass, it is put upon a smooth slab of stone, and kneaded by beating it with a pestle ; it is then rolled upon a stick, reheated several times, continually kneading it until the mixture is perfectly uniform. It is afterwards separated from the stick, laid again upon a stone table which has been previously covered with very fine corundum powder, and flattened into the form of a wheel by an iron rolling pin. The wheel is then polished by a plate of iron and corundum powder ; and finally, a hole is made through the middle of it by a heated rod of copper or iron.

" These wheels are made with a grain more or less fine, as the coarser perform the first rough work, and the finer cut the stones. They are mounted on a horizontal axis, and the workman, sitting on the ground, makes them revolve with a spring-bow, which he moves with his right hand, at the same time holding the stone with his left against the wheel, the latter being, from time to time, carefully moistened and sprinkled with corundum powder. The polish is given by wheels of lead and very fine corundum powder."

3.—CORUNDUM RUBBERS.—" The proportions generally used in making the corundum rubbers are, for the coarse, lac, 8, corundum, 1 ; for the medium, lac, 12 to 16, and corundum 1, by weight. The fine rubber is made by mixing the grindings of agates, carnelians, and the like, with lac ; and as the lapidary's wheels, upon which they are ground are made of corundum and lac also, the grindings must contain a portion of those materials; their proportion, in composition, must vary according to the nature of the stone from which they are ground ; but 6 of lac to 1 of grindings, may be considered a good proportion generally.

" The lac is first melted, and the corundum, after it has been reduced to a powder, mixed intimately with it. The composition is then moulded in the shape of a brick about $6 \times 4 \times 1\frac{1}{2}$ inch, with a handle of wood about 6 inches at one end, having a rise of about 30 degrees for the convenience of working it."

Some dentists employ old files thinly coated with a cement of emery and shell lac, in finishing the enamel or mineral teeth. The incorporation of the materials is greatly assisted when the emery or corundum is heated to the melting point of the gum resin.

CROCUS. *See* OXIDE OF IRON.

CRYSTAL, or ROCK CRYSTAL, is a popular name for Quartz, or pure crystalline silex, the finest and largest crystals of which are found in Madagascar Dauphiné, and the Alps ; the so called Bristol diamonds are nothing but fine specimens of quartz cut and polished.

The Brazilian pebbles for spectacles are lenses ground out of pure, transparent, colourless quartz, the stone is cut into slices by the lapidary, afterwards it is snipped into the form of the lenses, with nippers which resemble wide flat pliers, and are made of soft iron, in order that the quartz or glass may slightly imbed itself, to gain a hold, which could not take place with the hard steel faces of ordinary pliers ; lastly the pieces of crystal are ground into the form of lenses and polished by the optician, exactly in the same mode that he employs for glass lenses, and which will be described.

Many remarkable specimens of cups, tazzas, and other works of art have been formed by abrasion from the beautiful material rock crystal, or quartz ; some of these may be seen in the British Museum, and excite astonishment by the laborious perseverance they evince.

CUTLER'S GREEN HONE, see HONE SLATES, article 6.

CUTLERY is ground and polished with the various natural and artificial grinders, the constructions and applications of which are described under the article WHEELS in this Catalogue : the ordinary succession of the principal processes will be therefore alone adverted to in this place.

1.—FINE CUTLERY.—The manufacture of a razor blade of the best quality may be viewed as a suitable example of the mode of treating articles of fine cutlery : the succession of processes is as follows :—1st, the blade is moulded ; 2ndly, forged ; 3rdly, ground into form and *scorched*, or the black scale ground off : this is done on a dry coarse Wickersley grit stone ; 4thly, the blade is drilled for the joint and stamped with the name ; 5thly, hardened and tempered (see vol. 1, page 248) ; 6thly, ground on a wet Wickersley grit stone from 4 to 8 inches diameter ; 7thly, the shoulders of the blade are sometimes ground on a fine dry stone ; for this purpose the edge of the stone is *waxed up*, or kept keen by rubbing bees-wax on the side near the periphery to hold the particles of the stone together ; the wax keeps the stone from crumbling away, but the dry stone should be sparingly used after hardening, as it is liable to soften the edge of the blade ; 8thly, the blade is lapped on a lead lap of a diameter a little smaller than the grindstone employed in the 6th process—the lap scarcely alters in course of use, and gives the true curve to the surfaces ; 9thly, the tang and back are glazed on a leather glazer ; 10thly, the razor blade is polished on a soft buff wheel fed with dry crocus and revolving very slowly. This completes the manufacture of the blade, which is then ready to be handled preparatory to the setting, which will be described in Chapter XXXII.

The best penknife blades and scissors are treated in a similar manner to the above.

2.—COMMON CUTLERY.—All work should be scorched or dry ground to remove the scale before hardening, but this is frequently omitted in common works, and the usual routine after hardening is, 1st, the coarse wet stone ; 2ndly, the fine wet stone ; and, 3rdly, the buff with fine emery. Sometimes one or more intermediate stages between the extremes of the common and best cutlery are resorted to, according to price. Common razors, after being hardened, are, 1st, ground on a wet stone from 12 to 15 inches diameter ; 2ndly, lapped ; and, 3rdly, polished.

3.—EDGE TOOLS are treated the same as common cutlery.

DEVONSHIRE OILSTONE, see HONE SLATES.

DIAMOND, this remarkable and most useful gem has been considered at some length in the first volume, pages 175—180—first as regards the processes of splitting, cutting, and polishing diamonds for jewellery,—then its use in the hands of the glass-cutter and glazier—and lastly several of the uses of the diamond as tools, and which applications include the formation of the jewelled holes of ruby and sapphire for watches and chronometers, every process of which requires the intervention of the diamond.

In this place it is proposed to describe the three different modes in which the diamond powder is prepared for the use of various artizans, as the subsequent chapters will treat of its practical application by the lapidary, gem-engraver, and others.

1.—DIAMOND POWDER FOR LAPIDARIES' USE.—Lapidaries generally purchase small imperfect diamonds, and the fragments removed by splitting or cleavage, in preparing stones for jewellery. These fragments are crushed in a hardened steel mortar with a cylindrical hole about half an inch diameter, and nearly two inches deep, the bottom of the cavity is hemispherical or constitutes perhaps the third part only of the circle, the pestle almost fits the aperture of the mortar and is curved to the same degree, there is also a cover that fits a recess in the mortar to prevent the escape of any of the valuable dust.

The pestle is struck a few blows with a light hammer, and is twisted round between each blow, this readily crushes the diamond, which, although so incomparably hard, is brittle from its crystalline structure. The fragments are carefully collected, and mixed with a little of the oil of brick, in a small cup or any convenient vessel, which should have a cover to keep the prepared diamond from being wasted. When not wanted for immediate use, the prepared diamond is kept in a pasty condition between two very small watch glasses, cemented with soft wax around their edges.

2.—DIAMOND POWDER FOR SEAL ENGRAVERS.—This is required to be much more finely pulverized than for lapidary work, therefore having been crushed as above, the fragments are ground into a thick paste, with a few drops of olive oil, in another pestle and mortar of hardened steel, the surfaces of which are both exactly spherical with a curvature of from one to two inches radius ; this mortar has a tin cover that it may serve as the recipient for the powder which has been ground. Sometimes for reducing the powder after it has been crushed, flat grinders of hardened steel are employed, but these are less generally used than the spherical form. Rough diamonds of a dark steely colour are generally selected by the seal engravers, as these are considered the hardest stones.

3.—DIAMOND POWDER FOR WATCH JEWELLERS.—These artizans who use much larger quantities of diamond powder than the above, for cutting as well as for polishing rubies, sapphires, and topazes, pursue a different method. They purchase the fine dust, or *diamond bort*, that is rubbed off stones used for jewellery in the act of cutting them into facets, in which process two diamonds are operated upon at once, and caused mutually to abrade each other in forming the one facet on each stone ; see vol. 1, page 176. The diamond bort is usually washed for its separation into two or three sizes, exactly after the manner of washing emery, except that the process is carried on upon a very much smaller scale, and the finest olive oil is used instead of water, the diamond powder is generally laid by under a stratum of oil to prevent waste ; oil is employed because of its viscidity, it does not allow the diamond to subside so quickly as water, and it is moreover the fluid always employed in the using and preservation of the diamond by these artizans.

4.—THE APPLICATION OF DIAMOND POWDER to the splitting or sawing of minerals will be described in the chapter XXXIV. on Lapidary work. The coarser diamond powder used for grinding or cutting is generally burnished into the surface of the iron lap or *skive* of the diamond worker, and frequently also into the iron, copper, or other laps used by different artizans : in cutting sapphires the lapidary works the diamond powder into the copper lap, with a smooth piece of agate applied with gentle pressure. The finer diamond powder used for polishing, is simply applied on the surface of the tools, with the finger, or a small flattened wire used as a spatula. The gem engraver puts the diamond in minute hollowed disks of tin, two of which in fact are soldered to a strip of tin, and worn on the forefinger of the left hand as a ring: the one disk, of half an inch diameter, contains the mixed diamond paste, the other disk, one or two drops of the oil of brick, with which the tool is frequently lubricated.

5.—FICTITIOUS DIAMONDS.—The white sapphire is sometimes used in jewellery as a substitute for the diamond, and the zircon is said also to be so employed when deprived of its colour by heat : the so-called Bristol diamonds are crystals of quartz cut and polished, but those imitations which are considered to come the nearest to real diamonds, in point of lustre or colour, though not in hardness, are met with amongst the pastes of the first quality, which are made artificially, and polished on pewter wheels with rottenstone, and not on copper wheels, like most of the hard gems.

DUTCH RUSH, or the *Equisetum Hyemale*, is said to be a native of Scotland, and to thrive best in the marshy places in mountainous districts ; it is gathered in pieces two or three feet long, which are intersected by knots at distances of four to six inches. The rush is usually of the size of a writing quill, of a greenish-grey colour, with a groovy surface that feels rough like fine glass paper, from the quantity of silex disseminated throughout its exterior surface, and upon which circumstance depends its suitability to polishing hardwoods, alabaster, marbles, and some other substances. According to the analysis of Sprengel, Dutch Rush, when dry, contains rather more than 13 per cent. of ashes, viz. Silex, 6·38, Carb. Lime, 5·51, Potash salts, ·79, and Alumina ·46.

For the application of Dutch Rush, see WOOD, article 5, and ALABASTER, article 1.

EDGE TOOLS are treated of under the head CUTLERY.

ELECTRUM or GERMAN SILVER.—See Silver, Albata, and Brass. The respective modes being used, according to the nature of the works made in this triple alloy, which differs greatly as to value and quality.

ELVANS, the modes of working and polishing porphyry and granite, and also the elvans, which are of intermediate character between these two, are described in pages 169 to 172 of the first volume. By the lapidary, the elvans and porphyries are wrought like CARNELIAN, the granite somewhat differently, on account of its unequal hardness, see GRANITE.

EMERY.

1.—ORDINARY PREPARATION OF EMERY.—The following is the manufacturers' ordinary process ; the lumps of emery stone are broken up precisely after the manner of stone for repairing Macadamized roads, and into lumps of similar size. The lumps are then crushed under stampers such as are used for pounding metallic ores, and driven by water or steam power ; the stampers are considered to leave the particles more angular than they would be if ground under runners, a mode sometimes employed. The coarse powder is then sifted through sieves of wire cloth, which are generally cylindrical, like the bolting cylinders of corn mills, but the sieves are covered with wire cloth, having in general about 90 to 16 wires to the inch. The following table shows the numbers of wires usually contained in the sieves, and the names of the kinds respectively produced by them :—

16. Corn emery.	60. Coarse flour emery
24. Coarse grinding ———	70. Flour ———
36. Grinding ———	80. Fine flour ———
46. Fine grinding ———	90. Superfine flour ———
53. Super grinding ———	

No. 16 sieve gives emery of about the size of mustard seed, and coarser fragments extending nearly to the size of peppercorns, are also occasionally prepared for the use of engineers.

The sieves have sometimes as many as 120 wires in the inch, the very fine sizes of emery are however more commonly sifted through lawn sieves; but the finest emery that is obtained from the manufacturers, is that which floats in the atmosphere of the stamping room, and is deposited on the beams and shelves, from which it is occasionally collected.

The manufacturers rarely or never wash the emery, which is mostly done by the glass workers, opticians, and such others as require a greater degree of precision than can be obtained by sifting.

2.—WASHING EMERY BY HAND.—Washing-over or elutriation, as the process is called by chemists, is a valuable application of the law of gravity to the chemical, metallurgical and mechanical arts. Thus the alluvial deposits of some of the tropical rivers are washed for the separation of the particles of gold they contain. A small portion of the mud of the river is stirred in a large quantity of water contained in a broad shallow basin, the gold being several times as heavy as the earthy particles quickly subsides, and the mud which remains suspended for a long period in the water, is removed by pouring off the water from the valuable sediment.

In a similar manner the particles of emery and other powders may be separated according to their magnitudes, in a more accurate manner than can be accomplished by sieves. A portion of emery powder of uncertain size is thoroughly well mixed in a large quantity of water, as in a common wash hand basin, and at the end of 10 seconds the liquid is poured off from the sediment which has fallen down in that period ; the sediment is laid aside in a separate vessel. The bulk is again stirred and poured off at 10 seconds, and this second sediment added to the first, and which process is repeated until no further sediment is deposited in the period of 10 seconds ; the process requires watchfulness and a steady hand. A fresh deposit is similarly collected from the residue after a longer period of rest, say 20 seconds, until the whole quantity of emery is divided into grains of so many sizes, as may be required for the particular branch of manufacture for which it is intended ; thus—

3.—EMERY FOR THE CONSTRUCTION OF MECHANISM.—The author has been for many years in the habit of employing emery of twelve degrees of fineness, part of them prepared by himself by washing over, namely :

No. 1. Corn emery of commerce prepared by sifting
  „ 2. Grinding   „
  „ 3. Fine grinding   „
  „ 4. Superfine grinding   „
  „ 5. Deposited at the end of 2 seconds.
  „ 6.   „   5 „
  „ 7.   „   10 „
  „ 8.   „   20 „
  „ 9.   „   60 „
  „ 10.   „   3 minutes.
  „ 11.   „   15 „
  „ 12.   „   60 „

The emeries of the sizes 5 to 12 are preserved in glass bottles, to prevent them from becoming accidentally mixed or contaminated with foreign substances.

4.—EMERY FOR OPTICAL PURPOSES.—Mr. ROSS mixes four pounds of the flour emery of commerce, with 1 ounce of powdered gum arabic, and then throws the powder into 2 gallons of clean water. He collects deposits, as above described, at the end of 10 seconds, 30 seconds, 2 minutes, 10, 20, and 60 minutes, and that which is not deposited by one hour's subsidence is thrown away as useless for grinding lenses. The use of the gum arabic, which renders the water slightly viscid, was recommended by Dr. Green for preparing red oxide of iron, for polishing specula. See Trans. Soc. of Arts. Vol. L. p. 152.

5.—WASHING EMERY IN THE LARGE WAY.—Washing emery by hand as above explained is far too tedious for those who require very large quantities of emery, such as the manufacturers of plate glass and some others, who generally adopt the following mode :—Twelve or more cylinders of sheet copper, of the common height of about two feet, and varying from about 3, 5, 8 to 30 or 40 inches in diameter, are placed exactly level, and communicating at their upper edges, each to the next, by small troughs or channels ; the largest vessel has also a waste pipe near the top.

At the commencement of the process, the cylinders are all filled to the brim with clean water, the pulverised emery is then churned up, with abundance of water in another vessel, and allowed to run into the smallest or the three inch cylinder, through a tube opposite the gutter leading to the second cylinder. The water, during its short passage across the three inch cylinder, deposits in that vessel, such of the coarsest emery as will not bear suspension for that limited time ; the particles next finer, are deposited in the second or the five inch cylinder, during the somewhat longer time the mixed stream takes in passing the brim of that vessel and so on. Eventually the water forms a very languid eddy in the largest cylinder, and deposits therein the very fine particles that have remained in suspension until this period, and the water lastly escapes by the waste pipe nearly or entirely free from emery.

In this simple yet elegant arrangement, *time* is also the measure of the particles respectively deposited in the 12 or more vessels, their number being determined by the quantity of sizes respectively required in the manufacture to which the emery is applied. When the vessels are to a certain degree filled with emery, the process is stopped, they are emptied, the emery is carefully dried and laid by, and the process is recommenced.

6.—EMERY PAPER is prepared like glass paper, and of about six degrees of coarseness. The powders sifted through the sieves with 30 and 90 meshes per linear inch being in general the coarsest and finest sizes employed. When used by artizans, the emery paper is commonly wrapped around a file or a slip of wood, and applied just like a file, with or without oil, according to circumstances. The emery paper cuts more smoothly with oil, but leaves the work dull.

7.—EMERY CLOTH only differs from emery paper in the employment of thin cotton cloth instead of paper, as the material upon which the emery is fixed by means of glue. The emery cloth, when folded around a file, does not ply so readily to it as emery paper, and is apt to unroll, therefore smiths, engineers and others, give the preference to the emery paper and emery sticks ; but for household and other purposes, where the hand alone is used, the greater durability of the cloth is advantageous. Edwards' patent for emery cloth was taken out in December 1830.

8.—EMERY STICKS, are rods of deal about 8 to 12 inches long, planed up square, or with one side rounded like the half round file. Nails are driven into each end of the sticks as temporary handles, they are then brushed over one at a time, with thin glue, and dabbed at all parts in a heap of emery powder, and knocked on one end to shake of the excess, two coats of glue and emery are generally used. The emery sticks are much more economical than emery paper wrapped on a file, which is liable to be torn.

9.—EMERY CAKE consists of emery mixed with a little suet chopped small, rendered down, and mixed with a very little bees' wax, so as to constitute a solid lump, with which to dress the edges of buff and glaze wheels. The ingredients should be thoroughly incorporated by stirring the mixture whilst fluid, after which it is frequently poured into water, and thoroughly kneaded with the hands, and rolled into lumps before it has time to cool. The emery cake is sometimes applied to the wheels whilst they are revolving; but the more usual course is to stop the wheel, and rub in the emery cake by hand, it is afterwards smoothed down with the thumb.

10.—EMERY PAPER, OR EDWARDS' PATENT RAZOR STROP PAPER, is a new article in which fine emery and glass are mixed with the *paper pulp*, and made into sheets as in making ordinary paper. The emery and glass are said to constitute together 60 per cent. of the weight of the paper, which resembles drawing paper except that it has a delicate fawn colour. This emery paper is directed to be pasted or glued upon a piece of wood, and when rubbed with a little oil to be used as a razor strop, of which it is by far the least expensive of any previously in use. The patent for this invention was granted to the Rev. Mr Edwards, in November 1843, and he was rewarded for the same by the Society of Arts, in June, 1846.

11.—BARCLAY'S ARTIFICIAL EMERY STONE.—The numerous articles already given on emery, and various ways in which it is prepared and used will be concluded by a description of the invention of a Mr. Henry Barclay, who took out letters patent in August, 1842, for a very efficient mode of combining powdered emery into disks and laps of different kinds, suitable to grinding, cutting, and polishing glass, enamels, metals, and other hard substances. The process of manufacture is as follows :—

Coarse Emery Powder is mixed with about half its weight of pulverized Stourbridge loam, and a little water or other liquid, to make a thick paste, this is pressed into a metallic mould by means of a screw press, and after having been thoroughly dried, is baked or burned in a crucible, muffle, or close receiver, within a furnace, at a temperature considerably above a " *red heat*," and below the " *full white heat*."

In this case the clay or alumine serves as a bond, and unites the particles very completely in a solid substance, called *Artificial Emery Stone*, which cuts very greedily, and yet seems hardly to suffer perceptible wear or destruction.

Superfine Grinding Emery, is formed into wheels exactly in the same manner as the above, but the proportion of loam is then only one-fourth, instead of one-half that of the emery : these emery stones, which are of medium fine-ness, cut less quickly but more smoothly than the above.

Flour Emery, when manufactured into artificial stones, requires no uniting substance, but the moistened flour emery is alone forced into the metal mould and fired, as some portions of the alumine present seem abundantly to suffice to unite the remainder. These fine wheels render the works submitted to them exceedingly smooth, but they do not produce a high polish on account of the comparative coarseness of the flour emery.

Stourbridge loam is by no means the only ingredient used in uniting the particles of emery, as many other substances answer as well ; such as slate, Yorkshire gritstone, crocus, &c., and in this way the hardness and cut of the emery stone may be varied to a great extent.

Most of the grinders made of the Emery stone are formed with central holes, so as to admit of being attached to the lathe upon appropriate chucks or spindles ; and the substance is so porous as to absorb much water, which is gradually thrown to the surface by the centrifugal motion so as to keep the edge conveniently moist, or with excessive velocity, the water is thrown off as in trundling a mop. Mr. Barclay has made the disks of various diameters from ¼ inch to 8 or 10 inches diameter, but the difficulty increases with the size, as the large ones are liable to warp and crack in the firing.

When the emery stone laps are required to have plane surfaces, angular or convex edges, &c., that could not be readily moulded, the composition is partially fired at a low heat, then turned in a lathe to the specific form, and the firing at a nearly white-heat completes the manufacture.

The coarse emery stone has been tried in cutting glass, and is reported then to fulfil in itself the offices, first, of the iron disk fed with sand used in roughing, and secondly, of the Lancashire fine grit stone used in smoothing ; as when of proper consistence, the artificial emery stone cuts as quickly as the former, and as smoothly as the latter, and has the advantage of maintaining its form in an eminent degree.

Small fragments of these disks, spoiled in the firing, have been successfully used in scrubbing off the rough sand coat of door plates, mouldings, &c., cast in brass, &c., and indeed the Patent Emery Stone eminently deserves more extended use than it has, up to the present time, attained.

It remains to be observed that Mr. Barclay took up the subject of the Artificial Emery Stone from necessity, as in his professional employment of making artificial teeth and gums, of a kind of hard porcelain, he found the small grindstones, (tediously prepared by rubbing down waste flakes of the Yorkshire stone used for paving into flat plates, and which are afterwards drilled and turned to the requisite forms,) wore out amazingly quick, even when assisted by coarse sand and water ; but the present scheme fulfils the office of the grindstone in an admirable manner ; and some small artificial stones made as above have been in almost daily use for 3 or 4 years.

The project bears an evident analogy to Mr. Prosser's Patent for making buttons, various articles, and even fire bricks, out of dry clay in powder compressed in a mould and afterwards burned, and it offers certain advantages over the corundum wheels used in India, and described under the head CORUNDUM.

EMERALDS.—These valuable stones, the finest of which are found in Peru, are considered to be very soft gems, and in consequence they require more than ordinary care in their polishing, and still do not admit of such acute angles and edges being given to them as to many of the harder gems. The Emerald is worked just like CARNELIAN.

ENAMELS.—These are metallic surfaces covered with a thin coating of glass of various colours, and which is sometimes partially transparent, but generally opaque. The enamel or glass is ground to powder, mixed with some vehicle, such as turpentine, or oil of spike, and spread on as a thick coating of paint, and when dried, the whole is heated just sufficiently to fuse the enamel, and cause it to adhere to the metal.

The work is placed within a muffle, which is in many cases a miniature arched vault open at one end, placed in the midst of a small furnace, and surrounded by burning fuel, which keeps it at the red heat, although the fuel cannot possibly touch the work. In other cases the furnace is made of sheet iron ; it then measures externally about 20 inches long, 12 wide, and 10 deep, and is mounted on wrought iron legs that support it, so that the opening or door, which is at the one end, may be on the level with the eye of the artist, whilst from the opposite end proceeds the flue leading into a chimney. The whole apparatus bears some resemblance to a German stove, or rather, to a laundry stove considerably elevated, but the muffle, or a heated chamber corresponding therewith, is always provided for the reception of the work to be enamelled to protect the same from the flame and smoke of the fuel.

Many of the enamelled works can hardly be said to be polished artificially, as the lustre is produced simply by the process of fusion ; thus the enamelled faces of watches, when the ground has been fired, only require the figures to be added, as the vitreous surface is mostly smooth enough from the fusion without being polished ; and in less favourable cases the work is only ground to a level but dull surface, and afterwards just raised to the melting point, so as to fuse the surface, and thereby give it the polish.

The backs of gold watches and numerous articles of jewellery, including mourning rings, are so enamelled as to show various devices or inscriptions in gold, upon a ground or general surface of enamel ; in this case the work is engraved, all the parts where the enamel is to appear being cut away by the graver, and the spaces are afterwards filled in with the pulverised enamel, which is burnt in, and lastly, the whole is polished down to a uniform surface.

Formerly nearly all the enamelled works were polished by the lapidaries, who used, 1st, the horizontal lead mill with fine emery for grinding ; 2ndly, lead with rottenstone and water; and 3rdly, the leather lap or buff wheel with putty powder.   But the enamellers of the present day mostly polish their own work, and employ either an ordinary lathe with a mandrel upon which the laps are screwed like chucks, the cylindrical edges of the laps being alone used, or else they employ a polishing lathe similar to those of cutlers and others.

The French enamellers commonly select instead of emery, a hard white pulverised porcelain, called white emery, which is manufactured at the Royal Manufactory of Porcelain at Sèvres, and they afterwards polish with yellow tripoli ; the first is applied on a lead or wooden wheel, and the latter on a buff.

When enamels are polished by hand, the work is first roughed down with slips of water of ayr stone and water, used after the manner of a file ; after which the different artists use slips of boxwood, mahogany, or metal, first, with pumice-stone, and then with crocus, nearly as for gold.

FACETS, a few words are given on the cutting of the facets or gems at the conclusion of the article on Carnelian, but the subject will be considered more at length in the chapter on lapidary work.

FAYRER'S SWING HONE.—This is a flat and parallel slip of brass, in form like a hone, but with pivots at the ends by which it is suspended in two notches, so that this metal lap, or factitious hone, may accommodate itself to the angle at which the razor or other instrument is applied to it.   The one side of the brass is first used with fine oilstone powder and oil, afterwards the second side with pulverised water of ayr stone and oil, and the razor strop is afterwards resorted to, see Trans. Soc. of Arts, vol. 48, p. 248.

FELSPAR.—The fine varieties of this siliceous mineral, display most beautiful and varied iridescent colours ; namely, blues and greens in the Labrador Felspar, a beautiful apple green in the Amazon Stone, and a pearly white in the Adularia or Moonstone, the colours are best seen when the specimens are polished, which is effected as with Carnelian although Felspar is scarcely so hard.

FELT or Felted Cloth is very much used for polishing especially for marble. *See* CLOTH and MARBLE.

FISH SKIN is the skin of the Dog Fish, and some others which is dried as its only preparation.   The scales of the skin are hard and pointed and stand up obliquely, so that they cut or abrade very effectually in the one direction, but not in the other.   Fish skin is more durable but less generally convenient than glass paper, to which it probably gave rise.   It is however now but little used in polishing, although in clearing off rounded and irregular works, as in pattern making, from the fish skin being somewhat rigid, when bent round the finger it may be almost used as a file, and it has the further advantage of leaving nothing behind it, whereas, glass paper commonly deposits some of the particles of glass in the surface of the wood, to the detriment of any tools subsequently employed. The fins should be selected for fine works.

FLANDERS BRICKS, these which are now equally or better known as Bath bricks, are made in large quantities of a clay found at Bridgewater, and which contains a considerable proportion of fine sand. Besides the extensive employment of these bricks for domestic purposes, and in making founders cores, they are sometimes employed when rubbed to powder, in polishing bone, ivory, and soft metals, and also in dressing cutlers dry buff wheels, boards for cleaning table knives, &c. Trent sand is preferable when it can be procured.

FLAT SURFACES.—The principal modes of grinding flat or plane surfaces, will be described in Chap. XXXIII. sect. 1.

FLINT is not frequently polished by the lapidary but is then treated like Carnelian. Until of late years one of the greatest uses of this substance was for procuring fire, but percussion caps and Congreve matches have nearly superseded this employment of flint, which still however enters largely into the composition of porcelain, and has given the name to *Flint* Glass, although in this manufacture it is now rejected in favor of the more available article, the pure sand obtained from Alum Bay, Isle of Wight, Maidstone, and elsewhere. Flint is employed in the mechanical arts, as the " *bouldering stone*" for rubbing down to a smooth face the laps, buffs and glaze wheels of the cutler, and pulverized flint has also obtained the employment described in the succeeding article.

Flint. The late Mr. Larkin in finishing his beautiful wood models of crystals, employed calcined flint pulverized and glued upon wooden face wheels, as more fully described under the heads GLASS PAPER, and WHEELS, article 59.

FLUOR SPAR.—This substance from the confusion in the arrangement, and the frangibility of its crystals requires a peculiar and careful treatment whilst being turned into form, and which is described at page 168-9 of the first volume. The smoothing and polishing are conducted almost the same as in marble, but as fluor spar requires a longer continuance of the polishing process, it demands considerable care to preserve the square fillets of the work from being rounded in the polishing, and with which object the powders are sometimes applied on small square slips of metal or wood, the sides of which are used somewhat as a file so as to present a superior degree of definition and permanence in the form of the polishers, than would be obtained by the exclusive use of cloth applied with the fingers.

The lapidary pursues the same method in polishing fluor spar as carnelian, but he does not succeed so well as the Derbyshire workmen, and only produces what may be termed "a greasy polish."

FREESTONES.—Few or none of these admit of being polished, but many of them are rubbed smooth ; the rubber being in general a smaller piece of the same kind of stone, sometimes used alone, at other times with a plentiful supply of sharp sand and water.   In turned works, the stone rubber is smaller and held in the hand, the process being frequently conducted dry, and without additional sand.

GANNISTER STONE a species of slaty-stone somewhat resembling the Charnley Forest, or Mount Sorrel stone, and which is abundantly used in repairing the macadamized roads around Sheffield.   When calcined, pulverized, sifted, and applied on a straight buff stick of the bull neck leather, the Gannister stone is preferred to most other materials, for smoothing the threaded shoulders of pocket knives after they have been filed, as it is considered better to preserve the keen threads or projecting ridges of the shoulders than other abrasive powders.   The work is completed on a wheel brush fed with fine emery and oil, followed by another with crocus and oil.

GARNETS are worked by the lapidary just like Carnelian, so far as the succession of the tools is concerned, the production of the facets is further noticed in the chapter on lapidary work.   The fine large Garnets when cut *en cabochon*, or with a rounded face, are known as Carbuncles and are supposed to be the gems so designated also in the Scriptures.

GERMAN HONE.—*See* HONE SLATES, also the article on setting razors in Chap. XXXII.

GLASS is polished in various different manners, some of which are elsewhere particularized.   Thus Plate Glass, is roughed with sand, smoothed with emery, and polished with crocus.   *See* Chap. XXXIII. Sect. 1.   Glass Lenses, are roughed out with sand, figured with emery, and polished with putty powder.   *See* Chap. XXXIII. Sect. 4.   Cut glass for household purposes and toys, is roughed with sand, smoothed on a Lancashire grit-stone, then with pumice-stone, and lastly is polished with putty or rottenstone see Chap. XXXIII. Sect. 5.

Lapidaries in cutting glass for jewellery adopt the mode described in this catalogue as used by them for alabaster, with the exception that they omit the wooden mill.

Glass is used as a vehicle for polishing powders by watchmakers, watch-jewellers, and some others.   *See* BRASS, article 6, and MACHINERY, article 13.

GLASS PAPER.—In making this useful article, the fragments of broken wine bottles are carefully washed to remove all dirt, the glass is then crushed under a runner, and sifted into about six sizes as in manufacturing emery. The paper is brushed over with thin glue, and the pulverized glass is then dusted over it from a sieve, which completes the process.   Sometimes two coats of glue and glass are applied, or venetian red is mixed with the glue to give that tint to the glass and sand papers, and under Edward's Patent, thin cotton cloth is used instead of paper, as the vehicle for the glass.

See FLINT, an article recommended instead of glass for the above and other purposes.

GLAZERS, or GLAZING WHEELS.—Wooden wheels covered with leather when charged with fine emery receive the above names, but when supplied with crocus and used for finer purposes they are called polishers. Such wheels charged with emery cake, bouldered and waxed to deaden the emery are much used at Sheffield. *See* WHEELS, articles 50 and 51.

GOLD is in general polished much the same as silver although some variation is made as works in gold are in general much smaller and do not require such active means as those in silver.

1.—Gold is 1st polished with water of ayr stone in the stick used with water, 2ndly with slips of wood with coarse crocus, and 3dly with a buff stick and fine crocus or rouge. The black polish which is so much esteemed, is given with the naked hand and rouge, but the perfection of the polish depends on the peculiar texture of the skin, as the hands of some individuals do not at all answer the purpose.

2.—FLAT WORKS IN GOLD are treated by cutlers and others 1st with water of ayr stone in the stick with water, 2ndly charcoal in the stick with water, 3dly boxwood and rouge very nearly dry.

3.—CUT OR FACETTED GOLD is wrought upon pewter laps with crocus, the process closely resembles the cutting of facets on gems, *see* Chap. XXXIV., but the work is guided by the fingers alone.

GRANITE, after having been worked into form with heavy dumpy picks, and then with the hammer and chisel or diamond point, is 1st ground to a moderately smooth surface with a heavy iron plate fed with sharp sand or coarse emery and water, and put into reciprocal motion, or in turned works the granite is put in quick circular revolution against the rubber. 2ndly the work is smoothed with another iron plate and coarse flour emery. 3dly it is further advanced by wooden rubbers with fine flour emery, the rubbers being made the end-way of the wood. 4thly and lastly crocus is used on thick felt laid on wood or metal. On account of the softness of the mica compared with the quartz and felspar, which together constitute the granite, the hard rubbers must be persevered in until near the conclusion, to keep the work flat, otherwise the mica is too quickly worn away, and leaves minute hollows. Sometimes lumps of granite are used as rubbers instead of the iron plates.

2.—GRANITE, when worked by the lapidary is slit and roughly ground in the common mode adopted both with CARNELIAN and ALABASTER, namely the slicer with diamond powder and the roughing or lead mill with coarse emery ; afterwards it is found best to smooth it on a mahogany wheel with flour emery, and to polish it on the lead wheel with rottenstone ; but it requires great care to prevent the soft mica from being unduly worn away.

GREENSTONE.—*See* HONE SLATES, also the article on setting razors, Chap. XXXII.

GRINDSTONE.—Grit Stones or Grinding Stones are varieties of sandstones, some of which are described.

1.—" NEWCASTLE GRINDSTONES abound in the coal districts of Northumberland, Durham, Yorkshire and Derbyshire ; and are selected of different degrees of density and coarseness, best suited to the various manufactures of Sheffield and Birmingham, for grinding and giving a smooth and polished surface to their different wares."

2.—" BILSTON GRINDSTONE is a similar description of stone, of great excellence, it is of a lighter colour, much finer and of a very sharp nature, and at the same time not too hard. It is confined to a very small spot of limited extent and thickness, in the immediate vicinity of Bilston, in Staffordshire, where it lies above the coal, and is now quarried entirely for the purpose of grindstones."

3.—" CARPENTERS' RUBSTONE is a hard close variety, used as a portable stone for sharpening tools by rubbing them on the flat stone instead of grinding. It is also much employed for the purpose of giving a smooth and uniform surface to copper plates for the engraver."

A much softer variety of sandstone, is usually cut into a square form from eight to twelve inches long, in which state they are used dry by shoe-makers, pocket-book makers, cork-cutters, and others, for giving a sort of rough edge to their bladed knives and instruments of a similar description.

4.—" DEVONSHIRE BATTS.—A porous fine-grained sandstone in considerable repute, from the quarries of Black Down Cliffs, near Collumpton."

5.—" YORKSHIRE GRIT is a variety not at all applied as a whetstone, but is in considerable use as a polisher of marble, and of copper plates for engravers."

6.—" CONGLETON GRIT is a very similar stone of a softer nature, and made use of by the same description of workmen."

7.—SHEFFIELD GRINDSTONE is a hard coarse grit stone used for grinding large files, and similar purposes, it is obtained from Hardsley which lies about 14 miles north of Sheffield.

8.—WICKERSLEY GRINDSTONES are very generally used in Sheffield for most purposes of grinding, as knives, scissors, razors, saws, and edge tools generally. Wickersley stones are quarried at a village of that name about 9 miles east of the town of Sheffield.

9.—SHEFFIELD BLUESTONE is a finer grained stone than either of the last two kinds, and is very generally used at Sheffield for finishing the grinding of articles of cutlery, that have been prepared on the Wickersley stones. The act of grinding on a blue stone is called "*whittening*" and the blades of table and pocket knives are always thus treated in Sheffield. The bluestones are found very abundantly in the neighbourhood of Sheffield at from $\frac{1}{2}$ to $1\frac{1}{2}$ miles on the north and south sides of the town.

GUM LAC.—*See* LAC ; also CORUNDUM.

GUN METAL is polished like brass, which *see*.

GYPSUM.—*See* ALABASTER.

HACKING, a process employed in dressing rough grindstones, by notching or checkering the high parts with a hack hammer, which resembles a small adze of from one to three pounds weight, fitted with a short handle. The process is fully described under WHEELS, article 15.

2.—The periphery or *face* of soft metal laps and wooden glaze wheels, are also in some cases hacked by the cutlers, with a very light sharp hammer, the edge of which should be as keen as a chisel, and used very delicately ; but by far the more usual course is to score the edges of the wheels while they are at rest, with a pointed knife, which injures these tools less and entirely avoids the risk of spoiling the edge or angle of the lap, which should be scrupulously preserved.

3.—Lapidaries employ an entirely different mode of hacking or *jarring* their leaden pewter and copper polishing wheels, which are used with rottenstone and water, as fully described under the head CARNELIAN.

HARDWOOD.—*See* WOOD.

HELIOTROPE.—*See* BLOODSTONE, and also the article on CARNELIAN.

HONE SLATES.—A mineralogical distinction for various slaty stones that are used in straight pieces or slabs for whetting or sharpening the edges of tools subsequently to their having been ground on revolving grindstones. The following quotations are from Mr. Knight's paper in the Trans. of the Society of Arts, vol. 50, page 233.

1.—" NORWAY RAGSTONE.—This is the coarsest variety of the hone slates. It is imported in very considerable quantities from Norway in the form of square prisms, from nine to twelve inches long, and one to two inches diameter, gives a finer edge than the sandstones, and is in very general use."

2.—" CHARNLEY FOREST STONE is one of the best substitutes for the Turkey oil-stone, and much in request by joiners and others, for giving a fine edge to various tools and also penknives. It has hitherto been found only on Charnwood Forest, near Mount Sorrel, in Leicestershire." The best Charnley Forest Stone, is by some considered to come *only* from the Whittle Hill Quarry, the other stones from the neighbourhood are more pinny, or present hard places.

3.—" AYR-STONE, SCOTCH-STONE, OR SNAKE-STONE, is most in request as a polishing stone for marble and copper-plates ; but the harder varieties have of late been employed as whetstones." These stones should always be kept damp or even wet, to prevent their becoming hard.

4.—" IDWALL OR WELSH OIL-STONE is generally harder, but in other respects differs but little as a whetstone from the Charnley Forest. It is obtained from the vicinity of Llyn Idwall, in the Snowdon district of North Wales," and is now in more general use for small articles of cutlery than the Charnley Forest Stone.

5.—" DEVONSHIRE OIL-STONE is an excellent variety for sharpening all kinds of thin edged broad instruments, as plane-irons, chisels, &c., and deserves to be better known. This stone was first brought into notice by Mr John Taylor, who met with it in the neighbourhood of Tavistock, and sent a small parcel to London for distribution ; but for want of a constant and regular supply, it is entirely out of use here."

6.—" CUTLERS' GREEN HONE is of so hard and close a nature, that it is only applicable to the purposes of cutlers and instrument makers, for giving the last edge to the lancet and other delicate surgical instruments. It has hitherto been only found in the Snowdon mountains of North Wales."

7.—" GERMAN RAZOR HONE.—This is universally known throughout Europe, and generally esteemed as the best whetstone for all kinds of the finer descriptions of cutlery. It is obtained from the slate mountains in the neighbourhood of Ratisbon, where it occurs in the form of a yellow vein running virtually into the blue slate, sometimes not more than an inch in thickness, and varying to twelve and sometimes eighteen inches, from whence it is quarried, and then sawed into thin slabs, which are usually cemented into a similar slab of the slate to serve as a support, and in that state sold for use. That which is obtained from the lowest part of the vein is esteemed the best and termed old rock." The German Hone is now used almost exclusively for razors, as being very soft, it is cut by any instrument applied at an angle, and not laid flat down as a razor invariably is.

8.—" BLUE POLISHING STONE is a dark slate of very uniform character ; in appearance not at all laminated ; is in considerable use among jewellers, clockmakers, and other workers in silver and metal, for polishing off their work, and for whose greater convenience it is cut into lengths of about six inches, and from a quarter of an inch to an inch or more wide, and packed up in small bundles of from six to sixteen in each, and secured by means of withes of osier, and in that state imported for use."

9.—" GREY POLISHING STONE is a stone of very similar properties to the blue, but of a somewhat coarser texture and paler colours. Its uses are the same and both kinds are manufactured near Ratisbon."

10.—" WELSH CLEARING-STONE is a soft variety of hone-slate, the use of which is confined to curriers, and by them employed to give a fine smooth edge to their broad and straight-edged knives for dressing leather. They are always cut of a circular form."

11.—PERUVIAN HONE has been recently introduced as a whetstone, and is said to be imported from South America. It cuts freely with either oil or water, and is suitable for sharpening large tools that do not require a very fine edge.

12.—WELSH HONE. *See* article 4.

13.—OILSTONE WHITE AND BLACK. These are varieties of the Turkey-stone. *See* OILSTONE.

14.—ARKANSAS STONE, from N. AMERICA is of unequal texture and cuts slowly.

15.—BOHEMIAN STONES are imported from Germany, and are used by jewellers in the same manner as the blue and grey polishing stones for polishing small works, such as the settings around gems. The Bohemian stones cut well, and keep a good point for small work.

HORN handles for razors, knives, and similar works when moulded (see vol. 1, page 125) are scraped and then buffed with Trent sand and oil, and afterwards with rottenstone and oil as more fully explained under the head " Tortoiseshell ;" but upon which latter material the Trent sand is not used in its natural state, as it would be too coarse and vigorous in its action on that soft and expensive substance ; for buffing tortoiseshell therefore the Trent sand is first calcined and pounded, and then passed through a muslin sieve. *See* article TORTOISESHELL.

Horn is sometimes used by watchmakers as a vehicle for the application of polishing powders to flat works. *See* MACHINERY, article 13.

HYACINTH.—*See* ZIRCON.

IDWALL STONE.—*See* HONE SLATES, article 4.

IRON.—The modes of polishing the parts of machinery made in wrought and cast iron, are described in the general article MACHINERY in this Catalogue. *See* also WROUGHT-IRON and CAST-IRON.

IRON STONE.—A straight slab of the hæmatite iron ore, ground flat on the one face, is sometimes used by the Sheffield cutlers after the yellow German hone, in polishing the " *cannell* " or chamfers made by the German hone in setting razors.—The iron stone is very hard, and leaves a very smooth edge, almost fulfilling the purpose of the razor strop, but it must be used very lightly and sparingly. See the article on setting razors, Chap. XXXIII. Sect. 2.

IVORY.—The modes of polishing objects made of this useful and ornamental substance, differ according to the nature of the works ; and although the remarks here offered refer especially to the ivory of the elephant, that of the tusks of other animals, also the corosos or vegetable ivory, and bone are treated nearly or quite the same, when applied to similar uses.

TURNED WORKS.

1.—TURNED WORKS with plain surfaces may in general be left so smooth from the tool as to require but *very little polishing*, a point always aimed at with superior workmen by the employment of sharp tools. In the polishing of turned works very fine glass paper or emery paper is 1st used, and it is rendered still finer and smoother by rubbing two pieces together face to face ; 2ndly, whiting and water as thick as cream is then applied on wash leather, linen, or cotton rag, which should be thin that the fingers may the more readily feel and avoid the keen fillets and edges of the ivory work, that would be rounded by excessive polishing ; 3rdly, when the work feels smooth, or to hang less to the rag than at first, the work is washed with clean water on the same or another rag ; 4thly, it is rubbed with a clean dry cloth until all the moisture is absorbed, and lastly a very minute quantity of oil or tallow is put on the rag to give a gloss.

Scarcely any of the oil remains behind, and the apprehension of its being absorbed by the ivory and disposing it to turn yellow, may be discarded ; indeed the quantity of oil used is quite insignificant, and its main purpose is to keep the surface of the ivory slightly lubricated, so that the rag may not hang to it and wear it into rings or groovy marks. Putty powder is sometimes used for polishing ivory work, but it is more expensive and scarcely better suited than whiting which is sufficiently hard for the purpose.

2.—TURNED WORKS consisting of many parts are best polished separately, as they are then more accessible, and the whiting and water do not penetrate and clog the joinings of the several parts, and prevent their easy separation. Accurate workmen frequently polish screw threads, in order to make them move the more easily, and to endure the longer without wearing loose ; this is sometimes done with screws in ivory and the woods, as well as those in the metals, and is to be highly recommended.

3.—TURNED WORKS ornamented with the eccentric chuck, revolving cutters, &c. also require to be cut with exceedingly sharp tools, in order that but little polishing may be necessary.

The polishing of irregular surfaces is generally done with a moderately hard nail brush, supplied with whiting and water, and lightly applied in all directions, to penetrate every interstice ; after a period the work is brushed with plain water and a clean brush, to remove every vestige of the whiting. The ivory is dried by wiping and pressing it with a clean linen or cotton rag, and is afterwards allowed to dry in the air, or at a good distance from the fire ; when dry a gloss is given with a clean brush on which a minute drop of oil is first applied.

It is better to do too little polishing at first, so as to need a repetition of the process, rather than by injudicious activity, to round and obliterate all the delicate points and edges of the works, upon the preservation of which their beauty mainly depends.

FLAT AND FILED WORKS.

4.—SUPERIOR FLAT WORKS are accurately filed and scraped, then cleaned with fine glass paper folded around a square stick, afterwards with whiting also on a stick of deal planed very flat and square and used as a file ; some workmen cover the wood with one or two layers of flannel or cloth, but the naked wood, although somewhat tedious, will produce more exact surfaces and better defined edges.

5.—COMMON FILED AND CARVED WORKS are finished—1st, with Trent sand and water on flannel or a brush; 2ndly, scraped Flanders brick used in the like manner; 3rdly, wet linen or woollen rag with powdered chalk, which soon rubs down smooth, and to the condition of ordinary whiting.

6.—RAZORS AND KNIFE HANDLES are most generally finished by shaving or scraping, and 2ndly by buffing them on the wheels, as more fully explained under the head TORTOISESHELL; but the following methods are by some preferred.

7.—COMMON RAZOR HANDLES.—These are sawn out and filed, then scraped with an old razor blade, called a shaving blade; two razor handles or scales are then held at the one end in a pair of clamps in the vice, and rubbed lengthways— 1st, with chalk and water on felt or cloth, which cuts very quickly; and 2ndly with whiting and water for the finish.

8.—BEST RAZOR HANDLES.—Two scales are slightly rivetted together and buffed, 1st, on a buff wheel fed with Trent sand; 2ndly, buffed with rottenstone; 3rdly, they are *handed up* or polished with the naked hand and rottenstone. Other workmen entirely omit the rottenstone, which requires oil, and conduct the work with chalk and whiting, so that water may be used throughout the work.

9.—UMBRELLA AND PARASOL HANDLES, and many similar pieces are polished first with sand, and then with whiting, on cloth wheels consisting of several circles of thick cloth or felt, clamped between two smaller disks of wood; the cloth projects about an inch around the margin to make a soft elastic edge.

JACINTH or Hyacinth.—*See* ZIRCON.

JADE is polished by lapidaries like CARNELIAN but it only takes a greasy and not a brilliant polish.

JAPANNED WORKS.—Such of the japanned works as are baked in ovens, for the evaporation of the solvent of the varnish, are 1st forwarded with pumice-stone powder applied with water on list or flannel; 2ndly they are polished either with rottenstone or putty powder and oil, also on flannel; and 3rdly with the dry hand and rottenstone.

JARGOON.—*See* ZIRCON.

JASPER obtains just the same treatment as Carnelian in the Lapidary's art; it occurs of numerous colours and varieties, and is nearly equal to Agate in point of hardness.

JET is a soft bituminous mineral, and, like Cannel Coal, receives in the hands of the lapidary the same routine as ALABASTER; which see.

The articles on Jet and Cannel Coal (vol 1, page 162—3) describe an entirely different method of working these peculiar substances, and to which the reader is referred. *See also* CANNEL COAL in this Catalogue.

JEWELLERY.—*See* the articles on Gold, Silver, Enamels, and Saw-dust.

LAC or GUM LAC is used in India with powdered corundum in the formation of wheels and rubbers; *see* CORUNDUM. It is somewhat used in the same manner in England, but with emery instead of corundum.

LAPIS LAZULI "is used in jewellery, but is chiefly important as affording that beautiful pigment *ultra-marine*, so highly valued by painters on account of its great advantage in not changing by time or exposure."—In producing this pigment the mineral is simply calcined and then levigated. The lapis lazuli is difficult to polish on account of the irregularity of its substance, which abounds in soft parts that wear away more quickly than the remainder; it is treated as CARNELIAN.

LAPS, metal polishing wheels, *see* WHEELS, articles 37 to 47.

LAVAS, which are occasionally arranged as specimens, do not in general admit of being well polished, because of their being irregularly hard and soft, and also scoriacious; they are worked by the lapidary just like ALABASTER, which see.

LEAD is the basis of many of the laps, and is rendered sometimes harder by the addition of variable proportions of tin and antimony; *see* WHEELS, articles, 37 to 47.

Lead may be readily worked with rasps, but it clogs files so much as to render it difficult to produce a smooth surface by those instruments; in practice it is generally scraped for the smoothest surfaces. Lead is not often polished, it would require to be treated like pewter but with greater care, to prevent the formation of utters in the scraping or burnishing.

Lead when reduced to the white oxide, forms the commonest kind of putty powder, the process of manufacturing which is described under the head PUTTY POWDER.

LEATHER.—The leather principally used for polishing, in the manufacturing towns of Sheffield and Birmingham, is the beast hide, or the leather of the ox as prepared for the soles of shoes, which is much softer and open in the grain before it is hammered as for the soles of shoes. The hide is usually cut into parallel pieces or strips, which are glued around the edges of wooden disks; then constituting buff wheels if charged with emery, and polishers if dressed with crocus; and the leather is also fixed on straight sticks known as buff sticks.

The leather varies much in thickness, that about the neck of the hide being sometimes nearly an inch thick, and very soft, this part being designated as *bull neck*, a material for which the thick hide of the sea cow or sea horse is frequently substituted.

Occasionally the curried hides of the horse, and other leathers used in making harness, are employed for buff wheels; and in the metropolis in particular, the thick buff leather of old regimental belts is much employed for similar uses, but although cheaper it is softer and far less durable. Wash leather, prepared from sheep skins split in two, is also much used in polishing, but mostly after the manner of a dusting cloth, or to prevent the hand touching the goods.

LENSES.—*See* Chap. XXXIII. Sect. 4.

LIME is occasionally used as a polishing material on account of its cheapness, as the only preparation required is to slake the lime with a little water, it then falls to a fine powder and which is sometimes sifted. Lime is used for polishing the commonest works in bone, such as brushes, and also for Albata Spoons.

LIMESTONES.—The substances to which this name is applied differ greatly in hardness and compactness. Some are so soft as not to admit of being polished, and are treated much the same as the Freestones, (which see,) whereas, those limestones which do admit of being polished, are generally designated under the name marble, the mode of polishing which is minutely described under that head.

LITHOGRAPHIC STONES, are a fine *oolite*, a peculiar kind of fine granular limestone, principally obtained from the interior of Germany.

The surfaces of lithographic stones are required to possess different degrees of smoothness, according to the subject for which they are employed. When the drawing is to be made at once upon the stone, a certain amount of roughness or granulation is necessary, or it will not so well abrade the lithographic drawing chalk, and this granulation is required to be more or less fine according to the kind of drawing. But much smoother surfaces are required for those stones upon which the transfer process is to be employed, as for lithographic writing, which is first executed on paper, and then transferred to the stone, by passing them together through the press.

The stones are, 1st, rubbed smooth with another lump of lithographic stone, and silver sand applied with water, the sand is prepared of different degrees of fineness by sifting, as explained under the head Emery, the coarsest sieves employed have about 80 wires in the inch, the finest about 120. The stones for chalk drawing are left from the sand of appropriate fineness, but those required for the transfer process are, 2ndly, smoothed with a lump of pumicestone and water, and 3rdly, polished with a piece of snake stone, also applied with water.

LOAM is used with water by some manufacturers as a cheap material with which to grind in the conical plugs of brass valves and cocks. Loam contains more silex than the generality of the clays, but which also are occasionally used for polishing common works.

MACHINERY Composed of Wrought-Iron, Cast-Iron and Steel.—The engineer and mechanist employ nearly the same routine for polishing these three materials, more particularly in turned works, in which the variations principally depend upon the degree of finish required. This general article is therefore intended to apply to each of the three materials ; and some particular observations expressly suited to each of them, will be found under their respective heads of Wrought-Iron, Cast-Iron, and Steel.

TURNED WORKS.

1.—Large Sized Turned Works.—Such parts of machinery as come under this denomination, are in almost every case turned in self-acting lathes, which, under proper management, leave the surfaces very exact and smooth, so that many of them require no polishing whatever ; and which process is reserved for those exterior parts which meet the eye, when the machinery is erected.

Heavy works are made to revolve with considerably greater velocity than that proper for turning, and they are polished with a long stick of deal 1 to 2 inches thick, and 2 to 4 inches wide, the end of which is cut off square. The stick is dipped into a shallow vessel containing oil, then into another with dry emery after which it is pressed forcibly against the work, never being allowed to remain long in one position upon the lathe rest. Occasionally, for additional purchase, a bent bar of iron is used, to the end of which is fixed a block of wood, in imitation of the hanging tools for turning iron, figs. 423 and 424, page 527, vol. ii. Sometimes on the end of the polishing stick is placed a thick piece of leather for the application of the emery, of which two or at most three different-sized grains are used, namely, corn emery, grinding, and fine grinding emery.

2.—Medium sized Turned Works.—Many of these which are turned in power lathes running at a proportionate velocity, with tools properly formed and lubricated with abundance of water from a small jet, are left so smooth as hardly to want any polishing, or at most an inconsiderable amount of polishing with fine emery powder or emery paper ; but in other works less skilfully turned by hand tools and with little or no water, it is usual to reduce any very trifling irregularities of surface to a general level, by means of a smooth file, slightly greased, which is rubbed lightly over the work as it revolves ; careless workmen are apt however to rely too much on this practice, and having left the work full of ridges from the turning tool, to begin with a coarse file ; this practice is detrimental to the production of good true work, and the preservation of the angles.

Works of medium size are polished nearly as above described, but with a deal stick chopped to a chisel edge, or to a square point and thrust against the work ; sometimes instead of the point the side of the stick near the end is used as a crow-bar for additional purchase.

Generally two, but occasionally three sizes of emery are used, varying from grinding to flour emery ; but it is necessary between the application of each powder, to wipe the work entirely clean, with rags, cotton-waste, saw-dust, moslings, (or the curriers' shavings of leather), and also to use a fresh stick, or to chop a clean point, for every kind of emery.

3.—SMALL SIZED TURNED WORKS.—For these, emery sticks, (those with emery glued upon them,) and emery paper are much used ; but the loose powder applied as above although less cleanly, is in general somewhat quicker and also cheaper. For the plane surfaces and other parts of small-turned works, required to be particularly flat, emery paper folded around a smooth file or a flat piece of wood is used, or else flat pieces of mahogany, box-wood or metal, supplied with fine emery powder and oil are employed with still greater advantage.

In some few cases after the finest or flour emery has been used, fine crocus is applied similarly, or with a buff stick, but this is unusual as two sizes of emery are alone in general employed. Some parts of superior works in iron and steel, especially the rounded edges, are brightened with the burnisher, but such parts require to be previously polished quite smooth; both the work and burnisher must be wiped thoroughly clean from emery or dust, the burnisher is then held against the work as it revolves, a little oil being interposed to lubricate the surfaces.

4.—SCREW THREADS that are required to fit accurately and smoothly, and also to sustain frequent unscrewing, should be polished with a pointed stick and emery ; as frequently the removal of the rough edges will make that screw enter which appeared to be too large, and the smooth screw present far less friction and disposition to wear out.

5.—THE HEADS OF SCREWS are often finished with the side of an emery stick as they revolve in the lathe ; and if they are to be burnished the emery must be carefully removed from the notch by folding the rag and drawing it through like a saw or the process will fail, and the burnisher will be injured.

6.—SMALL ROUND RODS used for inferior purposes and not requiring to be cylindrical, are often ground bright against the edges of large revolving grindstones driven by power. The rod is held rather loosely in the hands of the workman and at a small angle to the axis of the stone ; then without any great attention on the part of the individual, the grindstone causes the rod slowly to rotate in his hands, so as to act on every part of its circum-ference, and the obliquity of the two axes also causes the rod to traverse endlong through the hands like a screw, and thus every part of the rod is acted upon successively by the grindstone.

7.—CYLINDRICAL WORKS that require great accuracy are ground by methods that will be explained in Chap. XXXIII. Sect. 2, but other cylindrical rods of inferior kinds, used only as levers and for similar common purposes, are often polished between two sticks, (supplied with emery and oil,) placed trans-versely to the cylinder, grasped in both hands, and rubbed lengthways on the work as the lathe revolves. Considerable friction may thus be given on opposite sides, and therefore without bending the cylinder, the figure of which is materially improved by the treatment. Sometimes for greater purchase, the sticks are united at the one end by a loop of string or wire, and compressed at the other, like nut-crackers, with one or both hands.

8.—LATHES FOR POLISHING.—In large manufactories it is usual to perform the polishing on common lathes kept entirely apart from those used for turning, on account of the mischief that ensues when gritty matters find their way into the fittings of the mandrel or other part of the lathe ; and careful workmen who use the same lathe for turning and also for polishing, avoid with scrupulous care the scattering of the powders, and frequently employ a spare center for the popit head, in polishing spindles and pieces requiring support at both ends, as the grit is almost sure to deteriorate the center employed in polishing works.

FLAT WORKS.

9.—LARGE-SIZED FLAT WORKS.—These are in almost every case, castings in iron, wrought in the planing machine ;—a machine that produces its results with so much accuracy and precision, that polishing is not frequently required as the concluding step. When however large planed works are polished, it is with rubbers of various kinds applied with emery and oil. Sometimes a flat lump of lead is cast upon the center of an old file, or of a still longer bar of iron ; at other times a bar of wood serves as the handle, and to it is fixed by screws or nails a piece of lead or wood, or wood covered with thick leather ; such rubbers are generally held in the two hands much after the manner of the spokeshave or drawknife, or they are worked by one very long handle as in smoothing a large slab of stone or marble. When the rubbers are large they are occasionally loaded with heavy weights, so that the workmen have only to drag them to and fro on the works, the forms of which latter are in general too diversified to offer much inducement to the application of machinery to rectilinear polishing.

10.—MEDIUM-SIZED FLAT WORKS.—Such of these as are of cast-iron, are also for the most part worked in the planing machine, and if at all polished, it is done with emery rubbers nearly or precisely as above described ; most of the flat parts of mechanism that are made in wrought iron and steel, are too irregular in their forms to admit of being worked otherwise than with the file. The black oxidized surfaces of forged works are often removed on the grindstone prior to the application of the file ; this application of the grindstone is in general highly economical, it being comparatively, much more rapid in its action, and less costly in respect to wear and tear than the file.

Sometimes, indeed, the flat parts of iron works are reduced on the grindstone to accurate plane surfaces, but this requires the assistance of mechanism, which is by no means common ; this subject, and also the application of revolving metallic laps to the production of flat works, will be noticed in the first section of Chap. XXXIII.

The coarser and larger of the filed works are sometimes left from the file, or without being subsequently polished ; in which case the coarser marks left from the file when used in the customary manner, or from point to heel, are removed by the method known as *draw-filing*, in which the file is drawn sideways along the work ; draw-filing is particularly employed in narrow pieces.   Large broad surfaces are occasionally finished by giving a circulating motion to the file, thereby producing curly marks.   Each of these latter processes are more effectual when the file is moderately supplied with oil, which lessens its disposition to become *pinny*, or clogged, by particles which stick into it, and scratch the work ; but the reader is referred to the previous chapter on the File, vol. ii., page 852, for more detailed particulars of these applications of this useful instrument.

Works requiring a finish superior to that of draw-filing, are rubbed with an emery stick, or with rubbers of the various kinds already noticed, and supplied with emery and oil.

11.—SMALL-SIZED FLAT WORKS, after having been draw-filed, are more usually finished with the emery stick, and often followed by emery paper of different degrees of coarseness wrapped on a file or a square stick.   The emery is moistened with oil for the more finished works, the dry rubber gives however the brighter surface, and it is sometimes applied with a curling motion, so as to diversify the grain left on the work.

Buff sticks supplied with crocus are often used for the last gloss, but on small flat surfaces they must be cautiously applied for fear of rounding them, a defect that is easily distinguished, and very objectionable.

Still smaller works and those required to be very flat are finished with square slips of stone with oil, or slips of mahogany, brass or tin, any of which are used with fine flour emery or oilstone powder and then with crocus.

12.—SMALL FLAT WORKS OF HARDENED STEEL.—As it commonly happens that in the process of hardening steel works they are more or less distorted from their intended figures, and as in many cases it is impossible or inadmissible to restore them to the plane figure by the hack hammer, (*see* vol. 1, p. 247,) grinding is then resorted to, metal laps generally of lead with a little antimony, and laps of copper or of cast-iron are also employed with emery and water.   When it is desired the works should present very true plane surfaces, the laps should be themselves very exact and flat.   There is however a constant tendency to depreciate the figure of the lap, because the outer part or exterior diameter gets the more worn, on account of the greater rapidity of its action at that part.   After the lap has been used, the mode of finishing described in the last article is also sometimes employed.

13.—WATCHWORKS IN STEEL.—Steel works of this diminutive kind are generally polished by the watchmakers, 1st with a steel rubber and oilstone powder, 2ndly, with a steel rubber and crocus of two degrees of coarseness, which is frequently called *red stuff* from its colour, and 3rdly with gun metal or glass rubbers supplied with fine crocus.

Some of the work is beautifully finished on tin or pewter revolving laps, into which the red stuff is embedded, occasionally with the burnisher, they are used nearly or quite dry, and when the laps are carefully preserved, they themselves present, under the magnifier, a beautiful smooth surface and which they impart to the work.

Many of the grinders and rubbers for watchwork, are made from one to two inches square, and of steel, glass, gun-metal, tortoiseshell, horn, or ivory, &c., the small pieces are laid down upon the anointed grinders, and rubbed about with the fingers, as if the work were a muller used in grinding paint, this mode also preserves the flatness of the respective objects in a most admirable manner.

MALACHITE, or the massive green carbonate of copper, is much used for jewellery and articles of *vertu*, the finest malachite is from Russia, and as it is traversed by numerous circular fissures ; from the imperfect joinings of the botryoidal masses of which it may be considered to be composed ; it is difficult to polish, and requires great care and attention ; notwithstanding its hardness it is considered by some lapidaries better to treat it as alabaster than carnelian, but each method is followed.

MARBLE is polished in different modes, which are jointly dependent on the nature of the marble, and the character of the work; some of the principal methods will be described.

Marble is generally worked by the lapidary after the manner of carnelian, sometimes of alabaster, but he is far less successful in this department of art than the sculptor and marble workers.

1.—MARBLE ORNAMENTS and small works intended for close inspection, and which require the highest possible finish.—" After the marble is sawn into slab the first operation is to grind it down with a flat coarse sand-stone and water, or with an iron plate, fed with fine sand and water, until all the marks of the saw are perfectly removed ; 2ndly, a fine sandstone, (procured from Bilston,) is used with water, until the marks made by the first stone are removed ; 3rdly, a finer sandstone which is found near Congleton, is applied to work out the marks of the former ; 4thly, pumice-stone with water, and 5thly, snake stone is used, and the last finishes what is called the *grounding*.

" Next comes the polishing, which is principally performed with rollers of woollen cloth or list made to the size of about three inches diameter. As the 6th process a rubber is charged with flour emery and a moderate degree of moisture ; this rubber is worked uniformly over every part, until the marble acquires a kind of greasy polish ; 7thly, the work is completed with a similar roll of cloth charged with putty powder and water. Some prefer as the polisher, an old cotton stocking not made into a rubber, and in some few of the more delicate works, crocus is used intermediately between the emery and the putty-powder. It is necessary to wash the marble after each operation, so that not a particle of the previous polishing material may remain, otherwise the work will be scratched."

2.—MARBLE WORKS TURNED IN THE LATHE.—" Turned works are polished as above, excepting that for the rolls of cloth are substituted two or three thicknesses of cloth supplied with emery or putty powder, and held upon the work by the hand, which is constantly moved about."

For the above paragraphs, and also for the practical remarks on turning marble, the author is indebted to Mr. Hall of the Marble-works, Derby ; and for the subsequent particulars to Mr. Thomas Smith, sculptor, of London.

3.—STATUARY and large works in marble, which are dependent on their general design and effect, rather than on elaborate finish, are executed by a different class of artists, and require only part of the above proceses to be resorted to. By Statuaries the marble is rubbed with two qualities of gritstone, the coarse, which is somewhat finer than Bilston, is known as *first grit*, and the fine as *second grit*. Thirdly, the work is smoothed with snakestone, after which the white or statuary marble is finished with putty powder and water, on a wooden *block* covered with thick *nap*, or felted cloth. (*See* article RUBBER.)

The Irish black marble is by some considered harder than the Derbyshire, and after the snakestone has been used, it is polished with tripoli on felt as above, and finished with putty powder or crocus, but the rubber is then covered with three thicknesses of stout linen.

The finest Welsh black marble is esteemed still harder and blacker than the Irish, and after the snakestone, is polished by laying a thin plate of copper or lead on the wooden rubber, and using therewith tripoli and water, and finally putty powder or crocus on linen as before.

The Irish marble is less brittle than the Welsh, and better suited to carved ornaments. Marble has of late years been sawn, ground, and polished to a very great extent, by means of machinery, much of which took its rise from the comparatively old machinery used for the same purposes in Derbyshire.

SCULPTURE.—The dull parts of sculpture are finished in four different manners, or rather, the complete process of smoothing is discontinued at various stages, so as to form four gradations, denoted by the respective paragraphs.

The marble is *First*, sometimes left from the long and very slender statuary's chisel, the reverse end of which is formed with a sharp circular edge or ridge, just like a hollow center, in order that the metal hammer, which is of soft iron, tin, or zinc, may be slightly indented by the chisel, so as to avoid its glancing off ; the chisel marks leave the surface somewhat rough and matted, intermediate between the granular and crystalline character.

Secondly, For surfaces somewhat smoother, rasps are used to remove the ridges left by the chisel, the rasps leave a striated or lined effect suitable for draperies, and which is made more or less regular according to the uniformity of the strokes, or the reverse.

Thirdly, Files are employed for still smoother surfaces of the same character ; and it is to be observed that the files and rasps are generally curved at the ends, to adapt them to the curvilinear forms of the sculpture. *See* the article on RIFLERS, in the chapter on FILES, vol. 2, page 834.

Fourthly, For the smoothest of the dull or unpolished surfaces, the faint marks left by the file are rubbed out with Trent sand or silver sand and water, applied by means of a stick of deal cut to a point, and rubbed all over the work in little irregular circles, as a child would scribble on a slate, and if the end of the stick is covered with two or three thicknesses of cloth, the marble receives a still rounder or softer effect than from the naked stick, for which the cabbage wood or partridge wood is sometimes used, and the end of the stick is slightly bruised, so that the fibres of the wood may assume the character of the stiff brush, known by artists as a scrub.

Mr. Thomas Smith adds that he has successfully copied the minute roughness or granulation of the skin, by a kind of etching which he was induced to try, by imagining that he could trace such a process to have been used in some of the most perfect of the ancient marbles that had not been exposed to open air. The work having been smoothed with sand as above, he takes a hard stubby brush, and therewith dots the marble with muriatic acid, and which quickly, yet partially, dissolves the surface. The stringency of the acid, which must not be excessive, is tested upon a piece of waste marble : the brush is hastily dipped in the acid, applied to the work, quickly rinsed in water, and then used for removing the acid from the marble. It is obvious the process calls for a certain admixture of dexterity and boldness, and sometimes requires several repetitions, the process occupying only a few minutes each time.

Fifthly, The bright parts of sculpture. Few of the works in sculpture are polished, and such as are, are required in the first instance to pass through the four stages already explained for producing the smooth but dull surface ; after which, slender square pieces of the second gritstone and of snakestone are used with water as a pencil, and then fine emery and putty powder on sticks of wood ; but the work is exceedingly tedious, and requires very great care, that the artistical character of the work, and any keen edges that may be required are not lost in the polishing. To avoid the tediousness and the risk of deterioration, it is not unusual in carved black marbles, and those of dark colours, after using the snakestone, to coat the work with varnish, by which a gloss is given without attrition. The pillars of the Temple Church, London, which are of Durbec marble, were in like manner French polished, after the manner of furniture, when that building was recently restored.

MARBLES FOR CHILDREN.—These are principally manufactured in Germany ; some are made of clay covered with a glaze and baked as in pottery ; others are made of alabaster and marble ; but the greater part are made of a hard stone found near Coburg in Saxony. The stone is first broken with the hammer into small cubical fragments, and about 100 to 150 of these are ground at one time in a mill, somewhat like a flour mill. The lower stone, and which remains at rest, has several concentric circular grooves or furrows ; the upper stone is of the same diameter as the lower, and is made to revolve by water or other power.   Minute streams of water are directed into the furrows of the lower stone.   The pressure of the runner on the little pieces rolls them over in all directions, and in about one quarter of an hour the whole of the rough fragments are reduced into nearly accurate spheres. Frequently a thick circular slab of oak or elm is used instead of the upper or revolving stone.—*Extracted from Gill's Description.   See* Tech. Repos. for 1828, p. 219.

The late Mr. Henry Guy's method, by which spheres of metal and other hard substances, are produced with perfect accuracy, will be described in Chap. XXXIII. Sect. 4, of this volume.

MARQUETRY WORK.—This term, probably derived from the French definitions, *marqueterie en bris* and *marqueterie en métal,* (see foot note, page 732, vol. 2) has been selected to denote a variety of works, also known as buhl work, reisner work, *parquetage,* mosaic, &c., in which two or more woods, metals, and other materials, are united by various modes of inlaying, some of which are entirely executed with the saw, as described in pages 731 — 739.   The methods of polishing these works depend on the materials of which they are respectively composed, and are generally as follows.

2.—MARQUETRY ENTIRELY OF WOOD.—This is reduced to a level surface with the toothing plane, and is then scraped with the joiner's scraper, which so far as possible is applied *obliquely* to the joints of the marquetry, as when the scraper is applied *parallel* with the joints, or broadside, it is liable to dig down, and if applied at right angles to the joints it does not cut so cleanly as in the inclined position, like the skew irons of some rebate planes.   The scraper is sometimes employed with such good effect, that the work only requires to be rubbed with a few of its own shavings, as in many draftboards made of holly and ebony.

When the scraper is less successfully used, fine glass paper on a flat piece of cork is employed to smooth the work, and the paper is preferable, if it is worn until it almost ceases to cut, and has become uniformly choked or clogged with the fine dust from the work, but which must not be allowed to collect in hard partial lumps, a condition that may readily occur with resinous or greasy woods, as these lumps would scratch the work.

3.—MARQUETRY IN WOOD AND METAL, and also those which contain ivory, pearl shell, tortoiseshell, and metals, require to be levelled very carefully with flat files handled after the manner of figs. 816 to 818, page 834, vol. 2, ending with a very smooth flat file, after which the scraper should be used if practicable, and followed by glass or emery paper employed very sparingly as above directed. When the metal preponderates emery paper is much to be preferred, and really good *sand* paper, which is of an intermediate character between glass and emery paper, has also been used, but as stated above, the paper of which kind soever, should have but very little cut, should be applied dry, and allowed to become clogged, so as to act principally as a hard dry rubber or burnisher.   If the polishing is at all in excess, the wood will inevitably be worn down so as to allow the metal or harder material to project above the general surface.

It is always particularly hazardous to resort to wet polishing with inlaid works, as if the water is carelessly used, there is risk of its penetrating to the glue and loosening the pieces, and if the woods are only superficially wetted they are apt to curl up at the edges and become warped ; and besides the grain of the wood is almost certain to rise with the wet and leave a rough unsightly surface. Oil is preferable only so far as not dissolving the glue, but oil or water are alike inapplicable to light-coloured woods, which are almost sure to become stained by the polishing powders, and the fluids used in their lubrication.

4.—MARQUETRY ENTIRELY OF METAL, which is less common and more recent than the foregoing kinds, is first smoothed with a flat file, secondly it is very care-fully scraped with a triangular or other scraper, thirdly it is rubbed with a stick of snakestone and water, fourthly with charcoal in the stick and oil, and it is finished with a coil of list or other rubber supplied with rottenstone and oil.

5.—MARQUETRY WITH VARNISHED SURFACES.—Many of the modern marquetry works, instead of having their surfaces polished simply by attrition as above described, are covered with varnish either applied with friction as in the so-called French polish, or the varnish is laid on in several coats with a brush and polished off with pumice-stone and rottenstone. Previously to their being varnished, which processes will be hereafter described, the marquetry works are levelled with the file or scraper as the case may be, and smoothed with glass paper.

MEERSCHAUM is scraped to a smooth surface, but it is so soft as scarcely to admit of being polished, otherwise than by dipping the meerschaum into melted wax to fill up its pores, and rubbing it when dry with a flannel ; and which is the usual process.

MILK MEERSCHAUM obtains a somewhat different treatment.

MILL a general termed used by lapidaries to represent their different wheels ; as roughing-mill, cloth-mill, etc. *See* the introductory article on WHEELS, also Chap. XXXIV. on LAPIDARY WORK.

MOSLINGS.—The thin shreds or shavings of leather shaved off by the currier in dressing cow, or calf skins. They are frequently used for removing oil from metals that are being polished and serve extremely well, being as bibulous as blotting paper. Cotton waste is similarly employed especially in the vicinity of cotton mills.

MOTHER OF PEARL.—*See* SHELLS.

NACREOUS SHELLS.—*Idem.*

NORWAY RAGSTONE. *See* HONE SLATES, article 1.

OILSTONE.—The Turkey Oilstone can hardly be considered as a hone slate, having nothing of a lamellar or schistose appearance. As a whetstone, it surpasses every other known substance, and possesses, in an eminent degree, the property of abrading the hardest steel, and is at the same time of so compact and close a nature, as to resist the pressure necessary for sharpening a graver, or other small instrument of that description. Little more is known of its natural history than that it is found in the interior of Asia Minor, and brought down to Smyrna for sale. The white and black varieties of Turkey oilstone, differ but little in their general characters, the black is, however, somewhat harder, and is imported in larger pieces than the white.

2.—OILSTONES FITTED IN CASES.—The rough irregular pieces of oilstone scarcely ever exceed about 3 inches square and 10 inches long, and are generally about one third smaller ; when cut into rectangular forms it is done with the lapidary's slitting mill and diamond powder, the blocks are then rubbed smooth with sand or emery on an iron plate. The piece of oilstone is generally inlaid in a block of wood, in which it is cemented with the putty used by glaziers, and to avoid the deposition of dust a wooden lid is usually added ; the lid is sometimes covered with a thick piece of buff leather which serves to absorb the oil from the tool and is used in the manner of a razor strop. The oil employed on the oilstone should be indisposed to dry or thicken, in this respect sperm oil is the best, but neats-foot oil is nearly as good, and has no offensive smell.

The joiner often puts three or more small points in the stock or bed of the stone, that it may take a firm hold of the work bench when dabbed down thereupon ; and the turner adds two fillets so that it may fit transversely on the bearers of the lathe.

3.—OILSTONE SLIPS, are small pieces of this useful stone cut into different forms by the lapidary. Some oilstone slips are wide thin pieces, the edges of which are rounded to adapt them to the curvatures of gouges, and such slips are usually cut wedge form, that the semicircular edges on the one slip may be of two sizes and curvatures ; these are used for gouges, for various figured tools used by turners, and also for plane irons for mouldings. Other Oilstone slips for polishing are cut into pieces from $\frac{1}{4}$ to $\frac{3}{4}$ inches square and 3 to 6 inches long, to be used after the manner of files, by mechanicians, watchmakers and other artizans.

4.—OILSTONE POWDER.—Fragments of oilstone when pulverised sifted and washed, are much in request by mechanicians. This abrasive is generally preferred for grinding together those fittings of mathematical instruments and machinery, which are made wholly or in part of brass or gun metal ; for oilstone being softer and more pulverulent than emery, is less liable to become embedded in the metal than emery, which latter is then apt continually to grind, and ultimately damage the accuracy of the fittings of brass works. In modern practice it is usual, however, as far as possible to discard the grinding together of surfaces, with the view of producing accuracy of form or precision of contact.

Oilstone powder is preferred to pumice-stone powder for polishing superior brass works, and it is also used by the watchmaker on rubbers of pewter in polishing steel.

ONYX, a variety of Chalcedony that is wrought by the lapidary like Carnelian.

OPAL.—This beautiful iridescent gem, although soft is very brittle and tender, on account of the numerous fissures by which it is traversed, and that apparently give rise to the splendid play of colours seen in precious opals of fine quality. Opals are always cut with rounded faces, and are more generally treated like alabaster than carnelian.

OXIDES OF IRON.—The red and black oxides of iron, and mixtures of them, are prepared by manufacturing chemists at Liverpool, Sheffield, Derby and elsewhere, as polishing powders, commercially known as crocus, rouge, red stuff, colcothar of vitriol, &c., and the same substances are also employed as pigments, under the names of red-brown, purple-brown, &c. The ordinary manufacture of crocus will be first noticed, and then the more exact method, required in the higher branches of scientific art, in order completely to avoid the accidental admixtures of silex and other impurities. As however these several matters have been elsewhere described with great exactness, it is conceived best to quote these passages, and it is to be observed that articles 1, 4, 6 and 7 are literal extracts from Mr. Thomas Gill's paper on the preparation of the metallic oxides, contained in Tech. Repos. vol. 1, pages 431-5.

1.—CROCUS AND ROUGE.—"These articles are manufactured at Liverpool," said the late Mr. Samuel Varley, "by persons who make it their sole occupation, in the following manner. They take crystals of sulphate of iron, (green vitriol or copperas,) immediately from the crystallising vessels, in the copperas works there, so as to have them as clean as possible ; and instantly put them into crucibles or cast iron pots, and expose them to heat, without suffering the smallest particles of dust to get in, which would have a tendency to scratch the articles to be polished. Those portions which are least calcined, and are of a scarlet colour, are fit to make rouge for polishing gold or silver ; whilst those which are more calcined, or have become red, purple, or bluish purple, form crocus fit for polishing brass or steel. Of these, the bluish-purpled coloured part are the hardest, and are found nearest to the bottom of the vessels, and consequently have been exposed to the greatest degree of heat."

2.—MR. ANDREW ROSS'S MODE OF PREPARING OXIDES OF IRON.—"Dissolve crystals of sulphate of iron in water ; filter the solution, to separate some particles of silex which are generally present and sometimes are abundant ; then precipitate from this filtered solution the protoxide of iron by the addition of a saturated solution of soda, which must also be filtered. This gray oxide is to be repeatedly washed and then dried ; put it in this state into a crucible, and very gradually raise it to a dull red heat ; then pour it into a clean metal or earthen dish, and while cooling it will absorb oxygen from the atmosphere, and acquire a beautiful dark-red colour. In this state it is fit for polishing the softer metals, as silver and gold, but will scarcely make any impression on hardened steel or glass. For these latter purposes, I discovered that it is the black oxide that effected the polish, (and this gives to the red oxide a purple hue, which is used as the criterion of its cutting quality in ordinary,) therefore, for polishing the harder materials, the oxide must be heated to a bright red, and kept in that state until a sufficient quantity of it is converted into black oxide to give the mass a deep purple hue when exposed to the atmosphere. I have converted the whole into black oxide ; but this is liable to scratch, and does not work so pleasantly as when mixed with the softer material. The powder must now be levigated with a soft wrought iron spatula, upon a soft iron slab, and afterwards washed in a very weak solution of gum-arabic as recommended by Dr. Green in his paper on Specula. The oxide prepared in this manner is almost impalpable, and free from all extraneous matter, and has the requisite quality in an eminent degree for polishing steel, glass, the softer gems, &c. *See* EMERY, article 4.

3.—LORD ROSSE'S MODE OF PREPARING THE PEROXIDE OF IRON.—"I prepare the peroxide of iron by precipitation with water of ammonia from a pure dilute solution of sulphate of iron ; the precipitate is washed, pressed in a screw press till nearly dry, and exposed to a heat which in the dark appears a dull low red. The only points of importance are, that the sulphate of iron should be pure, that the water of ammonia should be decidedly in excess, and that the heat should not exceed that I have described. The colour will be a bright crimson inclining to yellow. I have tried both potash and soda pure instead of water of ammonia, but after washing with some degree of care, a trace of the alkali still remained, and the peroxide was of an ochrey colour till overheated, and did not polish properly." *See* Phil. Trans., 1840, p. 521.

4.—JEWELLERS' ROUGE.—"Is prepared by persons in this metropolis, by decomposing sulphate of iron with potash ; well washing the yellow oxide of iron, to free it from the sulphate of potash ; and slightly calcining it, till it acquires a scarlet colour."

5.—SPECULAR IRON ORE when finely pulverized and washed, makes a polishing powder which is greatly recommended by Mr. Heath for razor strops and other uses. It closely resembles both in appearance and effect the crocus artificially prepared from the sulphate of iron.

6.—ARTIFICIAL SPECULAR IRON ORE.—" This is made in the following manner. Equal parts of sulphate of iron and hydrochlorate of soda, (common salt,) are to be well mixed, by rubbing them together in a mortar : the mixture is then to be put into a shallow cupel or crucible, and exposed to a red-heat : a considerable quantity of vapour will be disengaged, and the matter will run into fusion. When vapours no longer arise, remove the vessel, and let it cool.

" The mass will be of a violet-brown colour, covered with extremely brilliant scales resembling mica, and perfectly like the specular iron-ore. This mass must be dissolved in water ; as well to separate the sulphate of soda which is formed by the decomposition of the two salts employed, as to wash over the lighter particles of uncrystallized oxide, which forms an excellent polishing powder.

" The fire must not be continued too long, nor be too violent ; for then the powder would become black, extremely hard, and produce no good effect. The artificial specular iron ore is the more preferred, the nearer it approximates to the violet colour.

" The micaceous scales which subside after the washing over of the powdery part, afford an excellent material for razor strops, when applied to the strop with a little grease previously rubbed over it ; as we can vouch, from our own experience in the use of it, for several months past."

It has been suggested to the author by an experienced chemist, that the atomic proportions of the sulphate of iron and common salt, should be taken for the last process, and when it is considered that, as noticed by the Earl of Rosse, the present limit of perfection in the polishing of specula, depends mainly on the fineness and efficiency of the polishing material, it becomes evident that the subject demands every care in its investigation, and which may apologize for the length of the foregoing articles.

7.—An improved Tripoli, for Polishing Gold and Silver.—" The basis of this excellent Tripoli consists of a mineral substance, abundantly found in the coal and iron mines of Staffordshire, &c. &c.; known by the name of *clunch*, or *curl stone*. It had formerly been employed for no other purpose than as a material for mending the roads. It is a compound of *iron*, alumine, lime, and silex."—Mr. Gill proposed this application of *clunch* from the external and chemical resemblance it bears to *Septaria*—the well-known basis of the Roman Cement, the employment of which in polishing he had previously advocated in the *Annals of Philosophy*. He goes on to say—" The polishing effects of the calcined and pulverized *clunch* are however still superior to that of the *Septaria*, when prepared in a similar manner ; and are, indeed, in point of quickness of action in producing the polish, and in the beautiful black lustre which it gives to the gold or silver, far beyond any thing I have ever met with."

OXIDES OF LEAD AND TIN.—*See* Putty Powder.

PAINTED WORKS, such as the panels of carriages, are first grounded, or carefully painted three or four times in good oil colour, and when thoroughly dry and hard, the surface of the paint is rubbed smooth with a lump of pumice-stone plentifully supplied with water ; two pieces of pumice-stone are used and continually rubbed together to remove the paint accumulated on their surfaces. The finishing colour, which is frequently ground up in varnish, instead of oil, is then laid on, and the panels after having had three or four coats of carriage varnish, (a description of copal varnish,) are carefully polished first with a rag supplied with pulverized pumice-stone and water, and then with rottenstone and oil on other rubbers : the worsted stocking being here likewise in great requisition for the purpose.

PALLADIUM.—Palladium, platinum and silver when inlaid in the limbs of mathematical instruments, are treated much the same as platinum, which see.

PASTES, or factitious gems made in coloured glass, are polished after the mode employed for the gems themselves, and the succession of the mills and powders used by the lapidary for the purpose is nearly the same as that described under CARNELIAN. Facets on pastes, are cut on a lead mill with flour emery, and polished on pewter with rottenstone, but the particulars of this part of the lapidaries' art will be found in Chap. XXXIV. The description of the principal *Factitious Diamonds* will be found under DIAMOND, article 5.

PEARL SHELL, or Mother of Pearl.—*See* SHELLS.

PEBBLES.—Although these differ much in their colour and general appearance, they may be viewed as varieties of Agate, and are treated as such, or in the mode fully described under the head CARNELIAN.

PERIDOT.—*See* CHRYSOLITE.

PEWTER is seldom polished ; the articles when left from the turning tool or scraper, are burnished with plenty of oil, the oil is removed with a rag and whiting, and this is the only polish given. Pewter vessels are mostly cleaned with silver sand and water, or with liquids containing potash or soda, to remove the grease.

PEWTER is much used for laps and polishers by lapidaries, jewellers, watchmakers and many others. The metal of old pewter plates is preferred, but tin unalloyed appears to be nearly identical in effect.

PLASMA, which is a variety of Chalcedony, is polished like CARNELIAN.

PLASTER OF PARIS.—In removing the seams left from the mould a knife or scraper is first used and the work is then rubbed with Dutch rush, or fish skin previously softened in water. The cleaning off is best done before the plaster is dry.

PLASTER OF PARIS is made very closely to resemble ivory, by the following process, invented by Mr. Franchi, an Italian figure caster :—Plaster and colouring matter, are employed in the proportions of one pound of superfine plaster of Paris, to half an ounce of Italian yellow ochre reduced to the finest powder, they are intimately mixed by passing them together through a fine sieve, after which the plaster cast is made in the usual way. It is first allowed to dry in the open air, and is then carefully heated in an oven, (one that is used for culinary purposes will answer,) the hot plaster cast when thoroughly dry, is soaked for one quarter of an hour in a bath containing equal parts of white wax, spermaceti, and stearine, heated just a little beyond the melting point. The cast on removal is set on edge that the superfluous composition may drain off, and before it cools its surface is brushed with a brush like that known by house painters as a sash tool, to remove any wax which may have settled in the crevices, and finally when the plaster is entirely cold, its surface is polished by rubbing it with a tuft of cotton wool.

Mr. Franchi's specimens, some of which are very classical and in high relief, are cast in a peculiar manner in elastic moulds ; and although he states the above to be the usual proportions of the yellow ochre for a medium tint, the quantity may be reduced or increased for paler or darker shades. He adds that the brown discoloured parts in old carvings in ivory, are sometimes imitated in water colours with a camel hair pencil before the works are dipped in the composition, which entirely defends them from the action of the air, and permits them to be washed with soap and water if so required.

Mr. Franchi was rewarded by the Society of Arts for this invention in 1846.

PLATE GLASS.—The polishing of this beautiful material is slightly noticed in Chap. XXXIII. Sect. 1.

PLATINUM is very difficult to file and polish, but these processes are not often required, as the great use of platinum is for chemical apparatus, which are wrought almost exclusively with the hammer and soldered with pure gold. Platinum is sometimes inlaid in the limbs of mathematical instruments to receive the graduations, and then in filing this peculiar metal, the file is generally moistened with oil to prevent it from tearing up ; and in polishing platinum the mathematical instrument makers use 1st, water of Ayr stone ; 2ndly, blue stone ; 3dly, charcoal,—all with water ; and 4thly, they lay the grain with charcoal and abundance of oil, in order that the metallic particles may be floated away. It is necessary to use *two* pieces of charcoal, and these are rubbed together at short intervals, in order to remove from the one, those minute particles of metal which become embedded in the other, and that if allowed to remain would scratch the work.

POLISHING SLATES.—*See* HONE SLATES, articles 8, 9, and 15.

PORCELLANOUS SHELLS.—*See* SHELLS.

PORPHYRY is not much used in this country, but is successfully worked in Sweden,—first with the pick and chisels, and afterwards by grinding it into form with emery and water applied through the medium of heavy rubbers, also of porphyry. As in other cases it is needful to employ a gradual succession of emery as to coarseness. It is probable the final polish is obtained by rubbers of wood with flour emery, and wood covered with buff or felt and fed with crocus, much the same as in the treatment known to be applied to granite. From the homogeneity of porphyry it is less difficult to manage than granite, but they each demand great time and patience.

The Elvans of Cornwall require similar treatment to porphyry and granite, between which they are systematically placed.

By the lapidary porphyry is treated like AGATE or CARNELIAN.

POTSTONE, a magnesian mineral, allied to Serpentine and Steatite, is very soft when first raised, and then admits of being very easily turned with chisels of various forms. *See* vol. 1, page 166. The common practice in Germany for polishing the Potstone, is to use first sand and water, and afterwards tripoli and water, occasionally also rottenstone and oil for the highest gloss, the whole are mostly applied on woollen cloths.

When the lapidary polishes the Potstone, is it usually by the process recommended for Alabaster, unless from long exposure it has become hardened, and then it is worked as Carnelian.

" PUMICE-STONE is a volcanic product, and is obtained principally from the Campo Bianco, one of the Lipari islands, which is entirely composed of this substance. It is extensively employed in various branches of the arts, and particularly in the state of powder, for polishing the various articles of cut glass; it is also extensively used in dressing leather, and in grinding and polishing the surface of metallic plates, &c."

Pumice-stone is ground or crushed under a runner, and sifted, and in this state it is used for brass and other metal works, and also for japanned, varnished, and painted goods, for which latter purposes it is generally applied on woollen cloths with water.

PUTTY POWDER is the pulverised oxide of tin, or generally of tin and lead mixed in various proportions,—the process of manufacture is alike in all cases. The metal is oxidized in an iron muffle, or a rectangular box, close on all sides, except a square hole in the front side. The retort is surrounded by fire and kept at the red heat, so that its contents are partially ignited, and they are continually stirred to expose fresh portions to the heated air; the process is complete when the fluid metal entirely disappears, and the upper part of the oxide then produced, sparkles somewhat like particles of incandescent charcoal. The oxide is then removed with ladles and spread over the bottom of large iron cooling pans and allowed to cool. The lumps of oxide, which are as hard as marble, are then selected from the mass and ground dry under the runner, the putty powder is afterwards carefully sifted through lawn.

As a criterion of quality it may be said that the whitest putty powder is the purest provided it be heavy, some of the common kinds are brown and yellow, whilst others from the intentional admixture of a little ivory black are known as *grey putty*. The pure white putty, and which is used by marble workers, opticians, and some others, is the smoothest and most cutting; it should consist of the oxide of tin alone, but to lessen the difficulty of manufacture, a very little lead, (the linings of tea chests,) or else an alloy called *shruff* (prepared in ingots by the pewterers) is added to assist the oxidation.

The putty powder of commerce of good fair quality, is made of about equal parts of tin and lead, or tin and shruff; the common dark coloured kinds are prepared of lead only, but these are much harsher to the touch and altogether inferior.

Perhaps the most extensive use of putty powder is in glass and marble works, but the best kind serves admirably as plate powder, and for the general purposes of polishing.

2.—Putty Powder for Fine Optical Purposes is prepared by Mr. A. Ross by the following method, which is the result of many experiments. Metallic tin is dissolved in nitro-muriatic acid, and precipitated from the filtered solution by liquid ammonia, both fluids being largely diluted with water. The per-oxide of tin is then washed in abundance of water, collected on a cloth filter, and squeezed as dry as possible in a piece of new clean linen; the mass is now subjected to pressure in a screw press, or between lever boards, to make it as dry as possible. When the lump thus produced has been broken in pieces and dried in the air, it is finely levigated while dry, on a plate of glass with an iron spatula, and afterwards exposed in a crucible to a *low* white heat.

Before the per-oxide has been heated, or whilst it is in the levigated *hydrous* state, the putty powder possesses but little cutting quality, as under the microscope the particles then appear to have no determined form, or to be *amorphous*, and on being wetted to resume the gelatinous condition of the hydrous precipitate, so as to be useless for polishing; whereas when the powder is heated, to render it *anhydrous*, most of the particles take their natural form, that of *lamellar crystals*, and act with far more energy, (yet without scratching,) than any of the ordinary polishing powders. The whole mass requires to be washed or elutriated in the usual manner after having been heated, in order to separate the coarser particles.

Mr. Ross usually adds a little crocus to the putty powder by way of colouring matter, as it is then easier to learn the quantity of powder that remains on the polishing tool; and it may be added that this is the polishing powder employed by Mr. Ross in making his recently improved achromatic object glasses for astronomical purposes.

QUARTZ.—Pure silex, occurs both crystalline and amorphous and is polished after the mode described for Carnelian. The reader is also referred to the article Crystal, by which name Quartz is very commonly known in the arts.

RAGSTONE.—*See* Hone Slates, article 1.

RED STUFF.—A name applied by watchmakers to some kinds of crocus, or the oxide of iron, the manufacture of which is described under the head Oxide of Iron.

RHODIUM, which is an extremely hard metal, is generally figured and ground on an iron lap, into the surface of which fragments of diamond have been hammered. As a temporary expedient rhodium may be polished on a brass lap with oilstone powder and oil, using a high velocity.

ROCK CRYSTAL.—*See* CRYSTAL.

ROTTENSTONE is a variety of Tripoli, almost peculiar to England, and proves a most valuable material for giving polish and lustre to a great variety of articles, as silver, the metals, glass, and in the hands of the lapidary even to the hardest stones. It is found in considerable quantities both in Derbyshire and South Wales.

ROUGE.—*See* OXIDE OF IRON, articles 1 and 4.

RUBBERS.—The rubbers used in polishing often follow very nearly the form of the plane, the file, or the turning tool, accordingly as the respective artizans use the plane, file, or turning tool in their several avocations. For instance, the carpenter wraps glass paper around a square flat piece of cork ; the smith and others using files, fold emery paper upon that instrument, or use, after the manner of the file, square pieces of wood and metal fed with the several powders mixed with oil, and they also employ either the sides or the sloping ends of square slips of the polishing stones.

Many of the turned works in the metals, &c. are polished with pointed sticks of deal, by the ends of which the gritty substances are forcibly applied as the work revolves.

2.—THE RUBBER USED BY MASONS AND STATUARIES is frequently a slab of grit stone, to which a handle is attached by means of an iron strap, or cement. Sometimes the handle is short and perpendicular, at other times long and horizontal, or inclined at a small angle or loosely attached by an eye bolt, and stones of two or three qualities, from coarse to fine, are used in succession. The same forms are also given to the handles of flat plates of iron and lead that are fed with sharp sand for polishing stone, or with emery for metal ; and the plate may in this case be made of such a weight as to supply the required pressure, leaving to the workman alone to put it in movement to and fro upon the work, with strokes evenly distributed throughout its surface.

3.—THE BLOCK OR CLOTH RUBBER USED FOR MARBLE, consists of a wooden block about 12 or 14 inches long, 3 to 6 wide, and 2 to 3 thick, a hole is bored through the wood at one end for a transverse stick or handle which projects, horizontally on both sides, and there are fillets of wood on the top by which lumps of lead are temporarily affixed to give the required pressure. Felted cloth nearly half an inch thick, (called *nap*,) is fixed below the rubber by folding the cloth a little way up the ends and nailing it, or thinner woollen and also one or more layers of coarse linen cloth are also used according to the degree of hardness required.

4.—LARGE CLOTH RUBBERS for polishing marble are sometimes made of woollen or other rags placed in a rectangular iron frame, connected by two side screws which compress the rags into a dense mass, the surface of which is allowed to wear itself flat or it is levelled with a red-hot iron ; sometimes the ring is entire and the rags are fixed by wedges, at other times the ring is in two parts and connected by side screws to produce the compression, and a socket is added for the attachment of the handle by which the rubber is moved.

5.—SMALL CLOTH RUBBERS OR ROLLERS, used for various purposes in polishing, are commonly made of a coil of list or the selvedge of woollen cloth, wound up spirally to the diameter of two to four inches and tied round tightly with string. They are usually covered with a cloth of some kind that may easily be renewed.

6.—RUBBERS FOR FRENCH POLISHING are made of little balls of wadding, (that used for ladies dresses,) covered with a linen rag. The rubber is placed on the open mouth of the bottle which is then turned up, the varnish thus collected is covered with a second rag, and moistened with one or two drops of linseed oil, the varnish gradually exudes according to the degree of pressure given to the ball, which is of about the size of a walnut, and is thrown away after four or five minutes' use, as it hardens from the accumulation of the varnish and then scratches instead of polishing the work.

RUBY.—*See* SAPPHIRE, of which it is considered to be a variety. For the preparation of ruby holes for the pivots of watches, *see* vol. 1, pages 178—9.

RUMBLE or Shaking Machine.—This is a contrivance sometimes used for polishing small articles principally by their attrition against each other. The rumble is a cylindrical vessel with a side door for the introduction of the work, and is generally made to revolve as a churn by a winch handle or pulley, or is shaken endways by a crank in imitation of the mode of cleaning nails in a sack, and it is thence called a shaking machine. The following are some of the uses of the rumble in mechanical works :—

For scouring small castings to remove the sand coat.

For brightening iron tacks previously to their being tinned, water is in this case introduced.

For polishing steel pens with sawdust after they are hardened and tempered.

For polishing needles and brass pins with saw dust or bran.

For polishing bone buttons with Trent sand.

For polishing lead shot with black-lead powder.

For cleaning the rust from cannon balls by their attrition against each other.

For drying small articles in saw dust after they have been annealed and pickled with acid, as in the blanks for coin.

For dissolving gums in spirits of wine as in making lackers and varnishes —and to which processes might be added numerous others.

SAND, which is nearly pure silex, is used in sawing and smoothing building stones and marbles, and in many other of the preliminary grinding and polishing processes. River sand and pit sand are in general sharper than sea sand, which is more rounded by attrition. Stone masons prefer the scrapings of roads that have been repaired with flint stones, the particles of which become knocked off and abraded by the traffic ; and engineers sometimes employ grindstone dust, collected after turning the grindstone into form, or obtained by crushing the grit or sandstone with a hammer or pestle and mortar, as the grindstone dust cuts more sharply than Flanders brick, another form in which sand is employed.

2.—TRENT SAND is collected from the banks of the river of that name which runs into the Humber. It is largely employed at Sheffield, and somewhat throughout England generally, for polishing. This sand is remarkably fine and sharp, and serves very economically many of the purposes of emery and other polishing powders prepared by art, it is very much used for Britannia metal goods.

The Sheffield cutlers are in the habit of making the Trent sand with water, into balls two or three inches diameter. The balls when dry are burned for a few hours in the kitchen fire, and from being of a moderately dark brown, become brick red. The lumps are then crushed between the hands and passed through a fine hair sieve. The burnt sand is considered to cut quicker than the unburnt.

For common work they use the blue stone pulverized and sifted instead of Trent sand, that is, the blue grit stone, not the blue hone slate used for brass work, &c. Flanders brick when scraped may be used as a substitute for Trent sand, but being contaminated with the clay required in forming the brick, it cuts less keenly than the unmixed sand.

3.—SAND PAPER is made with the common house sand, and only of one degree of coarseness, but in other respects exactly like glass paper, to which it is greatly inferior ; as the particles of sand are less angular and cutting than those of glass, when applied upon wood, &c., but on metals sand paper assumes a character intermediate between glass paper and emery paper.

SAPPHIRE has been selected as one of the three general examples of lapidary work, described in this catalogue, namely Alabaster in explanation of the mode of working the softest stones, and other allied substances, Carnelian in explanation of the modes pursued with stones of greater hardness than Alabaster, but inferior in this respect to Sapphire, the subject of the present article. Sapphires are alone exceeded in hardness by the diamond, which last is pre-eminent over all natural substances, in point of hardness.

The previous articles on Alabaster and Carnelian may with advantage be here referred to, as containing much general information upon the lapidary art, and which will be more fully described in the 34th Chapter of this volume ; but it should be here observed that the harder and smaller the gems to be wrought, the harder are the metallic laps or mills respectively employed by the lapidary, and although sapphire may in truth be entirely wrought by the method employed for carnelian, the present will be found the more usual, as well as the more economical practice.

As gems are usually retained of as great size as their irregularities of surface will admit, sapphires and many other gems are seldom reduced in size except by grinding, or as it is more commonly called, by *cutting* them. When however they are *divided* it is more commonly done by cleavage or splitting, than by slitting or sawing, and which process when resorted to, is effected nearly as usual with an iron slicer fed with diamond dust, and lubricated with brick oil ; the slicer for sapphires is however very much smaller than for general lapidary works, and is principally met with in the hands of watch jewellers.

Secondly, the lapidary commonly grinds and cuts the facets on sapphires upon a copper lap, supplied with diamond dust and brick oil, which cuts more quickly and delicately than the lead mill with emery ; and 3rdly, these gems are polished upon a copper lap with rottenstone and water, the tool being jagged after the manner more fully described under the head CARNELIAN.

2.—The practice of the watch jeweller in making the pivot holes for watches in ruby and sapphire, is described in the first volume of this work, pages 178—9 : Diamond powder is used throughout, and of three degrees of fineness, the coarsest on copper tools, the medium on glass, and the finest on pewter tools for the last polish.

Phillips says the sapphire has obtained several names amongst mineralogists and jewellers, dependent on its colour and lustre, namely,—

White Sapphire, when transparent or translucent.

Oriental Sapphire, when blue.

Oriental Amethyst, when violet blue.

Oriental Topaz, when yellow.

Oriental Emerald, when green.

Oriental Ruby, when red.

Chatoyant, or *Opalescent Sapphire* with pearly reflections.

Girasol Sapphire, when transparent, and with a pale reddish or pale bluish reflection.

ASTERIA or *Star Sapphire,* exhibits 6 milk-white rays, radiating from the center of an hexagonal prism, and placed at right angles to its sides. The asteria is found in both the red and blue varieties of Sapphire, and is always cut *en cabochon* to show the figure.

All the above Sapphires, the Chrysoberyl, occasionally the Zircon and some others of the gems, are cut with diamond powder and polished with rottenstone, as above described.

SARD.—A variety of Chalcedony that is wrought by the lapidary like Carnelian.

SARDONYX.—*Idem.*

SATIN STONE or fibrous gypsum is treated much the same as Alabaster, but requires additional tenderness. *See* ALABASTER, article 3, also vol. 1, page 164.

SAW DUST is used by jewellers, brass finishers, and others, in drying the metals after they have been pickled and washed. The saw dust of boxwood is preferred for jewellery on account of its freedom from turpentine or resinous matter ; the saw dust of beech wood is next in estimation.

SCAGLIOLA, Keene's Cement, and other factitious marbles, are treated nearly the same as marble ; but they generally require less labour because they are accurately moulded into form, and are somewhat softer than the generality of marbles ; but when the materials are of unequal hardness the difficulty of the polishing is increased, from the softer parts wearing down too rapidly, and leaving the surface irregular.

SERPENTINE, when in large pieces, is treated like marble ; when the serpentine is in small pieces, that are recent and soft, the lapidary employs much the same mode that he would in grinding and polishing Alabaster, (*see* article 3,) or the routine for Carnelian, when from exposure to the atmosphere the serpentine has attained its greatest degree of hardness.

SHELLS.—On reference to vol. 1, pages 118—120, a few remarks on the descriptive characters of the porcelanous and nacreous shells will be found. Some of these shells are cut through to show their internal sections or structures, whilst others are simply polished exteriorly in their entire states, as specimens of natural history, or for their intrinsic beauty, some few of the shells are cut up in the manufacture of various useful and ornamental works. They are usually treated as follows :—

1.—PORCELANOUS SHELLS, which are generally univalve or single shells, such as the whelks, limpets and cowries, so far resemble porcelain or enamel as not to admit of being otherwise cut than with the apparatus employed by the lapidary ; and accordingly, when porcelanous shells are divided to exhibit their sections, it is effected by the Slicer, with Diamond Powder.

The porcelanous shells do not in general require the coarser or grinding tools, as few of them present the rough coat or epidermis of the nacreous shells, and it is therefore only commonly needful to restore or increase their natural polish with the list or brush wheel of the lapidary. Putty powder may be used, but rottenstone, from its greater hardness, is more effective on porcelanous shells : of course, similar wheels running in a vertical plane, such as those of the cutler and workers in horn and ivory, may be also used with equally good effect.

2.—NACREOUS SHELLS, which are generally bivalve shells, such as those of the various oysters, muscles, &c., are thus named from *nacre*, the French for mother-of-pearl, the covering of the *ostrea margaritifera* of the Indian seas. The nacreous shells are much softer than the porcelanous, and may be sawn, filed and turned with moderate facility, but from the quantity of lime they contain they feel harsh and scratchy under the tools.

The pearl shell is much employed in the ornamental art, and the usual course for its preparation into square, angular and circular plates, and cylindrical pieces, is first, with saws of different and ordinary kinds ; the pieces are then roughly shaped on the edge of a grindstone turned into grooves, and afterwards smoothed on the flat side of the stone : many use soap and water with the stone, which lessens its liability to become clogged. *See* also vol. 1, pages 119, 120.

3.—PEARL SHELL IN DETACHED PIECES, such as counters, silk winders, &c., immediately after having been ground, and when shaped on their edges, are smoothed with Trent sand or pumice-stone and water, on a buff wheel or hand polisher, and are finished with rottenstone.

The latter powder, although sometimes used with oil or water, is more frequently moistened with a little sulphuric acid, nearly or quite undiluted, this produces a far more brilliant polish, which may possibly arise from the partial destruction of the surface, thus developing in a more decided manner the striated formation of the pearl shell, and to which peculiarity of structure its variegated lustre is ascribed.

4.—PEARL WORKS COMBINED AS IN BOXES are most generally reduced to a flat surface by filing and scraping. Mr. Vanham says that first pumice-stone and then putty powder are used on buff sticks with water, and the final polish is given with a buff stick and rottenstone moistened with sulphuric acid, this mode is available for inlaid works with gold or silver, but not for those having tortoiseshell or other substances that would be attacked by the acid. The buff stick is expeditious, but for very flat surfaces, a flat deal stick covered with one layer of linen rag is preferable although slower.

5.—TURNED WORKS in general only require fine emery paper, and then rottenstone on woollen rag with sulphuric acid, but oil may be used instead of the latter.

6.—PEARL HANDLES FOR RAZORS.—The Sheffield manufacturers slightly rivet the handles together in pairs, after which they are 1st scraped, 2ndly " *sand buffed* " on the wheel with Trent sand and water, 3dly, " *gloss buffed* " on the wheel with rottenstone and oil, or sometimes with dry chalk rubbed on the same wheel, and 4thly they are " *handed up,*" or polished with dry rottenstone and the naked hand.

7.—PEARL SHELL, when polished by the lapidary, is treated in the mode followed with ALABASTER. *See* article 3.

8.—SHELL CAMEOS.—A very suitable material for cameos is found in the various conch shells or *Strombs*, the substance of which consists of two distinct layers of different colours, textures and hardness, and which may be considered respectively to partake of the nature of nacreous and porcelanous shells, the chemical compositions of which were noticed in vol. 1, page 118. The outer coat or layer in the most suitable specimens of conch shells is nearly colourless, of uniform texture, and like that on the nacreous shells admits of being readily operated upon by steel cutting tools, and which may be made to produce a smooth and well-finished surface, this outer layer is therefore suited for the carved parts of cameos, the ground being formed of the under layer of the shell, which in the most suitable kinds is of a dark colour, and allied to the porcelanous shells, being somewhat brittle and so hard and compact as not to admit of being readily cut with steel tools.

The best kind of conch shell for carving into cameos is found on the Southern coast of America, and also on the coast of the West India Islands, and commonly known as the " *black conch ;* " in these shells the contrast of colour is the most decided, the under layer being very dark or nearly black, especially in the old or full grown shells, which are the hardest and most compact, and also possess the greatest amount of the white or outer layer, the part to be carved. In the pink conch shell the contrast of colour is not so great, and as it does not at all resemble the onyx in which antique cameos were cut, it is but little used for the best works ; never- theless, some very beautiful specimens of carving on the pink conch shell are to be met with, and the delicacy of the colours gives a very pleasing effect.

The most suitable shell having been selected it is cut into pieces of the required forms for the cameos ; this process, which must be cautiously per- formed, is best effected by means of the slitting mill fed with diamond powder, described in the chapter on Lapidary Work, but the cutting may be also effected with a blade of iron or steel, such as a thin table knife blade notched to form teeth, and fed with emery and water, a process similar to that by which the stone mason cuts slabs of freestone and marble with a smooth blade of iron fed with sand and water.

The piece of shell having been cut out is next carefully ground to the general form of the cameo, as square, lozenge, elliptical or other shape, upon an ordinary grindstone, the face and back of the shell being also levelled and reduced to the appropriate thickness. A slip of Turkey oilstone may be used with advantage to give the last finish to the edges of the shell after the upper white layer has been removed from it, for when the shell has lost the support of the white layer, it will be found that the coarse cut of the grindstone will fill it with minute cracks, which frequently spread over the surface after the cameo has been some time finished.

Having prepared a piece of shell of the desired form and thickness it is next cemented on a block of wood about 3 inches diameter, or of a con- venient size to be grasped firmly in the hand ; care should be taken to place the piece of shell level and near the center of the block, in order that all parts of the cameo may be operated upon with equal facility. Now sketch with a pencil the contour of the subject to be carved, and follow this pencil- mark with a scratch point ; having removed the surrounding white substance by means of files and gravers proceed to develope the figure by the use of smaller tools. A very convenient form of carving tool for this purpose may be made of pieces of steel wire about 6 or 8 inches long, flattened at the ends and hardened ; they are lastly ground to an angle of about 45 degrees, and carefully sharpened on an oilstone. The largest tools may be made of wire about $\frac{1}{8}$ of an inch diameter ; smaller wire will serve for tools of a medium size, but for the smallest tools an ordinary darning needle left quite hard, and ground to the same angle, when inserted in a wooden handle, will be found very useful in deepening the finer lines. The advantage of this form of tool consists in the absence of any angles that would be liable to scratch the work, and a tool thus formed admits of being used either as a gouge, or as a chisel, according as the flat or round side is brought to act on the work.

To guide the tool in the act of cutting, the left hand should grasp the block upon which the cameo is cemented, the thumb being placed close to the cameo ; the tool held in the right hand should be so rested against the thumb of the left hand as to form a fulcrum, upon which the tool may be moved as a lever in short arcs of the circle, with a scraping action which removes the material as a powder, care being taken that every cut is made obliquely downwards towards the black ground ; should any of the cuts be made towards the surface, or even parallel therewith, there would be danger that small pieces would be chipped off, and which would be destructive to the cameo.

As in all other processes of producing form by reduction, the general shape should be first wrought with care to leave every projection rather in excess, to be gradually reduced as the details and finish of the work are approached. To render the high parts more distinct during the process of carving, it will be found convenient to mark them slightly with a black lead pencil. Throughout the cutting great caution should be observed, that in removing the white thickness, the dark ground is not damaged, as the natural surface of the dark layer is far superior to any that can be given artificially ; indeed, should the ground be broken up at one part, it would be requisite from its lamellar structure to remove the entire scale or lamina from the whole surface, a process that will be found very tedious, and much more difficult than the separation of the white from the black thickness.

In order that the finished cameo may possess a distinct outline at all points of view, it is desirable to adopt the system followed in antique cameos, namely, to leave all the edges of the figure quite square from the ground, and not gradually rounded down to the dark surface ; should this latter method be followed, it will be found that the outline is in many places undefined, owing to the colour of the white raised figure of the cameo gradually merging into that of the dark ground ; this evil is entirely avoided by leaving the extreme edge of the figure quite square, for about the thickness of one-fiftieth of an inch.

The surface of the cameo should be finished as nearly as possible with the cutting tools, as all polishing with abrasive powders is liable to remove the sharp angles of the figures, and deteriorate the cameo by leaving the form undefined. When, however, the work has been finished as smooth as possible with the cutting tools, the final polish may be given with a little putty powder used dry, upon a moderately stiff tooth brush, applied with care, and rather to the dark ground than to the carved surface : this is the concluding process ; after which the cameo is ready for removal from the block prior to mounting.

SILEX is the basis of tripoli, sandstones, sand and some other polishing powders. It constitutes from about 65 to 98 per cent. of these substances, and is the fourth or fifth of the polishing materials in the order of hardness,—silex being preceded by carbon and alumina, and probably by the oxides of iron and tin. *See* page 1029 of this volume.

Dutch rush and charcoal owe their abrasive qualities, and the enamel of teeth its hardness, to the silex they respectively contain.

See also CRYSTAL and QUARTZ.

SILVERSMITHS' work, after having been filed is generally rubbed, 1st with a lump of pumice-stone and water, 2ndly with a slip of water of Ayr stone and water, 3dly a revolving brush with rottenstone and oil, 4thly an old black worsted stocking with oil and rottenstone, and 5thly it is finished with the hand alone, the deep black lustre being given with rouge of great fineness. The corners and edges are often burnished with a steel burnisher, which is lubricated with soap and water if at all.

In this case and in all others of polishing with the naked hand, it is generally found that women succeed better than men, and that some few, from the peculiar texture and condition of the skin, greatly excel in the art of polishing. The skin should be soft and very slightly moist, as the polishing powder then attaches itself conveniently, and there is just sufficient adhesion between the hand and work to make the operation proceed rapidly. A dry hand becomes hard and horny, and is liable to scratch the work, and excess of moisture is also objectionable, as the hand is then too slippery.

2.—THE PLATED REFLECTORS FOR LIGHT-HOUSES are cleaned with rouge, which is dusted on from a muslin bag, and rubbed over them with a clean dry wash-leather.

A thin film of oxide will nevertheless occasionally form on the surface of the reflector, and this is removed with a piece of leather, with rouge moistened with spirits of wine, which dissolves the oxide, after which the dry rubber is applied as above.

SKIVE.—The iron lap used by the diamond polishers in finishing the facets of diamonds for jewellery. The skive is charged with fragments of diamond powder that are burnished into its surface.—*See* DIAMOND, also page 176, vol. 1.

SLATE.—The ordinary slate used for building purposes does not admit of being highly polished, but it is rubbed smooth, first with an iron plate fed with sharp river sand and water, and then with lumps of gritstones, of which two or three kinds gradually finer one than the other, are also used with water. The rubstones employed, depend principally on their relative abundance in the respective districts.

A lump of pumice-stone leaves a grain on slate suitable for writing upon, and the greyness is removed either by a slight rub of oil, or what is better a wash of common writing ink allowed to dry on. A disk of slate cemented to a wood chuck is useful to the amateur for receiving in the lathe rough sketches of eccentric patterns, and slate also serves for drawing boards.

As noticed in vol. 1, page 165, slate has been recently employed for chimney pieces, internal decoration and furniture, in which case it is rubbed smooth, then japanned like black and other marbles, and also of all colours and devices, after the manner of tea trays ; when the objects have been baked to harden the japan they are first smoothed with pumice-stone, and then polished with rottenstone, after the ordinary mode described under JAPANNED WORKS.

SLICER.—*See* SLITTING MILL.

SLITTING MILL or the Slicer, is a very thin sheet-iron disk, the edge of which is charged with diamond powder, and lubricated with brick oil. The slicer is the circular saw of the lapidary. *See* the chapter on LAPIDARY WORK.

SNAKE STONE.—*See* HONE SLATES, article 3.

SOAP AND WATER have been proposed by Mr. Reveley, to be used on hones instead of oil, in setting razors and other fine instruments, as being more cleanly and effective.

The hone is to be wiped clean with a wet sponge, and the lump of soap also wetted, is to be rubbed on until it produces a thin lather, which is to be sponged off when the hone is laid by.—*Trans. Soc. of Arts*, vol. xxxix. p. 137.

SOFT WOOD.—*See* WOOD.

SPECULAR IRON ORE.—*See* OXIDE OF IRON, articles 5 and 6.

SPECULUM METAL.—The mode of grinding and polishing this alloy will be noticed in Chap. XXXIII.

SPHERES.—Mr. Henry's Guy's method of grinding spheres will be described in Chap. XXXIII. Sect. 4. *See* also the article MARBLES FOR CHILDREN, in this Catalogue.

STEATITE, especially when first raised, is a soft unctuous magnesian mineral, and is thence called soapstone, but like Potstone, and Serpentine, which it nearly resembles in its constituent parts, it becomes considerably harder by exposure to the air. Steatite when recent, may be treated by the method practised in Germany with POTSTONE, (*which see* on page 1087,) and when indurated, by the same routine that is employed for alabaster by the lapidary. Many of the Chinese idols and other figures, are carved in Steatite, which has thence been called Figure Stone. *See* vol. 1, page 166.

STEEL.—The parts of Machinery made in steel, are polished as described in the general article MACHINERY, in this Catalogue, page 1072.

STRAGGLING.—A term indicating the mode of dressing the surfaces of grindstones, which is fully described under WHEELS, article 16.

SURFACES.—The principal modes of grinding plane surfaces are described in Chap. XXXIII. Sect. 1.

TIN is seldom polished except when in the form of tin-plate, for which purpose, rottenstone and oil, or whitening and oil may be used, dry whiting being lastly applied to remove the grease.

Works in solid tin are occasionally made by pewterers, and polished the same as that useful alloy. *See* PEWTER.

TIN, OXIDE OF.—*See* PUTTY POWDER.

TOPAZ ; of the Brazilian Topazes, there are the yellow, which is best known, the blue, and the white, the latter being more commonly called the Mina Nova. The Brazilian Topazes are worked like Carnelian, the Oriental Topaz, which is in fact a yellow variety of Sapphire, is treated like other Sapphires, and is cut into facets with diamond powder and polished with rottenstone, as more fully described under the head SAPPHIRE. The difference in hardness of the two gems is satisfactorily accounted for by their analysis, as the Brazilian Topaz contains about 50 per cent. of alumine, the Oriental about 98 per cent. of alumine ; this substance being next in hardness to the diamond.

TORTOISESHELL.—The covering of the *Testudo imbricata*, and on the working of which the reader is referred to vol. 1, pages 126—135, is usually polished after one of the following modes :—

1.—TORTOISESHELL HANDLES for razors and penknives, combs, spectacle frames, and many similar works, after they have been sawn out and moulded into form, (*see* vol. 1, page 130,) are smoothed with a float or single cut file technically known as a *quannet*, (*see* vol. 2, page 838,) and then shaved or scraped smooth with a scraper like that used by joiners. Cutlers often use an old razor blade the edge of which has been sharpened at right angles, by placing the blade perpendicularly on the oilstone.

The works are then very sparingly polished on a wheel covered with thick buff leather, such as the bull neck, or sea cow, and fed with calcined Trent sand and oil, (*see* article on HORN, page 1067,) and they are finished on a similar wheel supplied with rottenstone and oil, occasionally the latter wheel is alone used. Razor handles and some other works are often *handed up*, or finished with the naked hand and dry rottenstone, and works required to be very nice and flat are more generally treated as follows :—

2.—FLAT WORKS IN TORTOISESHELL, such as card and needle cases and others that require to be kept flat, are floated and scraped as above, and Mr. W. Vanham before referred to says, that he afterwards successively employs pumice-stone, putty-powder and rottenstone on three different buff sticks, and all generally with water but sometimes with oil, as the treatment varies according to the material inlaid in the tortoiseshell, which is lastly finished with the hand and rottenstone or whiting. When the works have mouldings and sharp edges that would be rounded by the buff stick, the same materials are used on slips of wood filed to the appropriate forms.

3.—TORTOISESHELL WHEN TURNED IN THE LATHE is usually smoothed with fine glass or emery paper, and finished with rottenstone and oil, on linen or woollen rag.

TOUCHSTONE is a compact black basalt or Lydian stone, of a smooth and uniform nature, and is used principally by goldsmiths and jewellers as a ready means of determining the value of gold and silver by the touch, as it is termed— that is, by first rubbing the article under examination upon the stone, its appearance forms some criterion ; and, as a further test, a drop of acid, of known strength, is let fall upon it, and its effect upon the metal denotes its value.

TRENT SAND.—*See* SAND.

TRIPOLI, according to Phillips, is an earth of a grey yellow or red colour, used in polishing, that was first introduced from Tripoli in Africa, whence its name, but it is found in France and elsewhere, and is said to contain nearly 90 per cent. of silex.

2. RED TRIPOLI has been largely prepared from a brick earth found near Battle in Sussex. When burned in lumps it is nearly as heavy as emery stone, after which it is ground and sifted, and presents the appearance of crocus, but is coarser and is used for similar but inferior purposes.

A Red Tripoli prepared by calcining and pulverising *Clunch* or *Curl Stone*, found in the coal and iron districts of Staffordshire, &c. is highly recommended by Mr. Gill. *See* the articles on the OXIDES OF IRON.

3. YELLOW TRIPOLI, sometimes called French Tripoli, is employed for polishing generally, and amongst other substances for light-coloured hardwoods that would be stained by the absorption of darker powders into their pores. A large quantity of fine yellow tripoli was obtained in digging the canal in the Regent's Park, London ; some additional particulars are given on this subject at the conclusion of the article on VARNISHED WORKS.

TURKEY OILSTONE.—*See* OILSTONE.

TURQUOISE.—The Oriental Calaite, or Turquoise, is a comparatively soft gem, found in the mountainous districts of Khorassan in Persia, those of a dark blue colour being the most esteemed. They are somewhat rarely engraved as seals, but are mostly used by the Persians, nearly of their natural forms, for ornamenting bridles, the handles of scimitars, &c., as the Orientals remove in general but little of the weight of gems in cutting and polishing them, which they effect on corundum wheels, although they are well acquainted with the use of diamond powder as an abrasive for such works as require it.

In Europe the turquoise is generally cut and polished by the method pursued with alabaster and other soft and rounded stones.

TURTLESHELL is worked and polished the same as TORTOISESHELL, *which see.*

VARNISHED WORKS of the finest kinds, such as the wood work of harps, are thus treated. The wood is covered with about six layers of the white hard varnish, and allowed thoroughly to dry between each, this entirely fills the pores of the wood ; the face is then rubbed quite smooth with fine glass paper. The ornamental painting is then done, after which about eight or ten coats more of varnish are laid on, and at every third coat the surface is rubbed with fine glass paper to remove the brush marks.

When all the varnish is put on, and has become hard, the surface is rubbed with fine pumice-stone powder and water on woollen rags, the work is allowed to stand for a day or two, and is then polished with yellow tripoli and water, after which it is washed quite clean with a sponge, and wiped dry with a clean wash leather.

The varnish is now touched at a few places, with the finger smeared with fine rendered tallow, which is then thoroughly rubbed all over with the ends of the fingers ; clean wheat flour is dusted over the work, and also well rubbed in with the fingers ; and after the removal of the flour, the surface is slightly rubbed with a clean old silk handkerchief, which completes the splendid lustre given to these instruments.

It should be observed that the rottenstone of commerce is sometimes ground very fine with a stone muller before use, and so is likewise the tripoli. The tripoli used by the Messrs. Erats, from whom these particulars were gathered, was obtained from the earth removed in digging the canal in the Regent's Park, London ; the dry lumps when cleared from the clay by which they are surrounded, are of a light brown yellow, and as hard as a stone, so as to require to be crushed with a hammer previously to being ground.

WASHING or the separation of powders into different degrees of fineness by washing over or elutriation.—On the advantages of the careful separation of the polishing powders some remarks were offered in the introduction to this division of the work (see page 1031) ; the practice of washing, which is within the reach of every one, is described in this Catalogue under the head EMERY, articles 3, 4, 5 and 6.

The author has been in the habit of washing some others of the polishing powders, but generally into two sizes only of each ; the times employed for their respective depositions, which are somewhat influenced by the specific gravities of the substances are subjoined.

POWDER.	No. 1.	No. 2.
Chalk	1 minute	2 minutes
Crocus	10 seconds	30 seconds
Oilstone Powder . . .	30 ,,	3 minutes
Pumice-stone Powder . . .	30 ,,	3 ,,
Rottenstone . . .	30 ,,	3 ,,
Tripoli	30 ,,	1 ,,

Washing is constantly employed in metallurgy, for the separation of the metallic particles from the earthy matters in the pounded ores ; in the manufacture of porcelain for the separation of the coarse and large particles from the fine clay, and prepared flint, therein used, and in the preparation of polishing powders and some drugs.

WATCHWORK.—As regards the parts in steel, *see* MACHINERY, article 13, and the parts in brass *see* BRASS, article 6.

WATER OF AYR STONE.—*See* HONE SLATES, article 3.

WELCH CLEARING STONE.—*See* HONE SLATES, article 10.

WHALEBONE.—Some of the applications of this peculiar substance are noticed in vol. 1, pages 135-6. To polish whalebone it is scraped with steel scrapers or pieces of window glass, rubbed with emery paper, and then with woollen cloth supplied with tripoli or rottenstone. The polishing lathe is also used for whalebone, which is then treated like horn or tortoiseshell.

WHEELS.—In almost every branch of the manufacturing and mechanical arts, the processes of abrasion are advantageously fulfilled by rotatory motion applied to various grinders and polishers. These are generally circular disks, made of a great variety of substances, and are for the most part fed with abrasive powders. Most of these apparatus, with the exception principally of the grindstone, are known by the cutler and the tool maker as *wheels ;* by the mechanician as *laps,* by the lapidary as *mills,* by the optician as *tools,* and also by many other conventional names ; the first name, or WHEELS, has been selected for the title of this article as being the most general. A few words will be first offered on the principal modes in which these wheels are employed.

1.—GENERAL MECHANICAL ARRANGEMENTS.—*Cutlers and tool makers* place the axes of the wheels *horizontally,* and employ both for the grindstone and the polishing wheels the same framework or apparatus. *Mechanicians* frequently employ nearly the same arrangement as cutlers and tool makers, and in some few cases mount the laps and wheels as adjuncts to the lathe.

Seal Engravers always use a small lathe mandrel, to which their delicate grinders are attached. *Lapidaries,* unlike the above-named artizans, mostly place the axes of their mills *vertically,* and frequently drive them by the left hand, as will be explained. *Opticians* fix their spherical tools for grinding and polishing lenses, horizontally, on the top of a fixed post, and rub the lenses or specula upon the same with an elliptical motion given by the hands, and they continually walk round the post, to change the direction in which the grinder and tool successively meet. *See* Chap. XXXIII.

These and other mechanical arrangements, will however be touched upon in the course of the chapters immediately following, and therefore, it is intended at this place principally to direct attention to the abrasive apparatus, and which will be classed under seven heads namely :—

A.—Wheels of Natural Stone such as Grindstones.

B.—Wheels of Factitious Stone, or Composition Wheels.

C.—Wheels of Metal, or Metallic Laps.

D.—Wheels of Wood, or Glaze Wheels.

E.—Wheels of Leather, or Buff Wheels.

F.—Wheels of Cloth, or Cloth Wheels.

G.—Wheels of Bristles, or Wire, or Brush Wheels.

In every case but the first, the cement, metal, wood, leather, cloth or bristles, are to be viewed solely as the vehicles or carriers by which the abrasive matters or powders are applied. And in speaking of these apparatus, their structure will be first noticed, and some observations on the modes of using them and keeping them in order, will be then subjoined. The first of the seven sections or the natural grindstones will be now considered under their principal although varied features.

SECTION A.—WHEELS OF NATURAL STONE, SUCH AS GRINDSTONES.

2.—The reader is referred to the article GRITSTONE, for the description of the principal varieties of the sandstones or gritstones used in the mechanical arts for various purposes, the most important of which uses is the grinding of various cutting tools ; indeed the removal of the grindstones from our workshops, would be an almost insuperable loss. The principal modes of employing grindstones will be now described.

3.—GRINDSTONES USED BY HAND.—In the most primitive method the tools to be ground are simply rubbed on the quiescent stone, as stonemasons and others whet their chisels on the foot pavement, after the manner of sharpening a tool upon a hone ; or smaller slabs of gritstones are employed after the manner of the butcher's steel, in fact as in whetting a scythe with the rubstone.

It is however very far more usual to fashion the grindstone as a thick disk, or very short cylinder, and to perforate it with a square central hole or eye, for the iron axis upon which the stone is mounted and put in rotation, as described in the succeeding paragraphs.

4.—GRINDSTONES MOVED BY WINCH-HANDLES.—These present the greatest degree of simplicity of all rotary grindstones, and must be familiar to almost every one ; when the stone does not exceed about one foot in diameter, it is commonly mounted on the upper edges of the little wooden box or trough, which serves both to support the pivots of the axis on which the stone revolves, and to contain the water with which it is moistened. The one extremity of the spindle is squared for the winch-handle, the central part is squared for the convenience of wedging on the stone with wooden wedges, and there are cylindrical necks or pivots on the axis, the bearings for which are sometimes of hard wood such as lignum vitæ, or far better of metal.

In the most common form, two iron staples which surround the pivots are simply driven into the top edges of the wooden trough ; in the best form, the trough and bearings are both in metal, and there is a small bar or rest parallel with the axis for supporting the tool which is held in the right hand, whilst the stone is turned with the left. The stones thus mounted sometimes measure nearly as much as 20 inches in diameter, and are used by general artizans for small tools and also by opticians for fitting in the lenses of spectacles.

5.—ORDINARY GRINDSTONES USED BY CARPENTERS, SMITHS, and many others, and which stones vary from about two to four feet in diameter, are often mounted very nearly the same as the last, so as to be worked with a winch-handle, which is then however turned by an assistant, but the frames for these larger stones are continued to the ground, or are sometimes let into the ground, and between the four legs of the frame is placed the water trough.

In these cases, there is no objection to the stone dipping a little way into the water whilst it revolves, as the surface velocity of the stone can be scarcely so great as to cause the water to be thrown off by the centrifugal motion ; but the stone should not be allowed to remain immersed at one particular part, or it will be there softened and become more disposed to wear irregularly ; the trough is consequently often suspended on a hinge or joint at the one extremity, and hung up by a chain at the other, so that it may be occasionally raised for moistening the stone.

6.—GRINDSTONES MOVED WITH TREADLES.—For stones from about 20 to 40 inches diameter, this method is highly to be commended, as the stone whilst in rotation, then supplies enough momentum to act as a fly-wheel, and in such cases it is only needful that some part of the iron axis for the stone should be formed as a crank of three or four inches radius, from which a connecting rod, or crank hook should descend to the treadle, jointed to the two back feet of the framework, nearly as in a turning lathe. A higher velocity may be thus given to the grindstone than with a winch-handle, and the workman does not require an assistant to put the stone in motion as when a winch-handle is used. The employment of the treadle, is even now far from being so general as it deserves to be, notwithstanding that it was known and published so long as three centuries back.

7.—GRINDING LATHES, OR SMALL GRINDSTONES DRIVEN BY FOOTWHEELS AND TREADLES.—Stones not exceeding a foot to a foot and a half diameter, do not present sufficient momentum to admit of their being driven as in the last example, unless a foot wheel of moderate weight is added to the lower part of the frame, the upper part of which then carries the grindstone spindle fitted with a pulley, so that a leather strap or a catgut band may communicate the motion of the foot-wheel to the spindle, in a manner analogous to that employed in foot-lathes ; whence this arrangement has been called the GRINDING LATHE. The same frame or lathe is commonly fitted with buff and brush wheels, and is then much used by cutlers for many parts of their works, that require but secondary care ; this apparatus is also used by many of the workers in horn, tortoiseshell, ivory and other materials ; but cutlers always polish the blades and superior parts of cutlery, upon the apparatus next to be described.

8.—CUTLERS' GRINDSTONE DRIVEN BY THE FLY WHEEL.—Cutlers' grindstones range from about 6 to 24 inches diameter, and are fixed upon square iron spindles from 12 to 30 inches long, terminating in steel pointed centers ; the stone is wedged fast near the right hand extremity of the spindle, and near the left is fixed the pulley for a leather strap which usually measures from 1 to 2 inches wide. The strap commonly proceeds from a hand-wheel of about 5 or 6 feet diameter, turned by a labourer who is situated at the back of the grinder, and the entire arrangement, from the length of space occupied is familiarly termed *the long wheel,* but in large establishments, the stones are generally driven by steam or other power.

The framework for supporting the grindstone spindle, usually consists of two long pieces or sleepers that lie on the ground and are united at their extremities, they have near the one end two perpendicular posts or standards, at the upper parts of which are placed the hollow centers for the spindle to run in ; lignum vitæ is the material preferred for the centers, horn is sometimes used, and in a few cases screws with steel centers are employed. The center block on the left hand for the centers near the leather strap, is usually pierced with three or four holes on a horizontal line, for the convenience of making the strap more or less tight, and also for adapting it to pulleys differing somewhat in diameter, without shifting the wheel. Sometimes the post for the center on the right hand, is fitted between two transverse pieces or bearers, and secured by a wedge, like the popit heads of very common turning lathes in order to serve for spindles of various lengths ; because the same frame-work is commonly used by the cutler not only for grindstones, but also various laps, buffs and glaze wheels.

The Sheffield grinders generally employ ash for the center blocks and wedges for grindstone spindles, and they mostly run all their stones and glazers in one set of holes, and adjust the length of the straps for various sized pulleys by using short pieces of strap of different lengths, which they apply by means of round buckles.

Between the standards and below the stone lies a long narrow water trough of wood lined with lead or of cast iron, sometimes called the " *dog pan*," but which should never contain enough water to reach the stone, as the centrifugal motion would splash the water about in an inconvenient degree ; the water is therefore at intervals thrown on from a pail with the hand, or is allowed to flow from a thread-like jet on the *side* of the stone very near its periphery. The workman is seated astride a board called the *horse*, which rests behind on the bearers or sleepers of the frame, and in front is propped up by a transverse bar of wood, which is shifted to or from the stone, to adjust the front end of the horse to a convenient height, dependent on the diameter of the grind-stone.

The edge of the horse near the stone is commonly shod with iron, that it may be used for supporting the turning tool employed in *turning up* the grindstone, and the horse has mostly also a piece of leather or sacking or a sloping board to keep off the wet thrown up by the centrifugal motion. The framework is sometimes furnished with a splash-board, which is placed almost perpendicularly on the other end of the trough, and projects above the top of the stone, so as to catch most of the water that flies off and reconduct it to the trough ; but the splash board is not always added.

9.—THE POSITION OF THE GRINDER WHEN AT WORK is highly favourable, he is seated before and rather above the stone, with his feet resting upon the ground or other firm support, and in the act of grinding and polishing delicate works, they are held by both extremities in the two hands, whilst the elbows rest upon the knees, so that the grinder can thus keep his person very steady, and is enabled to feel with great delicacy and exactness the position of the work upon the stones or polishers. But in polishing the handles, springs, middle parts of pocket knives, and other small pieces the cutler frequently employs the grinding lathe just described in article 7.

10.—LARGE GRINDSTONES FOR HEAVY EDGE TOOLS, SAWS, GUN BARRELS &c. Manufacturers in these branches use much heavier grindstones than cutlers, and mount them somewhat differently. Stones larger than 3 feet diameter and 4 or 5 inches thick, and those extending to the dimensions of 8 or 10 feet diameter, and 12 to 16 inches thick, are commonly wedged upon square spindles having *cylindrical necks*, that run on bearings either of hardwood or metal, and the pulley is generally placed at the extremity of the spindle and outside the one bearing, so that it may be changed agreeably to the decreasing diameter of the stone without the trouble of lifting the stone from its bearings, which is not commonly done until it is worn too small for its particular use. A deep groove is then turned in the periphery of the stone, and which, after removal from the spindle, is split in two by chisels and iron wedges to serve for smaller works.

The arrangements of the trough, horse and splash-board, for large grindstones differ principally in size alone from the preceding ; frequently however the axis of the stone is level with the ground, and the bearings are fixed on two sleepers, between which the earth is simply excavated to form the trough, as the grinders' tools are generally of the most simple and inexpensive kind.

11.—LARGE STONES ARE ALWAYS DRIVEN BY POWER, a drum of three to five feet diameter commonly extends across the grinder's shop, and the stones are arranged in a line on each side of the same. The *surface velocity* of the drum is commonly about 200 feet in a minute, and the diameter of the pulley being about one third that of the stone, the surface velocity of the latter is from about 500 to 600 feet a minute. This speed gives rise with large stones, to so much momentum as to endanger their being split, if there should be the smallest flaw in the stone, or that from neglect it acquires a *heavy side*, from being allowed to wear out of the true concentric figure. The centrifugal force then sometimes breaks the stone, and drives the huge fragments with frightful violence through the roof or walls of the building, to the occasional destruction of human life.

12.—FLANGES AND RINGS TO PREVENT STONES FROM BREAKING. The liability of grindstones to be broken by excessive centrifugal force, is materially lessened if not altogether averted, when four or six holes are made through the stone, and iron plates or rings covering about one-third to one-half of the diameter are bolted on each side, sacking, felt, pitch or some soft materials being interposed, so that the stone and two side plates when bolted together, may form a compact solid mass ; Flanges are also used as well as rings, but neither of them so generally as they ought to be, especially when from cupidity it is attempted to drive the stone as fast it will bear with *hoped for* safety, in order to hurry through as much work as possible.

In the new and unprotected stone, there is considerable body of the material or length of radius to withstand fracture, but when the stone is reduced to *half* its primary diameter, and its axial speed is *doubled* to maintain its original *surface velocity*, the risk is much increased, because there is then so much less bulk in the stone to resist accidental fracture.

13.—ENGINEERS' TOOL GRINDSTONES or those employed for keeping in order their working tools ; vary from two to five feet diameter, and four to eight inches thick, and as may be supposed, the structure of the framing is usually in metal, and much more engineer-like than the last. For instance, the trough is made either entirely of cast iron, or with cast iron sides united with a wide strip of boiler plate rivetted to each. The trough has usually feet to support the axis at two to two and a half feet from the ground, to suit the erect position of the workman, who holds the tool securely on a horizontal iron bar that is fixed near the stone, and at a convenient height by means of pedestals secured to the frame, this arrangement gives the choice of position in the rest or bar. The axis is cylindrical throughout, and the stone is fixed on its central part, as will be explained : the spindle lies in two plummer blocks or brasses, which are fixed on the edges of the trough, and one end of the spindle overhangs the same to receive the strap pulley, by which the stone is driven from the main shaft running through the building. There is likewise provision for changing the diameter of the pulley on the main shaft or on the spindle, to increase the velocity of the stone as it becomes reduced in diameter ; but unlike the generality of machines in the engineers' shops, the grindstone does not require fast and loose pulleys to connect or disconnect it with the power, as from its frequent use it is kept continually running when the engine is at work.

Engineers mostly fix the stone between cast-iron flanges or plates, the one keyed on the spindle against a shoulder, the other forced up by a screwed nut or key passing through a diametrical mortise in the spindle. Mr. Roberts of Manchester prefers the latter mode, and in hanging the grindstone he fits a square piece of wood into the eye of the stone, then bores it to fit the spindle, and afterwards having smoothed the central parts of the sides of the stone, he inserts two disks of soft pine wood between the cast-iron flanges and the stone,—the wood adapts itself to the trifling irregularities of both parts, and serves as a somewhat elastic cushion to ensure contact, and consequently a firmer grasp on the stone, to the extent of about one-fourth of its diameter, to which the flanges extend ;—by these precautions accidents rarely occur. Engineers sometimes use stones of the before-mentioned diameter of 8 or 10 feet for brightening the coarser parts of machinery, and such large stones are mounted nearly the same as those just described, but nearer to the ground.

14.—Turning up Grindstones.—As soon as the stone is wedged truly on its axis, it is turned on the cylindrical edge or *face,* and part way down each side. This is done with a rod of iron or steel drawn down at the end to about $\frac{3}{16}$ths to $\frac{3}{8}$ths of an inch square. The tool is not held radially but pointed downwards, at an angle of about 20 degrees, and is continually rolled over and over to present a new angle, which in its turn is rapidly worn away. The process is nevertheless much quicker than might be supposed.

In turning small grindstones driven by the long wheel, the stone is moved the reverse way, and more slowly than in grinding, so that the horse may be used for supporting the turning tool. In turning large grindstones driven by power, in which case the motion cannot be so readily reversed nor slackened, the workman goes to the back of the stone and supports the tool upon a wooden or iron bar placed across the water trough, and employs a larger pulley than for grinding. Sometimes a cross strap is allowed to run upon the edge of the stone itself, to reverse and reduce the speed of the stone when it is turned after having been mounted.

Large stones are seldom turned up, except when they are first set to work, but they are retained of a cylindrical or slightly convex figure, almost exclusively by the following process :—

15.—Hacking Grindstones.—At intervals during the time a large grindstone is in regular work, the strap is flung off and the stone is retarded by still applying to its surface the article to be ground ; but before the stone comes to rest, the high places are marked at six or more parts of its width, by holding a piece of chalk or charcoal steadily upon the horse, and gradually approaching it so as to mark the more prominent parts. When the stone has stopped, the grinder hacks or notches the high places denoted by the marks, by means of a tool called a "*hack hammer*," which is like a small adze of 2 or 3 lbs. weight, but longer and more curved in the blade, and with a very short handle. The grinder cuts with the hack hammer shallow oblique furrows about one inch asunder and crossing each other, producing a chequered surface.

When the stone is again used, the greatest wear occurs at these roughened places, and by a continual recurrence to the *dressing* the circularity of the stone is sufficiently well preserved, and with but little interruption to the work. It is very impolitic to defer the dressing too long, for fear of giving the stone a *heavy side*, and risking its safety.

16.—STRAGGLING OR RAGGING.—This process is principally adopted on fine and smooth grindstones into the surfaces of which particles of iron or steel have become embedded, and which greatly impede the action of the stone. In *straggling*, or *ragging*, the stone is kept running as usual whilst a piece of soft iron about a quarter or half an inch square, held upon the horse like the turning tool, is wriggled against the edge of the stone by a motion of the wrist, as in using a brad-awl, the iron is applied all over the surface, and lastly the edge of the bar is wriggled obliquely upon the top of the stone. This process also assists in correcting small inequalities in the figure of the stone.

17.—TURNING AND ROVING SMOOTH GRINDSTONES.—A different and perhaps more general mode of keeping the stone in order, especially when it is driven by the hand wheel, is followed by other workmen.

The motion of the stone is reversed, and the edge is turned with a bent tool, usually made out of an old file, by forging the end taper and to a thin wide chisel edge, and about one inch of the tool is then turned up nearly at right angles to the stem of the file. This tool is used as a hooked turning tool upon the horse, and it scrapes the surface tolerably true and smooth, and afterwards whilst the stone is at work its edge is cleared with the roving plate, a piece of either iron or steel plate just like a joiner's scraper, held upon the top of the stone not quite perpendicularly but meeting the stone at a small angle.

From its unstable position the roving plate chatters and jumps, and appears to fill the stone with minute furrows from dislodging some of the particles from its gritty surface. This mode also gives the stone a tooth, and as well as the last method serves to clear the stone from the thick dirty water or slush that otherwise fills its grain and considerably retards its action, frequently also the grinder throws a small handful of water on the stone, and applies his open hand very gently upon the same, in order to wash off the loose muddy coating it acquires whilst in use.

18.—GENERAL REMARKS ON USING GRINDSTONES.—In order to avoid the wasteful destruction of the stones they should be exposed to as equal circumstances as possible ; thus they should in the first instance be selected free from hard veins that impede, or flaws that accelerate the wear at the respective parts.

The object ground should be continually traversed backwards and forwards to use the stone alike all over, the stones should not be allowed to remain long out of condition, as they get rapidly worse, neither should they ever remain partially immersed in the water in the trough, which would soften those parts and expose them to more rapid wear, than the remainder.

In almost every case the grindstone is made to revolve *away* from the workman, so that should the work slip from his grasp it may be carried away from his person and not against him.   But this direction of motion leaves a wiry film on tools with thin cutting edges, and which the regular grinder occasionally avoids, by holding the tool *back-handed,* or with the edge towards his person.   Many of the tools used in turning metal do not require to be sharpened on the oilstone, and to avoid the wiry film, such tools are usually ground with the stone running towards the workman.

The Bilston grindstone has the preference for small tools from the comparative smoothness of its grain, and occasionally, a coarse and a fine stone are fixed on the same spindle ; and when the shop grindstone is driven by power, the workman goes to the front or back of the stone accordingly as the motion is best suited to his immediate want.

19.—GENERAL REMARKS ON GRINDING VARIOUS KINDS OF TOOLS.—The general position of the grinder described under article 9, serves for grinding all ordinary tools, such as chisels, axes, and many others of ordinary kinds, which are simply held to the stone by the hands, and receive the pressure of the arms and upper part of the person.

20.—*Massive works,* such as anvils, are suspended loosely by a chain, the man has then only to guide them, and their own weight supplies the pressure.

21.—*Large heavy plates,* such as the bright cast-iron fronts of stoves, are allowed to rest in an oblique position, jointly upon the surface of the horse and the stone, the grinder slides them about, to expose all parts of the surface to equal action, and often bears on them with his knees to increase the pressure.

22.—*Saws* are too thin and elastic to be thus treated, and such flexible objects are applied on a flat board to give them support, the man leans upon the board with his whole weight and moves them up and down at an inclination of about 45 degrees to grind each part successively and equally.

23.—*The blades of table knives* are before being handled ground on the side of a stick, about 2½ by 1½ inches and 2 feet long with a staple under which the shank of the blade is placed, the stick is rounded at the ends to serve for the two hands, and the workman sometimes applies also his knees to the central part, and the effect of the stone is then very rapidly felt on the blade.

24.—*Small works that are ground lengthways,* are sometimes nipped between the horse and the stone, an enormous pressure may be then given much less laboriously than by the arms, this is often done in grinding the surface of files preparatory to their being cut with teeth, and in *stripping* the teeth from old ones, prior to re-cutting them ; but this practice throws a great pressure on the stone, sometimes enough to check the speed of the steam engine.

25.—*Small works are in many cases difficult to be held unassistedly,* because of the risk of grinding through the skin of the fingers, or of burning them from the heat of the work, a small pointed stick is frequently used to press the work on the stone, and in some cases a small square piece of thick leather or felt, called a *patch,* is similarly employed. Sometimes also small tools are temporarily fixed by their tangs in a wooden handle to facilitate their presentation to the stone ; the handle is called a " *haftpipe* " and is commonly a short piece of hazel rod. But the more usual course at Sheffield is to employ a pair of tongs or pliers, the reins of which do not cross as pliers and scissors generally, but consist simply of two rods of iron retained by a link across their middle. The work is fixed by being inserted between the rods at the one end, and a wooden wedge driven in between the opposite extremities, binds the whole together very securely. The sliding tongs, fig. 861, page 862, Vol. II., are also used occasionally.

26.—ADAPTATION OF GRINDSTONES TO THE FORMS OF WORKS.—*Convex* works may of course be ground upon the cylindrical edge of the grindstone, as by rolling the work about, every part of the same may be brought into contact with the stone, in the same manner that round or convex works may be filed with a flat file ; but in grinding *concave* works, it is of course needful that the stone if not altogether a counterpart of the work, should be sufficiently modified in form to penetrate to the bottom of the hollow.

Thus in grinding a pruning bill, the hook of which is of small radius, it is indispensable the one edge of the stone should be rounded to the fourth of a circle ; in grinding that part of a table knife where the blade is united to the shank, a similar curvature in the stone is also required. In grinding hollow or fluted works such as the concave parts of gouges, it is necessary to turn the grindstone to the exact counterpart form, or into beads of different width and sweeps, and various other examples might be quoted.

In order to reach within that keen edge in the blade of a penknife which unites the square shank for the joint to the remainder of the blade, (which angle is technically called the *chorl,*) the edge of the stone is kept remarkably keen and sharp, this is assisted by waxing the side of the dry grindstone close to the edge, and which tends to prevent the same from crumbling away, and also prevents the stone cutting into the shoulders of the blade.

27.—WET AND DRY STONES.—Grindstones are almost always used with water, as in the humid state they cut more quickly, because the wet prevents the grain of the stone being choaked with particles of metal, but when the stone is used dry, although it cuts somewhat more slowly, it leaves a smoother grain upon the work, and on which account the dry stone is always resorted to by fork-grinders and needle pointers.

28.—*The dry stone* is somewhat used also by most grinders, but only for a small part of their work, as when vigorously applied it gives rise to so much friction ; that it frequently heats the work to a blue, or almost to a red-heat, and would destroy the temper of the tools, its use is therefore nearly restricted to the roughing-out of tools, *before* they are hardened, an operation called " *scorching* " : at this early stage of the manufacture of tools they receive no injury from the great heat sometimes thus given them.

29.—*Hardened and tempered blades* that have been ground on the wet stone, are often smoothed on a dry Bilston stone, in order to leave less work to be accomplished in the next stage of manufacture, by the metal lap with fine emery ; but the judicious cutler then applies the dry stone so moderately as not to reduce the temper of the blades, but only to smooth them.

30.—Danger of Using Dry Stones.—A still worse and more fatal mischief than spoiling the work attends the continual practice of dry grinding, as the fine particles of stone and steel that are given off, raise clouds of dust which are inhaled by the workmen, and so commonly does this contaminated atmosphere induce pulmonary complaints, that it is considered rare for a needle or fork grinder to live beyond the age of twenty-five or thirty, at which period they generally become afflicted with asthma and premature decay.

31.—To avert this calamity Mr. Abraham of Sheffield invented magnetic guards which were placed close to the grindstone, and sometimes also around the mouth and nostrils of the individual. (*See* Trans. Soc. of Arts, vol. 40, plate XXIII). The magnet attracted the particles of steel and together with them drew the greater part of the stone dust, but the men were too heedless to avail themselves of this philanthropic invention, notwithstanding its complete success.

32.—The only contrivance now employed is also due to Mr. Abraham, the stone is enclosed in a wooden case that only exposes a part of its edge, and from the box a horizontal tube also of wood, proceeds as a tangent from the upper surface of the stone to the external atmosphere. The current of air generated by the motion of the stone makes its escape through the tube, and carries with it nearly the whole of the dust arising from the process ; sometimes the tube alone is retained.

But even this contrivance, (which may be viewed as comparable with the revolving fan now used in blowing furnaces,) although so much less elaborate than the magnetic guards, yet nearly as effective, is also for the most part neglected, owing to the unpardonable heedlessness of the workmen themselves.

Mr. W. Lund invented an apparatus almost identical with Clark's revolving blower with a small fan, it was driven by a short band from the stone, and was described in the Mechanic's Magazine under the signature " Gulielmus," this also merely obtained a very limited use.

Section B.—Wheels of Factitious Stone, or Composition Wheels.

33.—Of Composition Wheels the corundum wheels deserve the first notice, they consist of particles of corundum cemented into a mass by means of shell lac, and which composition variously prepared is nearly the universal grindstone and polisher of the East Indies. The reader is referred for the details of their preparation to the article CORUNDUM in this Catalogue.

34.—BARCLAY'S ARTIFICIAL EMERY STONES.—The manufacture of these very useful grinding and polishing wheels, is fully described under the head EMERY article 11 : in most respects they are superior to the corundum wheels of the Asiatics described under the head CORUNDUM. They may each be made of various degrees of coarseness and rapidity of cut ; when properly compounded their texture is very uniform and free from the hard veins and flaws that sometime occur in grindstones.

35.—OPTICIANS *sometimes employ fine crocus made into a solid body* with wax, and moulded or turned into form (see the article on LENSES and SPECULA) in Chap. XXXIII. Sect. 4. The wax polisher is generally used with water, which greatly prevents the destruction of its surface and also assists in carrying off those particles of glass or metal which do not become embedded in the polisher. The introduction of this composition is ascribed to Mr. Varley.

36.—Crocus, mixed with powdered chalk and melted glue, constitute a composition employed by Mr. Bass in the formation of little wheels, employed by him in sharpening the long slender straight blades of his cork cutting machine. In cutting each cork the knife sweeps by against a square piece of cork, which, during the time, makes one revolution, and the four angles are removed in one piece. The knife in proceeding to and fro, is rubbed on its upper side by three of the crocus wheels which revolve slowly against it with slight pressure, and the lower side of the knife rubs against two or three hard steel rings, which act as burnishers and keep up the fine wiry edge required in cutting cork.

SECTION C.—WHEELS OF METAL, OR METALLIC LAPS.

37.—METAL WHEELS OR LAPS, made of nearly every metal and alloy in common use, have been more or less employed in the mechanical arts, as vehicles for the application of several of the polishing powders, but of all laps, notwithstanding their variety, those of lead slightly alloyed, and supplied with powdered emery, render the most conspicuous service. Generally the plane or flat surface of the lap is employed, at other times the cylindrical edge, as by cutlers, but the portion actually used is in either case called the *face* of the lap.

38.—LAPIDARIES, MARBLE WORKERS, sometimes also mechanicians and others, place the spindle vertically, so that the lap revolves in a horizontal plane, and in which case the lower end of the spindle is supported in a center fixed to the cross rail of the wood frame or bench, the upper in a bracket or overhanging arm extending from the platform, and beneath the latter is placed the pulley by which the spindle is driven. In some cases the upper center is dispensed with, and the spindle works in a metal collar just beneath the lap—after the manner of a lathe, if we conceive the mandrel to be placed perpendicularly.

The lap in all these cases revolves within a shallow trough, extended two to six inches above the lap, in order to catch the emery and water that are thrown off. The emery is usually applied dry, the lap having been previously moistened with a small brush dipped in water or with a mop made by twisting a wire around a few rags, the wire serving also as the handle, the dry emery powder then readily adheres to the lap, and less water is required than if the emery and water were previously mixed. In some cases the lap is screwed upon the mandrel of an ordinary turning lathe like a chuck, but which is hazardous, lest the emery should find its way to the collar of the lathe mandrel.

39.—CUTLERS' LAPS are fixed on spindles placed horizontally, in fact in the same form that serves for their grindstone and other apparatus. Cutler's laps measure from about 4 to 20 inches in diameter, the best razors being smoothed on laps of 4 to 6 inches diameter, and commoner razors on those from 10 to 12 inches, which act the more expeditiously but leave a thicker edge.

40.—DIFFERENCES OF CONSTRUCTION IN LAPS.—The lap is in some cases a thin disk of metal fixed by means of a screwed nut against a shoulder on the spindle, but it is better with lead laps to employ an iron plate cast full of holes to support the softer metal. The casting mould may in this case be either an iron disk with a central screw to fix the iron center plate at the time of pouring, or the mould may be made of sand and in halves after the usual manner of the foundry. In either case the iron plate should be made as hot as the fluid metal, which by entering the holes becomes firmly united to the iron especially if the holes are largest on the reverse side or that away from the lead.

41.—CUTLERS' NARROW CYLINDRICAL LAPS are sometimes similarly cast upon the edges of cast-iron wheels or disks, but it is far more usual to make a wooden center on account of its lightness. In order that the wood center may not contract nor lose its circular form, it is made in four quarters or of more pieces, with the grain pointing to the center ; the pieces are united by two circular disks of wood or metal, nailed to the sides, after this the edge is turned to the required width and cylindrical, with a groove in the center and a chamfer on each edge, to retain the lead.

A better construction is followed by Mr. Lund, he makes his wheels of common Honduras mahogany, or rather a species of cedar, in about thirty-two sections, and arranged in two layers or disks, sixteen in each, so as to break joint. No nails are used, and although the parts are only united by glue they are found to endure the transitions from heat to damp to which they are often exposed. In uniting them they are glued joint by joint, and quickly arranged together upon a flat board, and when nearly a half circle is combined, a few nails are driven round the margin to allow the last wedge or sector to be driven in tight ; when two such sectors are dry the last wedge is fitted into the space between them with the trying plane, and driven in tight to make out the last joint, the parts being restrained from slipping away by the use of a few nails as before, lastly the two circles when flattened are glued together and compressed by several hand screws.

The mould for casting laps, is in general an old grindstone in the center of which is placed the wooden disk, and around the latter is built up at the distance of 1 or 2 inches a border of soft clay. The metal, usually 1 part tin and 4 or 5 parts lead, (the lining of tea chests being preferred, on account of the tin with which it is alloyed and soldered,) is then melted and poured in, but the heat should be barely such as to scorch white paper. The lap when cold is fixed on the spindle, and its edge is turned true, the horse being used as the support for the turning tool.

42.—THE CYLINDRICAL EDGE OF THE LAP, and which alone the cutler employs, is called the *face,* and the dressing or coating of emery, which is never used by cutlers with water, is called the *head,* terms applied in common to his other wheels. In order to make the smooth metal retain the fine emery, it is *scored* or scratched with a pointed knife, by which two series of slight oblique furrows are scored in the face of the lap, to produce a faintly but coarsely checkered surface.

43.—IN LAPPING RAZORS AND LARGE ARTICLES, fine emery and oil are mixed up in a cup, a small quantity is spread on with the thumb whilst the lap is nearly at rest, the emery is then pressed in the lap with a spoiled razor blade, or a short bar of razor steel, (that from which the blades are forged,) whilst the lap is in motion, and when the lap is charged the work is drawn steadily across from end to end and entirely off the lap, to reduce it to an uniform surface.

After having preparatively lapped about one dozen of razor blades on both sides, which is called *the first course,* the process is repeated with finer emery, or else " *to fine the lap,*" the head is rubbed off with a piece of felt, or with thick woollen cloth, and the surface of the metal is rendered as fine as possible, with a smooth piece of flint, or with a steel blade ; and the lapping is completed in the last course on the nearly naked lap, a stick of charcoal being commonly used still more to deaden the emery before the flint is applied, and the charcoal moreover gives a black polish that could not otherwise be left from the lap.

44.—IN LAPPING PENKNIVES AND SMALL ARTICLES, it is more usual to charge the wheel whilst it is at rest, by rubbing on it a lump of emery cake, made of emery compounded with suet chopped fine and rendered down, and mixed with a very little wax, sometimes the dressing is rubbed in with the agate or bouldering stone, and as before explained, to fine the lap, at the conclusion the head is rubbed off and it is smoothed with the agate.

When the lap is coarse and the work is pressed heavily it produces a white colour on steel, and when the lap is fine and the work is pressed lightly, and gradually drawn from the one end to the other it gives a black polish—to attain this end the emery is worn down fine with the work, and afterwards with the bouldering stone, and the effect of the emery is still more deadened by putting a little bees'-wax on the face of the lap, the smoothness of which is tried with the finger before applying the work.

45.—Comparative Durability of Laps.—The metal wheels and grinding tools are from several reasons highly advantageous, as in the first place they admit of being fashioned with more exactness, and they longer retain that exactness than the natural stones and the compositions previously referred to. For instance when grit stones are in use, desintegration is constantly and rapidly going on, as in the course of work the particles of the stone are rubbed down and torn out ; so that the abrading surface is incessantly changing, by the gradual exposure of the part of the grindstone previously beneath. Much care is required to keep the edge of the stone circular and of the precise form required.

With the cement wheels, this progressive change as constantly, although more slowly occurs, from the abrading and structural materials being mingled.

46.—On the Action and Durability of Laps.—Metal laps are under very different circumstances from grindstones or cement wheels, as the metal constituting the lap has no cutting power in itself, but only derives it from the particles of emery which become embedded in its surface and act as the teeth of a file. Other particles of the emery lie continually between the metal lap and the article to be ground, and separate the two ; these grains have a partially rolling motion and, in all probability, have a tendency to grind both the work and the lap also. When the emery is crushed very fine, or that it is wasted, so that the lap and work come nearly in contact, the abrasion becomes so much reduced that fresh emery is generally thrown on to restore the action, and this again separates the lap and work ; which therefore rarely come into absolute contact. It must not be supposed, however, that although the metal is generally more cohesive than stone or cement, that it is not at all worn away, as the metal laps are likewise depreciated in form, but in a much slower degree than the cement wheels or natural stones.

47.—Metals employed for Laps and their Respective Purposes. — In the selection of the metals for laps, there is much of prejudice, and speaking generally it may be said the softer the metals the more readily do they retain the grinding powders, but the sooner are they worn out of form. In the following tabular view the more usual metals for laps and their purposes are given.

Brass is used by

Opticians, with fine emery and water for smoothing lenses and specula.

Cast-iron is used by

Glass-grinders, with coarse sand for roughing ;

Opticians, with sand or emery for rough grinding ;

Engineers and machinists, with emery and water for general purposes, in metallic construction ;

Diamond polishers, for polishing the facets of diamonds for jewellery ; the iron laps or *skives* are charged with diamond powder.

Copper is used by

Engineers and machinists, with emery and water for general purposes, in metallic construction. Copper is considered to retain the emery remarkably well ;

Lapidaries, with flour emery for grinding small and hard gems, and for cutting facets ;

Glass grinders, with emery for fitting stoppers into bottles ;

Glass engravers, with emery for their small disks and tools.

Lead, generally alloyed, is used by

Engineers and machinists, with emery and water, for metallic construction generally ;

Cutlers, with emery and oil, for fine grinding or perfecting the forms of cutlery prior to polishing the pieces ;

Lapidaries, with emery, first coarse and then fine, for grinding and smoothing most stones, except some few of the hardest, which require copper ;

Lapidaries, with rottenstone and water, for polishing most of the stones, except a few of the hardest, which require hard pewter or copper ;

Lead, mixed with a variable quantity of antimony or alloy, like type metal, is much used by engineers and mechanicians for laps.

Pewter is used by

Gold cutters, for cutting and faceting gold and silver, to which a most splendid lustre is given by means of crocus, which is generally rubbed into the lap with the burnisher ;

Watchmakers, with crocus or red stuff as above, for polishing some of their brass and steel works ;

Lapidaries, with emery for fine grinding, and also with rottenstone for polishing,—pewter being selected for those small and hard stones, for which lead is too yielding.

All these artizans select in preference the metal of old pewter plates, which consisted of pure tin with a minute addition of copper. Some of the modern pewters appear to be tin and lead in nearly equal parts, and are much the same when used for laps, as lead hardened with a little antimony, which is much less expensive. *See* articles Pewter, vol. i., page 284, and LEAD, page 277 of the same volume.

Tin may be considered as being applicable to all the purposes of the genuine old plate pewter, which is now difficult to be met with.

Zinc, alloyed with tin, which is much harder than tin or pewter, is said by Mr. Gill to be employed by the Geneva jewellers in lapping gold and silver works.

SECTION D.—WHEELS OF WOOD, OR GLAZE WHEELS.

48.—LAPIDARIES employ wooden wheels in smoothing soft and rounded stones. The wheels consist usually of beech, birchwood, or mahogany, cut out plankways, fixed on the spindle and turned flat. The wood wheels are fed with flour emery and water, as described under the article in this Catalogue on ALABASTER.

49.—GLASS CUTTERS employ the edges of similar wheels with pumice-stone and water for smoothing, and with putty and water for polishing ; the edge of the wheel is turned flat, angular or circular, according to the fashion of the work. Willow, poplar or alder, which are amongst the softest of our woods, are much used for the glass cutters' wheels : their face wheels, which are far less common, are mostly thick transverse sections of the tree, and consequently the grain is then upright at every part, and both more equable and durable.

50.—CUTLERS use wood wheels under the name of glazers ; these should be con- structed of two layers, each consisting of 6, 8 or more pieces with the grain radial, so that the periphery may be entirely formed of the end grain of the wood ; walnut, oak, crab-tree, birch and mahogany are severally used, but the latter is on the whole the best. The cutlers' wood or glaze wheels are mostly fed with emery cake, already described, and which is applied whilst the wheel slowly revolves.

The edges of glazers are occasionally scored with a pointed knife, to enable the emery cake to penetrate, and for fine work, they are also boul- dered down with a flint, or other hard and smooth stone, and waxed to render the edge smooth, just in the manner recently explained in reference to cutlers' laps. Sometimes a wood wheel fed with emery and oil is first used, and afterwards a wood wheel with emery and wax.

SECTION E.—WHEELS OF LEATHER, OR BUFF WHEELS, GLAZERS AND POLISHERS.

51.—This title includes three different kinds of apparatus, all of which have wooden centers covered with leather, and are thence sometimes indiscrimi- nately called buff wheels, but they are distinguished into three kinds as above by practical men, thus :

First. Buff wheels which are covered with thick soft leather, sometimes half an inch thick, the bull neck being commonly employed. In the metro- polis old regimental belts are sometimes used from economical motives, instead of the new kinds of leather above named, but this seems to be a questionable policy, as the belt leather is less durable, and although it may serve for glazers, it is too thin for buff wheels. The *coarse buff*, or *sand buff*, is supplied with Trent sand and oil, the *fine buff*, with rottenstone and oil ; these are not used for steel but for softer metal such as brass, Britannia metal, &c., and for horn, tortoiseshell and ivory.

Secondly. Glazers are wheels covered with harder leather, upon the face of which emery is attached by glue, they are almost invariably used dry, and for steel. The leather used for glazers and polishers in the manufacturing towns of Sheffield and Birmingham is " beast hide," that is, the same leather which when hammered is used for the soles of shoes, the leather is cut into strips, and used without having been hammered, the thick and thin parts being selected according to circumstances ; as glaze wheels require moderately thick leather supplied with emery; and polishers soft thin leather employed with dry crocus.

Thirdly. Polishers are wheels covered with thin soft leather, and supplied with crocus which is rubbed on dry, and without the intervention of glue or oil. In Sheffield one kind of leather is tanned expressly for polishers, it being important that the whole of the grease should be extracted, as if any remain in the leather it will not polish properly. The polishers are used alone for steel, and with very small velocity.

52.—THE SMALLEST BUFF WHEELS, called bobs, are used in polishing the insides of the bowls of spoons—they are simply disks of leather, nearly an inch thick, known as sea cow or bull neck; they are perforated so as to be mounted on spindles, and are turned of a nearly globular form. *See* ALBATA.

53.—BUFF WHEELS AND OTHER LEATHER WHEELS, WITH WOODEN CENTERS differ much in size, those for cutlers usually measure from $\frac{1}{4}$ to 4 inches wide by 4 to 20 inches diameter, although they are sometimes of twice that diameter; they have wooden centers or disks usually cut out the plankway of the grain, in similar woods to those used for glazers, but they are better when constructed of various pieces in sectors, the best mode being that recommended in article 41, or two layers of sectors each consisting of about sixteen pieces and glued up so as to break joint. The largest of these wheels, say those exceeding two feet diameter, are generally made up of one set of middle sector-like pieces, screwed fast between two circular iron plates which are themselves keyed on to the spindle, and then a set of felloes is nailed or screwed around the periphery on each side; making the thickness out to three, four, or even five inches. When the wood centers have been constructed according to some of the above modes, and turned cylindrical or rounded as the case may be, they are turned smooth on the edges and then covered with one thickness of leather.

54.—IN COVERING THE WHEELS, the wood, and also one side of the leather, are plentifully glued, the extremity of the leather is fixed down by two or three nails driven a little way into the wooden disk, the leather is stretched tight and nailed at short intervals, and its other end is also fixed down, and when the entire surface is covered with one strip if possible, the glue is allowed to dry. It is a matter of great importance that the ends of the leather should be made to butt closely one to the other to make good joints, otherwise the work jumps when a bad joint passes beneath it. The nails are afterwards withdrawn, the leather is turned true and regular with a flat chisel. Sometimes the glazers are required to be very hard, and in this case the leather is soaked in water for a few hours before being glued on the wheel, it is then secured as above whilst in the wet condition, and in drying the leather contracts and becomes considerably harder.

Buff Wheels even of the small diameter of 10 or 12 inches are frequently made three or four inches wide, and covered with soft leather half an inch thick. In such cases the thickness of the wood centers is also very nearly three or four inches, or the width of the leather, which however is allowed very slightly to project, and the sides of the wood are considerably hollowed in the sweep of a circle from the edge to the center to allow the works to be turned round on the edge of the leather in reaching into hollow and rounded angles, as already noticed the buff wheels are used either with Trent sand or rottenstone mixed with oil, and for various materials excepting steel.

Emery Wheels, when the leather with which they are covered has been turned smooth, are brushed over with glue, rolled in a heap of dry emery powder, and afterwards on a smooth board to consolidate the head and make the periphery smooth.

55.—COARSE EMERY WHEELS are always used dry, and they give off a splendid display of sparks with some of the risk of overheating the work that attends the use of the dry grindstone; the finer emery wheels are sometimes used just as explained with the wooden wheels, namely they are dressed with the emery cake, and bouldered down with the flint, to bring the head to a smooth and regular condition.

Tool makers use the buffs or glazers immediately after the grindstone, and select the coarse and fine buffs according to the degree of finish required. It may be observed the dry wheels give the brighter gloss, but do not generally leave the work so smooth as those which are greased.

56.—IN RENEWING THE FACE OF THE EMERY WHEEL, or in putting on a "new head," the wheel is wetted with a sponge and cold water, and allowed to soak for about an hour, the used emery is then scraped off with an old knife, and the surface of the leather is made somewhat rough; after which it is again glued, and rolled first on the emery and then on a flat board as originally. It is useless to attempt "to put one head upon another," or to apply new emery, until that which has been used has been thoroughly scraped off.

57. — THE POLISHERS FOR RAZORS AND FINE CUTLERY are soft leather wheels charged with crocus, which are always used dry. It is necessary that both the polisher and blade should be *hot*, as without a moderate and equal degree of heat, short however of that producing a colour on the steel, the process does not succeed, and a good polish is not produced. It is therefore usual with some workmen before commencing work to take a piece of razor steel, which is held against the revolving polisher to prepare it for the work itself, by crushing and regulating the powder with which the polisher is charged.

58.—ACTION OF THE POLISHER.—Although the polisher is made to revolve much more slowly than the other wheels, the razor is moved to and fro from end to end, very quickly and with considerable pressure, to distribute the heat equally; and the blade is not drawn slowly across and off as in lapping, on the contrary the work is moved endlong actively, and pulled off quickly. In examining the work, the polished part is occasionally wiped clean with the patch or thick piece of cloth or felt, which serves both to protect the fingers from the heat of the blade, and also to supply the polisher with crocus, as the patch is dabbed upon a small quantity of dry crocus close at the work-man's hand, and is then rubbed on the polisher, to transfer the powder to the wheel.

Occasionally the surface of the polisher becomes very hard from being somewhat scorched by the heat generated in polishing, and its surface is then more or less filled with scratchy lines which disfigure the blade, at such times the wheel is stopped, and the face of the polisher is *roughed up*, or thoroughly scraped with an old razor blade or knife as in erasing writing, in order to remove all the *old head* or polishing stuff, and render the leather a little rough, and quite soft ; after which the polisher is recharged by means of the thumb or patch.

59.—THE FLAT SIDES OF WHEELS are not often covered with buff leather except by lapidaries, but in imitation thereof glass and emery paper are frequently glued on flat chucks of wood and used for finishing the flat surfaces of small works in the metals, woods, ivory, and other substances, and Mr. Larkin dusted the naked wood with a covering of pulverised flint, as noticed in the previous article on FLINT.

60.—A FLAT POLISHING MACHINE actuated by rotary motion is used in America for flat works, such as brass hinges, parts of locks and other metal works. The principal part consists of an endless strap of leather, which is put in motion by its encircling a foot wheel as in a lathe, but the strap instead of giving motion to a pulley, passes over and in contact with a narrow flat board, the edges of which are rounded or furnished with small cylindrical rollers to lessen the friction, sometimes two oblong holes are simply made in the bench. The strap is charged with emery glued on exactly as in the emery wheels or buffs. The work when applied on that part of the strap which is flowing over the flat surface of the board is polished with considerable rapidity and a tolerable approach to a plane surface.

SECTION F—WHEELS OF CLOTH, OR CLOTH AND LIST WHEELS.

61.—THE CLOTH USED FOR WHEELS is usually thick woollen cloth such as that for white great coats, and the blankets of printing machines, felted cloths are likewise used. Sometimes the cloth or felt is simply glued around the edge or upon the face of the wooden wheels precisely the same as in buff wheels, and is employed for similar purposes.

62.—OPTICIANS' CLOTH TOOLS, consist of a circular piece of cloth cemented by means of pitch upon the surface of one of their brass concave or convex tools of the required curvature, the cloth if new is seared with a hot iron to remove the nap before it is cemented down.

Sometimes the opticians' metal tools are covered with a broad strip of thick silk or lute string, which is folded around the edges and cemented at the back of the tool. The cloth and silk tools are always used with putty powder. *See* the articles LENSES Chap. XXXIII. Sect. 4.

63.—THE LAPIDARIES CLOTH MILL is a face wheel having an annular surface about two inches wide, there is first a center of wood of about 6 inches diameter, then a spiral coil of wide list or cloth which is wound up closely until the diameter of the cloth becomes about 10 inches. The cloth is secured partly by tacks driven first into the wood centers, and then by small nails driven into the plate of wood that forms the back, and the outer coil is nailed around the edge of the principal disk, so that the whole forms an annular face with a loose pliant surface, the top of which is dressed level with an iron heated to a dull red.

The list or selvedge of woollen cloth is commonly used, and as this is thicker on one edge than the other, it is the practice of many lapidaries to roll on two coils at once by aid of two individuals, the thick edge of the one coil being downward and of the other upwards ; this mode equalizes the tension and prevents the list gathering up as a cone—and in this case it is only usual to nail the list at the beginning and ending of the coil.

The list wheel is employed generally with pumice-stone and water, and from its elasticity it yields admirably to the curved surface of shells and stones ; it is also employed for plane surfaces on many soft substances, as explained under the article ALABASTER in this Catalogue.

64.—IVORY WORKERS' LIST WHEELS consist of 10 to 20 circular pieces of cloth screwed fast between two disks of wood about 2 or 3 inches smaller than the cloth, which therefore forms a pliant edge projecting an inch or upwards beyond the wood, and which is well adapted to the curvilinear surface of umbrella or parasol handles, and many such works—the wheel is fed with Trent sand, loam or chalk, or it is better to have one wheel for each of these substances. *See* IVORY.

SECTION G.—WHEELS OF BRISTLES, OR WIRE, OR BRUSH WHEELS.

65.—WHEEL BRUSHES OR BRUSH WHEELS are very largely employed in the arts ; they are made both hard and soft, and of all diameters from about 2 to 8 inches, with the hairs placed radially so that the outer rows lean a little towards the center to give them more stability.

Wheel brushes are used with emery, crocus, rottenstone, putty powder, whiting, and in fact all the polishing powders both with oil and dry, and they are employed for curved, indented, chased, open and pierced works, but it is to be remembered the brush rapidly obliterates keen angles, the preservation of which requires particular care and patience, and the employment of hard buffs or the wood and metal polishers already described—as the greater the degree of exactness that is required in the angles and edges of polished works, the greater should be also the degree of hardness in the face of the grinders and polishers employed.

66.—WHEEL BRUSHES MADE OF IRON AND BRASS WIRE, instead of hairs, are occasionally used after the manner of scratch brushes made of metal wire, and for the same general purposes ; as for cleaning and scratching the metals preparatory to gilding and silvering, but not for polishing. The ends of the wires are a little curved to soften the abruptness with which they would otherwise meet the work.

WHITING is common chalk, ground, washed for the separation of sand and other impurities, and dried in lumps. *See* CHALK.

WOODS.—Many variations will be met with in the modes by which the woods are polished, and which depend greatly on the qualities of the woods themselves, as to hardness, fibre and colour; consequently under this head it is preferred nearly to follow the arrangement of the turnery and other woods, enumerated in the tabular view in page 70 of the first Volume.

TURNED WORKS.

1.—WOODS OF SOFT GRAIN AND LIGHT COLOURS, such as alder, ash, small beech and birch wood, sallow, willow, and also holly, horse chesnut, sycamore and some others, which woods are used respectively for common toys, and the best Tunbridge wares, are in many cases so smoothly turned as not to require any polishing whatever, or at most, only the friction of a few of their own shavings.

The less-experienced may find it necessary previously to employ glass paper, and it is then desirable to polish the work first whilst it revolves in the one direction, which lays down flat such of the loose filaments as are not polished off; and then by reversing the motion of the lathe, these parts are as it were brushed up, and generally removed. The alternating motion of the pole or spring lathe, is therefore desirable in polishing such woods. A few shavings are mostly used after the glass paper to remove the loose dust and brighten the surface. Many of the toys and works here referred to are coated with the white sandarac varnish, and some few are subsequently polished.

2.—WOODS OF MEDIUM HARDNESS AND COLOUR, namely, apple tree, plum tree, and old beech wood, box, elm, oak, walnut, and also mahogany and some others, although in general turned with the tools for soft woods, and in the same manner as the first group, are polished in almost every case with glass paper. They are then in general coated either with boiled linseed oil, which is applied with a brush or rag, allowed to soak in for a short time, and is afterwards rubbed off with shavings; or else they are covered thinly with bees-wax dissolved in turpentine, and applied on a flannel. As much as possible of the bees-wax is afterwards rubbed off with a clean flannel, to prevent the stickiness that occurs from an undue quantity of the dissolved bees-wax, which never thoroughly hardens. Some workmen judiciously add a little powdered resin to the bees-wax and turpentine, this gives a little more consistency to the wax and lessens its stickiness, but the quantity should be moderate.

Some workmen use the wax in its natural state, and rub it in by softening it with the friction caused by a stick of deal wood, applied successively over the surface of the work, and afterwards remove as much as possible of the wax with a flannel. For woods that have been stained black, the black wax or composition prepared for the shoemakers, (and called *heel-ball,*) is almost always thus applied, unless indeed the works are lackered after the manner of French polishing.

3.—WOODS OF THE HARDEST GRAIN AND DARKEST COLOURS, and some others such as the foreign hardwoods for turnery enumerated in the tabular view on page 70, vol. i., are sometimes polished precisely after one of the modes already described, in other cases they are lackered, the mode of fulfilling which will be afterwards described, but when the lacker is used it should be applied directly after the glass paper, and without either oil or bees-wax having been used previously.

It should however be observed that careful workmen place but little reliance on the advantage to be derived from polishing, as in truth the work should be left so smooth and exact from the turning tool as to require little or nothing to be afterwards done to it. The practice employed by the mechanist of rubbing the emery or glass paper face to face to abrade any coarser particles is here likewise desirable, and also that of wrapping the papers around a parallel slip of wood in polishing flat surfaces and some others, as this tends to preserve the keenness of the angles and fillets of works turned in the woods. In polishing within the bottom or lid of a snuff box, it will be found advantageous to wrap the fine polishing paper around a small cubical block of wood, one or two of the faces of which are rounded or made cylindrical ; this will tend to lay an even flat grain over the work.

4.—HARDWOODS POLISHED WITH TRIPOLI.—A lustre that may be termed a natura polish is given to some of the hardwoods of close grain, as in the best flutes made of cocoa wood and ebony, and some other works ; that is to say the surface of the wood is polished entirely by abrasion, the same as the metals, marble, and many other materials. The process is sometimes conducted with tripoli powder, at other times with Dutch rush ; and it is needful in each case that the work should have been smoothly turned, and then rubbed with fine glass or emery paper, which latter is frequently preferred.

A moderate quantity of yellow tripoli is placed on flannel slightly moistened with oil, and applied just like glass paper, the motion of the lathe being occasionally changed in direction, and sometimes stopped, whilst the flannel is rubbed lengthways, to diversify the direction of the friction thus applied. It is desirable not to use a second supply of tripoli, unless at an early stage, but to allow the powder to become embedded in the flannel, and worn down to a smooth face, on which account but little oil should be used. The tripoli then becomes gradually finer and drier, and with careful management will produce a surface entirely free from scratches and highly polished, without the adventitious aid of lacker ; this mode produces a far more durable surface, wood being a much harder substance than the shell lac, the basis of the varnish for hardwood.

5.—HARDWOODS POLISHED WITH DUTCH RUSH.—A dozen or more short pieces or joints of the rush just divested of the knots and tied up at the ends as a faggot are used with water, applying all sides of the rush to wear it down smooth alike ; and in this case, as in the last, the same polisher is continually used throughout the process, in order that it may become finer with the progress of the polishing. After a sufficient period, and when the rush feels inactive, it is laid by and allowed to dry, when it is again used in the dry state, and serves to bring up a polish nearly or quite equal to that produced by the tripoli. Some artizans employ subsequently to the rush, putty-powder or rottenstone, but this is only admissible when the surface of the wood is so smooth and dark as to be incapable of retaining the powders in its pores, or of becoming stained by them.

6.—TURNED WORKS CARVED AND ORNAMENTED with the eccentric chuck, or revolving cutters, &c., do not admit of any polishing beyond the use of a clean dry brush ; sometimes a drop of oil is placed on the brush, but the oil although it may leave a temporary gloss, is eventually absorbed in the wood, and renders the surface more dull than before.

Occasionally the ornamented works are coated slightly with thin varnish laid on with a brush, this is not to be recommended, and unless the patterns are very bold, and the varnish is very dexterously applied, it is almost certain to fill in the hollows to a degree that is highly prejudicial to the appearance of the work.

That sharp tools and proper treatment completely obviate the necessity of any polish on engine turned works in hardwood, beyond that of a dry brush, is abundantly proved by several of the most tasteful and finished specimens ever executed, which were the work of a lady, and are in the author's possession. The proper course was pursued ·in their formation ; namely, *that of polishing very highly the facets forming the cutting edges of the tools,* in the manner that is elsewhere explained, and allowing the tool to cut gradually, or without plunging it too rapidly or too rankly into the work.

FLAT WORKS.

7.—FLAT WORKS IN WOOD.—The majority of the joiners' works wrought with the plane, and others executed with the file, come under this denomination. Their flat surfaces are in general scraped with the ordinary joiner's scraper, a thin plate of sheet steel, the edge of which is sharpened on the oil-stone and burred up with the burnisher. (*See* page 484, vol. ii., fig 331.) Afterwards the wood is cleaned with glass paper, of two or more sizes, wrapped around a flat piece of cork glued on a block of wood about 3 × 4 inches square, or on a piece of wood on the flat surface of which one thickness of woollen cloth is stretched and nailed around the edges which acts with greater accuracy than the elastic cork, and keeps the work flatter.

8.—SMALL FLAT WORKS IN WOOD are often rubbed *upon* the sheet of glass paper, which is then laid on the flat bench or other board—a practice analogous to that pursued by watchmakers and others. In some cases also small flat surfaces in wood are finished on face wheels, or plane disks of wood on which glass paper is glued ; this practice is somewhat common for the mechanism of piano-fortes, and many years back an analogous method was pursued by Mr. Larkin, which is described under the head FLINT.

9.—POLISHED FLAT WORKS.—It may be generally said that the several modes of polishing, already described in reference to turned works of wood, are all more or less practised also in flat works ; indeed, they were always used until comparatively of late years, when the so-called French polish, (to be hereafter spoken of,) has nearly obtained a monopoly in the embellishment of furniture and other works ; the carved surfaces of which are still, however, mostly varnished with a brush as in painting, and not by attrition. But the old fashioned polish due to linseed oil, applied daily for a year or two, although tedious, produced an equally beautiful and far more lasting polish, although it must be admitted the oil has the effect of rendering the woods somewhat darker. In conclusion of these remarks the reader is referred to the article MARQUETRY in this Catalogue.

WROUGHT IRON.—The parts of machinery made of wrought iron are polished as described in the general article MACHINERY in this Catalogue : two other examples are alone here given.

The parts of stoves and similar works in wrought iron, are sometimes ground, but in general they are filed, draw-filed, rubbed with an emery rubber, and burnished with the two handed burnisher having a stirrup for the foot ; as in such works the glittering polish on a comparatively scratchy surface, is considered to be good enough for the purpose.

Round knobs, crooked arms, bows of keys, stirrups, bridle bits, and pieces free from sharp angles, are often polished by wrapping once or twice around them, a piece of soft rope or string smeared with the polishing stuff ; and by using a sawing motion with the two hands, a considerable friction is applied all around the objects. The screws of corkscrews are mostly thus dressed.

ZINC.—Door plates made of rolled zinc are cut out, scraped to a clean surface, hammered flat and then planished, after which they are by some workmen smoothed, 1st, with a stick of blue stone and water ; 2ndly, with emery paper wrapped on a piece of wood or cork, and moistened with oil ; 3rdly, with rottenstone and oil on a coil of list.

Other workmen employ immediately after the scraper, 1st, pumice-stone, either in the lump or powder ; 2ndly, flour emery and oil on a flat woollen rubber ; and 3rdly, rottenstone in the same manner.

ZINCOGRAPHIC PLATES FOR PRINTING.—In order to give these the fine grained surface required in this branch of the graphic art, they are, 1st, rubbed with ordinary sand, and 2ndly, with fine sifted sand, the rubber is of list rolled up tight and used with water ; the zinc plate is then ready to receive the drawing which is made with the ordinary lithographic chalk upon the plate, or is transferred from the transfer paper and fixed by an acid preparation.

Zinc plates are equally susceptible with lithographic stones of the transfer process, and which by Wood's patent method of " Anastatic Printing," may be employed in producing fac-simile copies, *by transfer,* of engravings or books of the very earliest dates in their respective arts.

ZIRCON is the generic name of three varieties of gems known as the Hyacinth, the Jargoon, and the Zirconite, they are sometimes so hard as to require to be cut into facets with diamond powder the same as Sapphires. " The exposure of some varieties to heat, deprives them of their colour, and they are said to have been sold in that state in place of the diamond."

CHAPTER XXXII.

GRINDING AND SHARPENING CUTTING TOOLS.

SECT. I.—GRINDING CUTTING TOOLS ON THE ORDINARY GRINDSTONE.

THE various apparatus, materials, and processes, employed in grinding, and polishing, having been generally described in the preceding Catalogue, it will be only necessary in the present chapter, to offer a few examples of the grinding and sharpening apparatus commonly employed by amateurs, together with a brief notice of the modes of restoring the edges of the most usual tools, and which will serve to convey a sufficiently precise idea of the modes of sharpening those not described, as the edges of all cutting tools may be considered as either rectilinear, or circular, or combinations of the two forms.

The present chapter will therefore contain one section on the grinding of cutting tools on the ordinary grindstone, one section on the sharpening of cutting tools on the oilstone, and one section on setting razors, in all of which cases scarcely any guides are employed, but the tool is applied with the unassisted fingers. These will be followed by one section on sharpening cutting tools with artificial grinders, in which from the greater amount of exactness generally required, guides of various kinds are usually employed, and the chapter will conclude with a few miscellaneous examples of the less usual modes of restoring the edges of cutting tools.

Of all the tools in the workshop whether of the amateur or of the practical man, the absence of the grindstone would be the most severely felt, without it the restoration of the edges of the tools would be scarcely possible, and upon their perfection much of the practical success of cutting processes depends.

Sharp tools, produce with the least expenditure of time, surfaces so nearly finished as to require but very little polishing, whereas blunt tools leave the lines and mouldings less accurately defined, and the additional friction or polishing employed to gloss over the defects makes a bad case worse, and obliterates all the keen edges that would impart to the work a defined and exact character.

The ordinary mischief in polishing is excess, and the amateur is most strenuously counselled to *polish the tool* upon the oilstone, or other fine abrasive employed for setting the edge, and he may be assured that it will then not only cut in a much more agreeable manner, but likewise that it will impart its relative degree of perfection to the work, in like manner that the coin or medal is polished by the bright and accurate surface of the die, and not by any subsequent process.

The primitive tools whether of stone, wood, bone, or metal, were probably sharpened by rubbing them on flat gritty stones, a method still resorted to in the absence of other means, although when the substances are hard and much is required to be ground away, it is exceedingly tedious; and perhaps one of the earliest efforts at mechanical contrivance, coeval with the introduction of the draw well, and the potter's wheel, (also a revolving flat stone,) was the rotation of the grindstone upon an axis, fixed within a central aperture cut within the same, and now often denominated the eye. The spindle was doubtless supported in a horizontal direction in notches made in the top of two stakes fixed in the ground, or in some simple frame, and a transverse handle was fixed to the axis to enable one man to turn round the stone, whilst another applied to its surface the tool to be ground.

This primitive apparatus, a little improved in its mechanical details, still exists in almost every village and also in many workshops, notwithstanding, as will be shortly shown, that a far more economical mode for tools of a medium size has been employed for at any rate three centuries.

Fig. 1027.

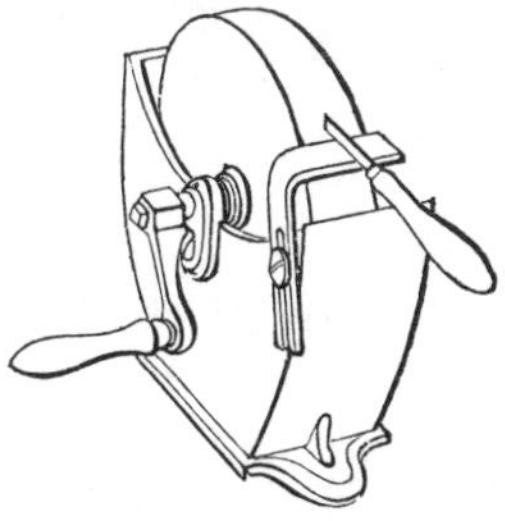

Small grindstones not exceeding a few inches in diameter, are commonly fixed in a similar manner in boxes of wood or iron. Fig. 1027, represents one of these of about one foot in diameter, the bearings of which are screwed to the cast iron trough; a stone of this diminutive size may be turned by the left hand, whilst the tool supported on the iron rest is held in the right, this arrangement is usually adopted for small tools, such as those employed by watchmakers, jewellers, engravers, and others, in which the quantity of material to be removed is inconsiderable.

The succeeding figure is copied from an engraving in a work by Hartman Schopperum, printed at Frankfort on the Maine in 1548. In this case the stone is moved by a treadle, which is an admirable plan for grindstones from about twenty to forty inches diameter, that are intended for sharpening tools, as the weight

FIG. 1028.

of the stone serves as the fly wheel, and the whole process may be carried on by one individual. This mode is less common than it deserves to be, the treadle should however be extended beyond the crank rod, and the foot should be applied at the opposite end, the same as in the ordinary turning lathe.

An oval tub made of staves like a barrel is sometimes used as a trough, its diameters should be about as two to one; the axis of the stone is placed across the shorter diameter, and it runs in collars of hardwood or metal fixed to the sides of the trough, which is supported at a convenient height upon four legs ; the treadle is joined to the back legs, and it communicates with the crank, which overhangs the bearing in the manner of the last figure.

Grindstones are also fitted up in a variety of other frames, either of wood or metal. The ends or pivots of the spindles are either cylindrical, conical, or turn between conical center points. The water-trough is stationary in some cases, in others it is joined to the frame by a joint or hinge at the one extremity, and

Fig. 1029.

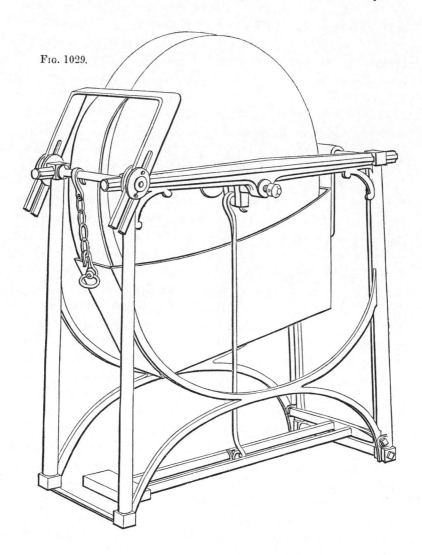

supported by a chain at the other, in order that it may, from time to time, be lifted up to moisten the edge of the stone, which, as previously explained, should never be allowed to rest in the water, as that part would be softened, and would therefore wear away more rapidly than the remainder, and hasten the departure from circularity. The frame is generally provided with a support on which the tool or the hand is rested, and also with a splash-board to catch the wet thrown off by the centrifugal force, and conduct it back into the trough.

Fig. 1029 represents an arrangement suitable for grindstones of from two to three feet diameter. In this case the frame is entirely of iron ; the stone is worked by a treadle leading to the cranked spindle, mounted between centers ; and instead of the stone being fixed to the spindle by wooden wedges, which are liable to be disturbed from their original setting by extreme change from wet to dry, they are secured by the improved plan, introduced by Holtzapffel & Co., of casting a lead center in the eye of the stone, by means of a proper mould, so as to leave a central and cylindrical aperture, and the spindle is turned to the corresponding diameter, and provided with a screw and nut, which press the stone against a flange on the spindle, which has a pin to ensure the rotation of the stone.   In this manner the stone is fixed with great solidity, and with the power of removal from one spindle to another, when the reduction of the diameter of the stone calls for the change. Fig. 1027 is also mounted upon its spindle in a similar manner. The rest for the tools in fig. 1029 admits of being placed at any height or distance from the stone that may be required, and a leather flap suspended from the rest serves the purpose of the splash-board, mentioned in the last paragraph.

A small grinding and polishing machine adapted for the use of the amateur is represented in fig. 1030. This machine is fitted with five spindles, two of them have grindstones, the one for rough usage, the other to be reserved for the more particular tools, the three other spindles are fitted with a metallic lap of lead hardened with a little antimony, a buff wheel with emery, and a circular brush. The spindles are driven by an iron foot wheel and treadle, somewhat after the manner of a lathe, as explained under the head WHEELS in the catalogue, page 1104, article 7. The stones of about the diameter of 7 inches are

fixed upon roughened iron spindles by means of melted lead
poured in between the two; by this plan such small stones are

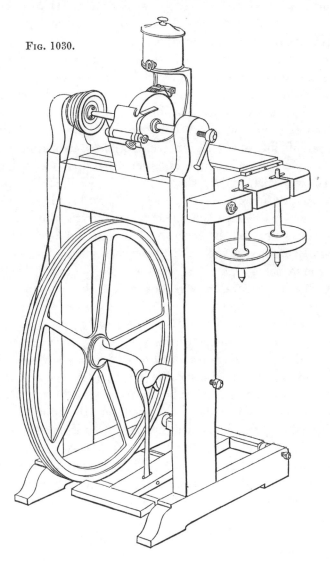

FIG. 1030.

not liable to be split, which frequently occurs with wooden
wedges, either from their being over driven in the first instance,
or from their subsequent expansion by wet.

The spindles were formerly made with centers at each end,
and a pulley for every spindle, but they are now made with a
center point at the one extremity, and a truncated cone with a

driving pin at the other, and the spindles work respectively between a center screw and a hollow notched cone fixed in front of the pulley, which is free to revolve upon its own bearing, when connected by the band with the foot wheel and treadle beneath. By this arrangement which is somewhat similar to the center chuck and driver of the common turning lathe, the spindles can be readily exchanged, by unwinding the center screw, without the displacement of the band. The machine is provided with two iron rests for the tools, that are each applicable to the edges of the grindstones and the face of the lap, they are of different bevils and susceptible of adjustment by the screw. On the back of the cast iron trough is mounted a water cistern with drip valve, the water from which falls upon the stone slightly in advance of a piece of tow, held in contact with the stone by a clamp, this effectually prevents the water from being thrown off, by the centrifugal action, and keeps the stone uniformly moist. A box at the back of the frame serves to contain the polishing powders, brushes and scraper. The other parts of the apparatus will be sufficiently explained by an inspection of the figure.

The ordinary cutlers' wheel and the large grindstones for tools have been already described in the catalogue, pages 1105 to 1108, and their arrangement will be sufficiently obvious without the aid of diagrams. Large stones are however sometimes furnished with a contrivance called a *dolly bar*, for adjusting the height of the water in the trough without the continual necessity for adding small quantities to maintain it at the most suitable level, the dolly is a large wooden bar suspended from a pulley attached to the splash board, and partially immersed in the water, when the dolly is lowered it causes a corresponding elevation of the water so as just to reach the grindstone. This contrivance in common with all those of the grinder is exceedingly simple, and although dirty the grindery is often very picturesque.

The restoration of the edges of most cutting tools for wood and soft substances is effected by the successive action of the grindstone and oilstone, the former being employed to remove the principal bulk of the material, so as to prepare the tool for the action of the slower but more delicate oilstone, which produces a much keener and more accurate edge than can be obtained with the grindstone. Tools for cutting the metals and hard materials are frequently left from the grindstone without the application of the oilstone, which is chiefly resorted to for setting a smooth edge upon the finishing tools.

Tools that are required to possess a delicate edge of a definite form, should in all practicable cases be ground upon the one bevil only, the second face then admits of being carefully formed in its manufacture, and the accuracy thus given should be scrupulously maintained, as it is clearly much easier to produce the required form by the abrasion of the less important face, than when both angles of the edge have to be renewed every time the tool is sharpened. For example, the axe and chipping chisel which require considerable strength, and but a moderate amount of accuracy, are commonly ground with two bevils, while the plane iron and paring chisel, which require accurate edges and greater delicacy, have the one face made quite level in the first instance, and in the process of sharpening, the second face of the angle is alone operated upon ; in screw tools, and moulding tools for turning, this is still more imperative. The razor, which requires delicacy of edge rather than accuracy, is sharpened on both faces, but in this case as will be shown hereafter the back of the instrument serves as a guide for the formation of the edge.

The grindstone should be kept in order so far as possible by the equal distribution of the wear; narrow tools especially, should be constantly traversed across the face of the stone to avoid wearing the latter into ridges, and the extreme edges of the stone should be exposed to their fair amount of work, or otherwise the stone will become hollow and unfitted for grinding broad flat tools. By the equal application of the tools, the face of the stone may be kept tolerably flat with but little recourse to turning or hacking, which processes have been explained in the preceding catalogue under the head WHEELS, articles 14 to 17. When however the stone loses its circularity, or becomes eccentric from being worn irregularly, it is better at once to resort to one of the means of correction, as otherwise the stone becomes rapidly worse, and the difficulty of holding the tools steady is considerably increased.

As a more scientific way of keeping grindstones in order, it has been proposed that two grindstones should be mounted with their axes parallel, and adjustable by a screw to keep their surfaces always in contact, and by giving them different surface velocities they would respectively abrade and correct each other, but the contrivance although simple is too refined for the majority of the grinders' shops, and is scarcely required for the limited purposes of the amateur.

The flat side of the stone is but little used notwithstanding that its broad surface appears so suitable for the purpose, but which is certainly not the case, in the first place the spindle would be found to be in the way of large tools or their handles, and secondly, the constant reduction of the stone arising from the friction of the work rubbing away its granular particles, would soon cause the flat surface to degenerate into an imperfect cone, and would leave a lump in the center, or if the stone were kept perfectly flat, it would be at the expense of its thickness, and the wedges by which it was at first secured, would be gradually exposed and loosened.

The stone is turned either to or from the operator according to circumstances, and in all practical cases it is best that it should run towards the extreme edge of the tool, and not from it, as in the latter case the last portion bends away from the stone and leaves a film or wire edge upon the tool, which the reverse direction avoids. The edges of the tools should be always ground parallel to the axis of the stone, or *transversely*, and not in the direction of their length, as the former position makes their edges concave to the same radius as the stone, and therefore keener and better prepared for the action of the oilstone.

In grinding the *ends* of rectilinear tools the stone should run towards the operator, as in turning, and for their *sides* or edges, it is perhaps the most convenient that the stone should travel the reverse way or backwards. Pointed tools are ground much the same as flat tools, but the choice of method is in some respects a matter of personal convenience.

In grinding the bevils and edges of instruments in their manufacture, the workman is seated on a board called the *horse*, and generally rests his elbows on his knees for steadiness, as explained on page 1106. The work is mostly applied to the stone by the hands alone without the employment except in rare cases of any guide beyond the sense of touch, which some of these workmen possess very acutely, and the amateur will find it desirable and sometimes imperative to trust to the feel alone in holding the tool upon the grindstone.

To grind the various tools with an uniform bevil requires considerable practice, as of course the least variation or tremor of the hand makes a corresponding irregularity in the bevil, after a time however the fingers acquire considerable sensibility and readily appreciate when the tool lies fair and flat upon the stone. In some cases even the practical men apply the tools upon a guide block that bears the same relation to the periphery that should exist between the respective edges of the tools, that is, if the edge of a tool is required to be exactly at right angles to the broad surface of the same, the guide upon which it is applied should point directly to the axis of the stone, or be as a radius. If the tool should differ 10 or 20 degrees from the right angle, the rest is inclined upwards or downwards to the same angle. There are also instruments in which the rectilinear tool is grasped, so that the end to be ground forms with the two legs of the instrument a triangular base, the feet are applied to some fixed plane surface, and the tool or the third leg rests upon the grinding surface. These instruments will be described in Section III.

The broad flat surfaces of tools are traversed quickly to and fro upon the top of the grindstone, as a short period of rest would grind a hollow place of the same curvature as the edge of the stone, and it is to lessen this evil as far as possible that the largest stones are employed for saws, the sides of which are required to be flat and parallel. In the razor on the other hand the curvature is desirable, and the four inch stone is there the nominal desideratum, still smaller grindstones are very often employed.

The following examples of the mode of grinding a few of the most usual tools for wood and metal, will explain the methods pursued by artizans generally for grinding the edges of their tools; and which differ from the practices of the cutler, and grinder, only so far as is called for by the nature of their respective apparatus.

In grinding an ordinary plane iron the stone travels towards the operator, and the tool is applied about half way up the stone from the axis, the rest is not generally used, but the iron is grasped firmly in the right hand to guide the tool, the position of the hand being the same as that for sharpening the tool explained in page 1144 while the pressure is principally given with the fingers of the left hand applied near the edge of the tool.   The iron is inclined vertically so that the chamfer may be ground to the angle of about 25 degrees with the face of the blade, but horizontally the iron should be held quite square to the face of the stone, or parallel with its axis, in order to prevent either corner being reduced below the proper line.   To assist the inexperienced in determining when the plane iron is held square, the top iron is sometimes kept on during the grinding, but it is set back about one eighth of an inch from the edge, so as to be quite out of the reach of the grindstone, as the action of the top iron would be materially injured, or altogether spoiled, if its form were interfered with, it is however a safer and more cleanly method to remove the top iron before grinding.

To assist in keeping the arms steady, they are pressed firmly to the sides of the body as far as the elbows; and to traverse the tool across the face of the stone, the workman swings bodily from side to side without moving his foot, so as to shift the tool gradually, and almost constantly, without disturbing the position of the arms, which would be liable to grind a second facet upon the bevil of the tool, or otherwise to grind the edge rounding instead of in a right line.   The grinding should be continued until nearly the whole of the bevil made in the sharpening on the oilstone has been removed, but unless the iron be notched, it is advisable to avoid grinding it to an absolute edge, which would be liable to produce a wiry film, the removal of which is troublesome.

To ensure the bevel being ground flat, it is in all cases necessary that the tool should be held at the same angle throughout, and also that the edge of the tool should be applied at the same height above the axis of the grindstone.   Should the edge of the tool be shifted upwards a little during the grinding, a second facet would be ground somewhat more acutely, and if shifted downwards another facet somewhat more obtusely; the combination of the two movements would produce a rounded instead of a flat chamfer, whereas if the tool be held quite steady, the chamfer will be ground slightly concave, from the circular form of the stone, and which is desirable in tools for wood, as they then cut more keenly.

Carpenters' chisels are ground in exactly the same manner as plane irons, but chisels below about half an inch wide are more difficult to grind square, as the oblique position of the tool in plan, is not so readily detected in narrow chisels.

Carpenters' gouges are ground in the same manner as chisels, except that while the fingers of the left hand are held quite steady to give the requisite pressure, the tool is rotated in the right hand, backwards and forwards, in an arc of about one third of a circle, much the same as in boring a hole with a bradawl. Gouges that are sharpened from the inside do not admit of being ground on a flat stone, they are therefore in general thinned with a slip of gritstone in the same manner as the moulding plane irons explained in the next paragraph.

Moulding plane irons are not generally ground because from their complicated forms they would require grindstones fashioned expressly to suit nearly every kind, but preparatory to sharpening with the oilstone slip, the bulk of the material is removed either with files, or narrow slips of gritstone applied in much the same manner as the file. The irons of moulding planes like those of ordinary planes are always made principally of iron, with a thin facing of steel to constitute the cutting edge, the file may therefore be successfully applied to remove the bulk of the iron, leaving little more than the thin steel edge to be abraded by the oilstone slip. As mentioned at page 493 of Vol. II. care is required in restoring the edges of moulding plane irons to keep the figure of the cutter in the proper position to fit the plane. Concave plane irons may be successfully ground on the conical grinders employed for concave turning tools, and explained in the fourth section of this chapter.

The soft wood turning chisel is ground with two bevils meeting at an angle of from 25 to 40 degrees as explained on page 513 of Vol. II. and as there shown the edge is placed oblique at an angle of about 25 degrees. In grinding this chisel the stone should revolve towards the edge of the tool, the rest is not generally employed, but for the one bevil the handle is grasped with the right hand, whilst the pressure is applied with the fingers of the left, much the same as in grinding the plane iron; but the shaft of the chisel must be held at an angle in order to place the edge square upon the grindstone. When the chisel is turned over to grind the second bevil, of course the angle at which the shaft is held must be reversed, and also the position of the hands, the left then grasping the handle and the right supplying the pressure. As in the plane iron it is desirable not to grind the tool quite to an edge, but to leave a narrow line of the facet produced in sharpening.

In grinding a turning gouge, which requires to have an elliptical edge as noticed on page 512 Vol. II. the stone generally travels from the operator. The tool is held much the same as a turning chisel, except that the oblique position of the shaft is uncalled for, and to give the elliptical form to the edge, the gouge is twisted in the hand half a turn backwards and forwards; and it is at the same time traversed across the face of the stone, not in a straight line against the rest, as for most rectilinear tools, but out of contact with the support, and in a semicircular path like an inverted arch, the sides of the gouge being applied nearer to the top of the stone than the middle of the gouge; a few trials will render this action familiar.

Flat tools for turning hard wood, ivory, and steel, are ground with the stone running towards the operator, and the tool is applied face upwards on the rest, and inclined vertically to the suitable angle for the edge, which is generally from 60 to 80 degrees, but flat tools and chisels must be held square horizontally to avoid producing oblique edges. The handle of the tool is grasped in the right hand whilst the fingers of the left applied near the edge serve to steady the tool, which is gradually traversed across the face of the stone, but to keep the edge straight care must be taken that both hands are moved equally, or parallel with the axis of the stone, otherwise the edge of the tool will become rounded.

Flat tools for brass are ground in the same manner as the above, except that the vertical inclination is not required, and the tool is pointed to the axis of the stone as in turning a cylinder.

Right and left side tools are most conveniently ground with the stone running backwards, and the tool is applied at the top of the stone, with its face or upper surface towards the operator, and its shaft parallel with the axis of the stone, the tool being inclined backwards in order to give the required bevil. For grinding the end, the stone travels forwards as usual, and the tool is applied on the rest as in grinding a flat tool.

Triangular tools that are required to cut very keenly, are ground in the same manner as the side tools, and by which the edges are made slightly concave; but when the triangular tool is required to be less penetrative and more durable, it is applied on the top of the stone, at right angles to its axis, and traversed quickly backwards and forwards as in grinding a flat surface.

Square tools for turning brass are ground in the same manner as triangular tools.

A graver is held point upwards on the rest, with the stone running towards the operator, and it is best to remove the extreme point by grinding a minute triangular facet, at right angles to the principal chamfer, but less in size than a pin's head, the tool performs as well, and the point is considerably strengthened; it requires only a touch on the stone. Many of the tools for metal are used at once from the grindstone, which could not be the case if a film were left upon them, as explained at page 1135.

Point tools are ground in the same manner as flat tools, except that the tool is held horizontally at the suitable angles for the point.

Large pointed drills that cut in the one direction only are ground the same as point tools, except that for the second edge the drill is turned over and applied at the same angle as for the first edge.

Small pointed drills that cut in both directions are generally sharpened on the oilstone without grinding. When the latter process is resorted to, however, the tool is held like a pen near the top of the stone, which runs backwards.

Round tools are held upon the rest much the same as flat tools, except that they are not traversed in a line across the stone, but while the extremity of the tool is kept nearly stationary, the handle is moved horizontally through a semi-circle around the part of the tool supported on the rest, and which serves as the imaginary axis.

Round tools that are much bevilled are sometimes ground in a manner similar to the gouge, but without the rotation on the axis of the tool therein called for.

Heel tools for turning iron are supported upon the rest exactly in the position for turning, shown in figs. 415 and 417, page 525, Vol. II., but the handle is a little more depressed, to place the bevil at the suitable angle, and the tool is swept round in a semicircle like the round tools, the point of the heel serving as the axis of rotation.

Slide rest tools for metal turning are generally held upon the rest, and as they are mostly used direct from the grindstone without having recourse to the oilstone, it is desirable in all possible cases that the stone should run towards the edge. They are applied to the grindstone after the same general method as the hand tools of corresponding forms, but as explained in pages 530 to 534 of Vol. II., the fixed tools require additional care to preserve the proper angles for cutting, and the tool-gage, figs. 438 and 439, may with advantage be resorted to for determining the proper forms.

Detached cutters for fitting into cutter bars, such as those shown in figs. 440 to 442, page 535, Vol. II., are too small to be held in the fingers, they are therefore fixed in socket handles of appropriate forms, or otherwise they are grasped in a hand-vice, which serves as the temporary handle for applying them to the grindstone.

Screw tools and moulding tools used by hand, that are cut to their respective forms on steel hobs or cutters, as explained on page 591, Vol. II., are sharpened only upon their upper surfaces, as the forms of the tools would be impaired by grinding their ends. They are frequently sloped off on the face, and this method serves sufficiently well for tools applied to the hardwoods and ivory, but as explained on page 520, Vol. II., the slope increases the angle of the edge; and the method of nicking in the tools, shown in fig. 407, by applying them transversely on the grindstone, is far preferable for screw tools intended for iron and steel.

SECT. II.—SHARPENING CUTTING TOOLS ON THE OILSTONE.

THE completion of the edges of tools after grinding is effected either upon the Turkey oilstone or one of the family of hone slates described on page 1065. These stones differ exceedingly in quality, some being so hard as scarcely to take any hold of the tool, whilst others are altogether as soft. The latter are best for broad tools, as they cut rapidly, and are then less exposed to being irregularly worn than when used for narrow tools.

On the whole, the preference is given to the Turkey oilstone for ordinary tools, and the yellow German hone for razors and delicate instruments. The Turkey stone being crystalline, is cut into square blocks with the slicer, fed with diamond powder; but the hone slates may be split through their natural fissures into rough parallel blocks; and before use they are ground flat by rubbing them on a wide stone, or iron plate, fed with hard sand or emery. The stones are afterwards mounted in a wooden stock, as explained on page 1081.

In sharpening, as in the majority of mechanical operations, the work becomes a copy of the tool, and a flat oilstone, now the tool, will produce the most correct edge with the least expenditure of time. The oilstone should be kept flat principally by an even distribution of the wear; the stone or iron plate must, however, be occasionally resorted to for restoring a level surface.

The oilstone should be moistened with good clean oil not disposed to dry; otherwise it becomes thick, like glue or varnish, and entirely prevents the action of the stone upon the tool. Soap and water have been recommended for razor hones, but its rapid evaporation is unfavourable to its use.

The angles at which the tools are sharpened for different materials have been already treated of in the preceding volume. It is there mentioned that the ultimate angles of the ordinary tools for wood vary from about 25 to 45 degrees, according to the hardness of the wood; and the manner in which the tool is applied. The smallest angle, or about 25 degrees, is used for the spokeshave iron. Paring chisels and gouges are generally sharpened at about 30 degrees, and plane irons at about 35 degrees. Turning chisels and gouges vary from about 30 to 45 degrees. The screw tools and moulding tools for hardwood and ivory are made at from 50 to 60 degrees. Tools for iron and steel have angles of from 60 to 70 degrees; and those for brass and gun-metal from 80 to 90 degrees.

In all cases in which the sharpening of the tools is completed upon the oilstone, the principal part of the material is removed upon the grindstone, at an angle a little less than that forming the ultimate edge of the tool, the greatest differences being made in the tools for soft wood, which only require a moderate degree of strength in their edges, such as the plane irons, paring chisels, and gouges, which are generally ground about 10 degrees more acutely than they are sharpened. In the tools for metal, which require considerable strength in their edges, the difference is not more than about 2 degrees. It is therefore necessary in all cases that the shaft of the tool to be sharpened, should be held at such an angle to the surface of the oilstone, as to place the edge of the tool at the required angle. Thus, if a tool with one bevil only, such as a plane iron, is to be sharpened at an angle of 40 degrees, the shaft of the tool is held at an angle of 40 to the face of the oilstone; but if a tool with two bevils, such as a turning chisel, is to be sharpened at an angle of 40, its shaft must be held at half that angle, or 20 degrees, so as to place the second bevil at the angle of 40. It consequently results, from the tools being placed at two different angles on the grindstone and oilstone respectively, that the chamfer of the tool presents two bevils, the one produced by the grindstone, the other by the oilstone, and which, in the case of the tools for soft wood, are quite distinct, but in the tools for metal gradually slide into each other.

It has been explained at page 1137, that some practice is required to enable the tools to be held steadily upon the grindstone at the proper angle, the same remarks apply to setting tools upon the oilstone; but in the latter case the difficulty is increased by the necessity for rubbing the tools backwards and forwards upon the quiescent stone. With a little care and practice, however, the hands acquire the habit of traversing the tool at the same angle in parallel lines, and which is quite essential, as should a rocking motion be given to the tool in the direction of the bevil, during the stroke, the chamfers, instead of being flat, would become rounded, and the ultimate edge of the tool would be thereby thickened and unsuited for its purpose.

Rectilinear tools that are sharpened upon the one bevil only, require to be laid flat on the face to remove the wire edge; this is done as the last process of setting; the tool should be rubbed upon the face no more than is absolutely necessary, and not in the least degree tilted up, which would produce a second bevil, and greatly increase the angle of the edge, at the same time destroying the accuracy of the face given in the manufacture of the tool.

The method of sharpening a plane iron has been described somewhat in detail at page 496, Vol. II., the peculiar mode of holding the plane iron is there stated as follows :—" The iron is first grasped in the right hand, with the fore finger only above and near the side of the iron, and with the thumb below ; the left hand is then applied with the left thumb lapping over the right, and the whole of the fingers of that hand on the surface of the iron ; the edge should be kept nearly square across the oil-stone, as when one corner precedes the other, the foremost angle is the more worn." This method of holding the tool gives great steadiness and command of position, and it should be adopted with all rectilinear tools that will admit of its application ; as the back of the tool is then firmly supported upon the three fingers of the right hand, assisted by the two thumbs placed beneath, while the pressure is given almost exclusively by the fingers on the top of the blade.

Narrow chisels that are too small to be grasped in both hands, are held in the right hand much the same as a plane iron, and the pressure is principally given by the first two fingers of the left applied near the edge of the tool, and over the forefinger of the right hand.

Chisels that are required for paring across the end grain of moderately soft wood, are considered to hang better to the work when they have a very slight keen burr or wire edge, thrown up on the face of the tool ; to produce this they are sharpened quite smoothly as usual, but for the last finish the bevil is passed once or twice over the stone as in sharpening, and which raises a minute wire edge sufficient for the purpose.

Cabinet-makers' gouges that are sharpened externally, and are required to have the edge square across the end of the tool, are held in the right hand the same as small chisels, and traversed straight along the oilstone with the shaft at right angles to the side of the stone ; the first two fingers of the left hand are applied within the concavity of the gouge, and serve as a fulcrum upon which the tool is twisted about one-fourth of a turn, with each stroke backwards and forwards upon the oilstone, so as to subject all parts of the chamfer equally to the action of the stone ; this is continued until the edge has been uniformly sharpened. The flat oilstone cannot be applied to remove the wire edge from the concave side of the tool, but which is effected with a slip of oilstone having a convex edge, as described on page 1081, the gouge is held in the left hand whilst the oilstone slip is rubbed up and down the inside of the gouge with the right hand, care being taken to keep the slip flat on the face of the tool to avoid making a second chamfer; at the last finish the side of the slip is generally swept once or twice around the outside of the edge.

Gouges that are sharpened from the inside must be set entirely with the oilstone slip, but the gouge is in this case generally rested against the bench, and the process is more tedious.

It is at all times rather difficult to keep the curved edge of the gouge level across the end. When the edge has become irregular from repeated sharpening, it is restored by placing the gouge perpendicular upon the oilstone, and reducing the end to a level surface; after which the edge is sharpened as above described.

Moulding plane irons are held in the left hand face upwards, that the operator may the more exactly see the part to which the oilstone slip is applied; the straight portions of the edge are sharpened upon the ordinary oilstone, and to remove the wire edge the iron is laid flat on the oilstone in the same manner as a chisel.

The turning chisel for soft wood, is sharpened in the same manner as the paring chisel, the only differences arising from the double chamfer and the oblique edge; the extreme point of the turning chisel requires to be made quite keen, that it may be used for turning flat surfaces.

The turning gouge, when sharpened upon the flat oilstone, is held in the same manner as the cabinet-maker's gouge, but to sharpen its elliptical edge, the tool is traversed in a concave sweep upon the face of the oilstone, whilst the gouge is twisted in the hand exactly as described for grinding this tool. Sometimes both the outside and inside of the turning gouge are set with the oilstone slip; in this case the gouge is held in the left hand, and rested against the popit head, or any convenient part of the lathe, whilst the flat surface of the oilstone slip is rubbed lengthways upon the chamfer of the tool around each part, and then the round edge of the slip is rubbed within the concave flute.

The wire edge left by the grindstone upon the gouge must be entirely removed before the tool is fit for use, it is expedited by drawing the chamfer of the tool through a notch cut by itself in a piece of wood as hard as beech, a few touches of the oilstone slip will then render the edge perfectly keen and fit for use.

Tools for turning hardwood, ivory, and those for finishing the metals, are sharpened upon the oilstone much the same as the corresponding tools for soft wood, the principal difference being that they are held upon the stone at a greater angle, according to the material upon which they are to be employed; the appropriate angles and forms for the various materials have been fully explained in the second volume of this work. Tools for steel cut the most keenly and smoothly when left from a fine grindstone. Tools for iron cut rather more smoothly when finished on the oilstone, but the edge is not so enduring, and therefore with tools for iron the oilstone is only occasionally resorted to for giving a smooth edge for the last finish of the work. Tools for brass and gun-metal, when left from the grindstone, cut too rankly, and are said by workmen to *drag;* they are therefore always sharpened upon the oilstone, and the finishing tools for brass and gun-metal are frequently burnished, as mentioned at page 522 of the second volume; in this case the burnisher is placed at right angles to the face of the tool, and passed once, or at most twice, across the edge with moderate pressure.

Finishing tools for soft wood are sometimes burnished with the back of the turning gouge, applied at an angle to throw up a wire edge which is used with a scraping action. The broads figs. 372 and 373, page 515, Vol. II., are thus employed for flat surfaces. Right side tools, fig. 382, ground at an angle of about 30 degrees, and burnished, serve for the interior of boxes, and ordinary paring chisels are used in like manner for finishing cylindrical and convex works. The method of sharpening the joiner's scraper with the burnisher is explained at page 484, Vol. II.

SECT III.—SETTING RAZORS.

PERHAPS of all cutting instruments, the razor possesses the most general and personal interest, in respect to the conditions required for its perfect action, and it is therefore proposed to notice at moderate length the principal circumstances on which the perfection of its edge depends.

The razor notwithstanding the peculiarity of its outline, conforms strictly to the ordinary wedge form section of most cutting tools, but as it requires the most delicate edge that can be produced, it is so formed as to facilitate to the utmost the process of sharpening. For instance in the plane iron, chisel, penknife, lancet, and most other instruments, the angles of the one or both the sides of the wedge or cutting edge are determined by the particular inclination at which the tool is held upon the stone, but if the hand wavers, the setting or facet instead of becoming a plain flat surface, becomes rounded and ill defined.

In the razor on the other hand the proportion between the width of the blade, and the thickness of the back, is almost always such that when the blade is laid perfectly flat on the hone, or so that the edge and back both touch, the suitable angle is obtained, and which varies from about 17 to 20 degrees; the exact measure of the angle is very little studied, although in reference to the principle of cutting tools some little variation ought to be made, in choosing the thickest edge for the strongest beard. It does sometimes happen that the razor is not laid quite flat on the hone, but that it is slightly tilted, this occurs when a wide razor that has been ground on a large stone is required to be sharpened for a stiff beard; but it so rarely occurs that the razor is placed otherwise than flat on the hone, that the exception may be overlooked.

The magnified sections of razors in figs. 1031 to 1036, which for distinctness are drawn three times their full size, and for comparison, of the same angle or 18 degrees throughout, exhibit various modes adopted to avoid the necessity for sharpening the entire side of the imaginary wedge, represented by the dotted lines, by hollowing the sides in different ways. It is apparent that it would be much more tedious and difficult to wear down the imaginary flat sides represented by the dotted lines, than the small portion of the same which are supposed to remain; and indeed the entire dotted line if sharpened, would most probably become rounded instead of flat. The concavity therefore facilitates the placing of the razor on the hone, it thins the edge leaving but little for the stone to abrade, and it prevents the finished appearance given to the sides of the razor being detracted from by the sharpening.

Figs. 1031 and 1032, represent the section of that description of razor blade which is by far in the most common use, as before observed the widths of the blade and the thicknesses of their backs are such as to give in each an ultimate edge of 18 degrees when the blade is sharpened on the hone, but fig. 1032, is ground

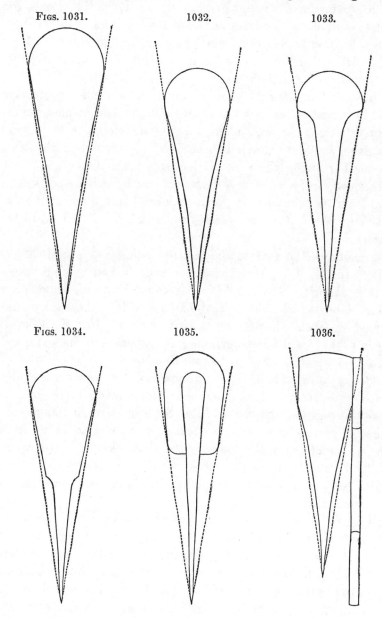

Figs. 1031.   1032.   1033.

Figs. 1034.   1035.   1036.

transversely on a wheel of four inches diamater, and fig. 1031, on one of twelve inches, the general extremes of curvature. It is clear that the former possesses an edge that is thinner and more flexible, and that presents a narrower edge or plane to be abraded by the hone ; and which latter in consequence will cut with greater precision and delicacy than if it had to abrade the entire surface. The curvature in most general use for best razors is intermediate, or from 5 to 6 inches, but stones of from 12 to 15 inches diameter are from motives of economy resorted to for common razor blades.

In some few cases the edge of the razor is ground lengthways on the stone, so as to become nicked in, in the manner represented in fig. 1033, and in this way any degree of thinness may be given, and also extended throughout any desired width. This mode of grinding the razor is however more difficult, and the feebleness of the edge may be thereby easily carried to excess ; and from the vibration to which they are liable when applied to a strong beard, they are called by the Sheffield cutlers, *rattler* razors.

Sometimes the two methods of grinding are combined, as shown in fig. 1034, in this case the razor is first ground transversely as for fig. 1032, and it is subsequently ground lengthways so as to be nicked in for about half its width ; these razors are known by Sheffield workmen as half rattlers. For the sake of variety the longitudinal grinding is sometimes only extended about one quarter of an inch from the edge.

Other razors as in fig. 1035, are made as very thin acute blades fixed in a detached back somewhat like a dovetail saw, in this case the edges of the blade and of the back are simultaneously whetted on the hone ; but no advantage appears to result from the construction, on the contrary the blade cannot be reground without removal from the stock, which implies the risk of its being reduced below the edge of the stock so as to prevent its replacement.

Fig. 1036 represents another of the modes in which razors are occasionally constructed, in this a loose frame or guard of brass is added to the blade. The idea in this case is to prevent the liability to accident incurred by nervous or infirm persons from the tremor of their hands. The frame is intended to act as a muzzle or guard to prevent the edge penetrating to any serious depth, and the instrument is known as a guard razor.

The keenness of the edge of the razor is commonly tried by making a faint incision in the thick skin covering the inner edge of the palm of the left hand, but the cutler also tries the razor upon the thumb or finger nail. The razor is either placed in a line with the finger and obliquely across the end of the nail, or a still more sensitive test is to place the blade at right angles to the finger, and allow it to rest upon the back of the nail, that of the third finger being by some considered the most sensitive. In this manner a very minute notch in the edge is quite perceptible, and the keenness may also be appreciated by the degree in which the razor hangs to the nail, as the keen blade will make the deeper incision, and appear to offer a more dragging yet smooth resistance, whereas the blunt razor will slide over with less penetration and drag.

A more scientific method was proposed by Mr. Kingsbury in his pamphlet on the razor, namely the examination of the entire edge with a magnifier, and which process when applied in a sufficiently powerful degree will doubtless exhibit the causes why the razor fails in its purpose, and which are sometimes threefold, namely first the razor may be notched, secondly it may have a loose pliant film or wiry edge, or thirdly, instead of a keen acute edge it may be blunt and obtuse, which is generally due to the excessive use of the razor strop ; upon each of these considerations some few observations will be offered.

First, notches are liable to occur in a razor from the blade having been overheated, either in the forging or hardening, a fault which is irretrievable, as it renders the steel permanently brittle, and altogether incapable of receiving a fine acute edge, as the particles of the metal break away at the extreme edge on the hone. The brittleness may occur in a somewhat less degree, when the razor without having been overheated is simply left too hard, so as to require to be let down or tempered a little lower than at first.

Secondly, the wire edge generally occurs from the hone being too much used, as when the two faces of the wedge are rubbed away beyond *that point at which they first meet*, the slender film of steel commences to form, because the extreme edge is then so thin that it bends away from the hone instead of being rubbed off. The wire edge is more liable to occur when the one side of the blade is more whetted than the other, and if it be obstinate in its resistance to removal, it frequently indicates further that the blade is too soft, as if the razor blade be made too hard, the metal will be brittle instead of flexible, and the thin extremity break off instead off forming the filmy edge.

The temper of the blade ought to be such as to be indisposed to become either permanently notched or wiry from the action of the hone.   But in the application of the various grinding and polishing wheels, especially the latter, there is always some risk, as the temptation to expedite the work causes too much vigour to be occasionally used, thereby giving to the blade so much heat as to reduce its temper; an error the unscrupulous may easily gloss over, by touching the work more lightly, and thereby removing the colour, or that index whereby the temper of the instrument is commonly estimated.   But the experienced cutler is generally able to distinguish by the feel of the cut, or of the action of his own particular hone, between such blades as either exceed or fall short of the appropriate temper.

Thirdly, in a new or a recently ground razor, the thick obtuse edge shows that the blade has not been sufficiently rubbed on the hone, and in a used razor, it more commonly indicates that partly by the using of the razor, and partly by its being inter-

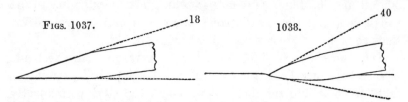

Figs. 1037.   18   1038.   40

mediately stropped to renovate the edge, it has been too much rounded; so that instead of the two narrow facets constituting the edge being plane surfaces and meeting at from 17 to 20 degrees as left from the hone, they are seen to have become considerably rounded, so as probably to meet at more than double the original angle, a condition explained by the diagrams figs. 1037 and 1038, in which for perspicuity the extreme edges are shown about twenty times their true size.   This fault or the rounded edge is also readily detected with the magnifier, and is almost sure to occur from the use of a soft strop, as the leather immediately against the edge from being indented, rises as an abrupt angle and mutilates the keenness of the blade.   If however the razor at any of its stages of manufacture or setting have been treated without uniformity, it may possess at different parts of its edge all these errors, but which is less to be expected than that the one error should prevail.

If neither of the above three faulty conditions are discernible by the careful use of a lens of one half to one third of an inch focus, (or of a linear power of twenty or thirty,) such razor will in general be found to act with satisfaction, but the keenest razor when delicately examined with a lens of one fifth to one tenth of an inch focus, (or a linear power of fifty to one hundred,) or still better with a microscope of not less than equivalent power, will present a faintly undulating and irregular edge, which resembles rather a ripple mark, than the angular teeth of the edge of the saw, to which it is usually compared.   Indeed the edge of a razor of ordinary quality, bears the microscopic examination much better than might be expected; but as no surface polished by art is free from scratches, it must happen that every such scratch when continued to the edge formed by two planes meeting at so small an angle, deprives the otherwise continuous edge of a small portion of its material, and thence constitutes a notch, but the notches are the smaller, the finer the abrading surface used in producing the edge.

When however the errors are so minute as to require to be thus magnified some fifty or one hundred times, to render them visible, they are too minute to be detected by the skin, the nail, or the employment of the instrument on the beard.   Having explained the good and bad condition of the razor, the practice of setting the instrument will be now the more easily understood, and it is proposed first to describe the sharpening of a new razor, and then that of one which has been rendered dull by use.

Various kinds of whetstones are more or less used in sharpening razors, commonly in pieces measuring from eight to ten inches long, by one and a half to two inches broad, and great importance is deservedly attached to their being perfectly flat on the face, with which view they are occasionally rubbed on a large gritstone with water, but in use they are always supplied with oil and kept remarkably clean.

The Charnley Forest stone is generally preferred for the first stage or for striking off the wiry edge of the blade.   The Turkey oilstone is sometimes used for the same purpose.   The Green hone or Welsh hone, which is harder than the Charnley Forest, and generally in smaller pieces, is occasionally used for razors, and is by some preferred to Charnley Forest for finishing pen and pocket knives, and especially for setting surgeons' instruments.

The yellow German hone, particularly the slabs from the lower strata known as old rock, is greatly preferred to all the above for the principal office in setting razors, as it cuts more slowly, smoothly, and softly, than any of them.   The Iron stone or slabs of the hematite iron ore, are occasionally used for giving the final edge, it consists principally of oxide of iron, and chemically resembles crocus, but that it is in a compact, instead of a disentegrated form.   The iron stone is however so very hard that it appears to act more as a burnisher than a hone, and renders the edge almost too smooth, so that when at all used, the razor is in general only passed once or at most twice on each side along the iron stone.

Taking the razor from the last stage of its manufacture described at page 1051, it is to be observed that as the glazers and polishers revolve *away from*, and not towards the edge, they always leave a thin filmy edge, which as the first step towards setting, is *struck off* on a Charnley Forest stone.   The blade is grasped in the right hand by its tang, and near to the cutting part, and is placed square across the one end of the stone but tilted about ten or twenty degrees, and is then swept forward along the stone, edge foremost in a circular arc, so as to act on the entire edge; each side in general receives only one stroke, and this produces a comparatively obtuse edge measuring from forty to sixty degrees.   Should this fail to remove the wiry edge, the blade is placed perpendicularly upon, and drawn with a little pressure across, a strip of horn, (generally a spoiled razor handle,) which is fixed down to the bench, the friction of the horn against the edge generally suffices entirely to remove the wiry film, otherwise the blade is struck once more on each side along the stone.   Should the film of steel be left on the stone, it is removed before another blade is applied.

One object in the striking off, is to avoid the necessity for so far wearing down the back of the razor, as to give it the appearance of an old one that has been repeatedly set, and it is also especially required in wide blades ground on large stones, as the wiry film is then very difficult to remove otherwise.

The next and principal part of the setting is accomplished almost invariably on the German hone. The razor is held as before, but it is now placed quite flat down, or so as to touch on the back and edge. Some prefer a long sweeping stroke backwards and forwards, others prefer small circular or elliptical strokes, and others a short zig zag movement, but all gradually work from heel to point, or draw the razor forward so as *to act on all parts alike*, and most persons lift the razor endways towards the conclusion, allowing its point still to rest on the hone, with the view of sharpening the circular end of the blade. The choice of these methods seems to be principally a question of individual habit, and to be nearly immaterial, provided the entire edge is acted on alike, and that at very short intervals the razor is turned over so as to whet it upon its opposite sides alternately, but it is general to conclude the process by sweeping the razor edge foremost, once on each side steadily along the hone, as if in shaving off a thin slice of the hone, this lessens the disposition to the wire edge.

The line of policy is just to continue this secondary process, until the new facets constituting the wedge of seventeen to twenty degrees, exactly meet at the extremity of the more obtuse angle given by the striking off, and which if mathematically done, would prevent the formation of the wiry film, which is one of the most troublesome obstacles in the process.

Should the film nevertheless arise, it is to be removed by passing the blade occasionally across the slip of horn, and continuing the whetting for shorter periods on each side, some persons indeed suffer the film if very minute to be abraded on the razor strop, but which latter unless very cautiously used is a very mischievous instrument. It is of course to be understood that the hone is not given up, until at any rate the notches are no longer perceptible, when the blade is drawn across the thumb or finger nail, which detects them more faithfully than the slip of horn, and that when viewed edgeways, the edge is merely discovered as the meeting of the two sides of the blade, and not from possessing itself any visible thickness or width.

As before observed, the blade is by some persons passed once on each side along the iron stone, but this practice is by no means common, and may, according to the questionable doctrine advanced by some cutlers, spoil the blade by rendering it *too smooth, or too free from the saw-like teeth*, but which it would appear can hardly be the case, unless it also increase the angle of the edge, or render it less acute and keen.

When the edge of the razor admits of being drawn smoothly across the horn, and the edge is not distinguishable by the eye, the hone may be considered to have fulfilled its purpose, and the razor is slightly stropped, but in this case, as the edge of the blade becomes somewhat embedded in the leather, it would cut if moved forwards as in setting, and therefore the razor is always stropped backwards, and usually from heel to point.

Disregarding the high sounding names and praises bestowed on various razor strops, it may be added that within moderate limits, they are the better the harder their surfaces, and the less they are supplied with abrasive matter. As when they possess the opposite qualities of softness and superabundance of dressing, or that they are used in excess, they rapidly round the edge of the razor, and change its edge from the well-defined angle of seventeen or twenty degrees produced by the stone, to twice that angle or more, and entirely unfit it for use.

Perhaps for the razor strop a fine smooth surface of calf skin, with the grained or hair side outwards, is best, it should be pasted or glued down flat on a slip of wood, and for the dressing almost any extremely fine powder may be used, such as impalpably fine emery, crocus, natural and artificial specular iron ore, black lead, or the charcoal of wheat straw; each of these two latter act as abrasives in consequence of containing a minute portion of silex. Combinations of these and other fine powders, mixed with a little grease and wax, have been with more or less of mystery applied to the razor strop. The choice appears nearly immaterial, provided the powders are exceedingly fine, and they are but sparingly used.

One side of the strop is generally charged with composition; on the other side the leather is left in its natural state, and the finishing stroke is in general given on the plain side.

It is of great importance that all razor strops be kept scrupulously clean, and with which view they are provided with sheaths, which should be marked so as to prevent the composition being accidentally carried over to the clean side of the instrument. The strop should be always employed in the most sparing manner, so as rather to wipe than rub the razor; many, indeed, never strop the razor *after use,* but simply wipe it dry on clean wash leather, a silk handkerchief, or a soft towel, and only employ the strop *before* using the razor. A good mode was suggested to preserve the edges of surgical instruments from rusting when laid by, namely, the drawing them lightly through a tallow candle; this leaves a minute quantity of grease on the edge, which defends them from the air, and becomes deposited on the strop before the blade is used.

When a razor, from continued use and stropping, has become dull, it mostly arises from the edge having been rounded and thickened as explained by the diagram, figs. 1037 and 1038; in this case the setting, if attempted by the amateur, may with advantage be only so far pursued as barely to remove the rounded part. On close inspection it will be seen the part of the facet towards the back is first touched by the hone, the effect of which is seen by the less polished surface it leaves; and if the setting be only continued until the bright rounded part is all but removed when examined with a magnifier, no wire will be formed, and the blade will be again brought within the province of the razor strop. The razor, after having been repeatedly set, becomes so wide in the bevil or facet, as to require to be re-ground, to thin it away to the first state, as the blade should always be so thin as to be sensibly pliant at the extreme edge, when pressed flat on the thumb nail and slightly tilted; but the re-grinding should be done with a proper regard to the relative width of the back of the blade, and the preservation of its proper temper.

SECT. IV.—SHARPENING CUTTING TOOLS WITH ARTIFICIAL GRINDERS.

Fig. 1039 represents the upper part of a horizontal grinding machine, principally intended for grinding and setting the edges of cutting tools, by means of revolving laps of metal fed with the various abrasive powders. The lower part of this apparatus exactly resembles that of the vertical grinding machine, fig. 1030, page 1132, but to place the sides of the laps in a horizontal position, this apparatus is furnished with a vertical spindle, or mandrel, upon which the laps are screwed after the manner of chucks upon an ordinary turning lathe.

The mandrel is mounted in a rectangular frame of cast iron, which fits between the bearers, and is secured in its place by a wedge beneath, as shown at *w*. The upper side of the iron frame is made as a platform, and is fitted in the center with a cylindrical steel collar, within which the mandrel revolves, while its lower end rests upon a center screw passing through the bottom of the iron frame, and by means of which the mandrel can be elevated to the required position, nearly level with the upper metal platform, which is dotted in the drawing, and serves as a support for the tools. This second platform stands upon three feet, which are fitted with pins that enter corresponding holes in the under platform ; by this arrangement the upper platform can be readily removed when the laps are exchanged. The band for driving the mandrel proceeds from the foot wheel over the two oblique guide pulleys *g*, to the pulley *m*, fixed on the vertical

Figs. 1039.   1040.

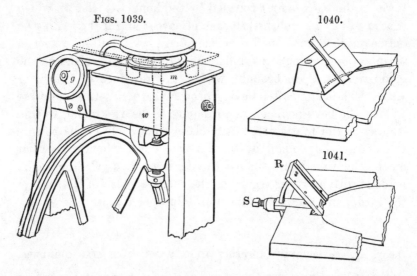

1041.

mandrel, and the tension of the band is adjusted by shifting the mandrel frame to the right or left upon the bearers.

The general application of the revolving laps has been already described in the Catalogue of Abrasive Processes, under the head Wheels, articles 37 to 47, pages 1113 to 1117, and it only remains to observe, that the lead lap supplied with emery of different degrees of coarseness, is used for grinding the tools to the required angle ; they are afterwards smoothed upon the brass lap fed with flour emery, or oilstone powder, and the final polish is given with the iron lap supplied with crocus; the two latter powders may be applied either by putting on the oil and powder separately in small quantities, and mixing them with a brush, or the materials may be mixed in a cup previous to their application.

Various guides have been employed for determining the exact angle at which the tools should be applied to the revolving laps, and also to remove the difficulty of grinding the bevils of the tools perfectly flat, the most simple guide consists of a block of wood shown in fig. 1040, and made to the same angle at which it is required to grind the tool, the block is screwed upon the upper platform of the horizontal grinding machine, and the back of the tool being held steady upon the bevilled side of the wooden guide block, the chamfer of the tool is readily ground to that particular angle, this method however requires a separate guide for every different angle.

An instrument that has been called a quadrant rest is shown in fig. 1041, and which removes the necessity for several guide blocks, this instrument is made of brass, and consists of a base piece that is let into the platform of the horizontal grinding machine, a rising plate R is connected to the base piece by a joint at the edge close to the lap, and it is retained at any required angle by the arch piece and binding screw S, a steel rib is fitted on the upper surface of the rising plate against which the tool is held whilst being ground.

For determining the exact angle at which the instrument is fixed, the arch piece is either graduated into degrees, or small holes are drilled at every five degrees, into which the point of the binding screw enters. The tool to be ground is held with its back upon the upper surface, and one side in contact with the steel rib, but the quadrant rest like the wooden guide blocks, is unprovided with the means of determining the horizontal angle of the tool, which is therefore left to the dexterity of the operator ; they are both objectionable also on account of always presenting the tool to the same part of the lap, which is thereby liable to be worn irregularly. These objections are entirely removed in the instrument next described.

The instrument for grinding and setting ordinary turning tools having rectilinear edges shown in figs. 1042 to 1045, is a modification of an instrument that has been long used for sharpening the ends of tools employed in eccentric and ornamental turning, for which works the tools are in general all of one exact size, and therefore admit of being held in the same socket, but this would not answer for the common turning tools made of different sizes according to their respective purposes.

The principle employed in the construction of the instrument fig. 1042, is to fix the tool to be ground to a triangular frame having two points of bearing, and allow the point of the tool to be ground to form the third bearing, if therefore the two feet of the instrument are supported on a plane parallel with the

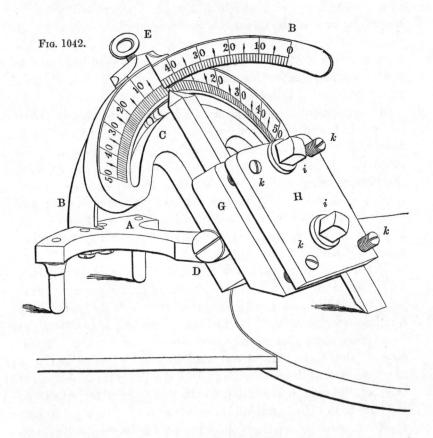

Fig. 1042.

grinding lap, whilst the third leg of the triangle, or the tool to be ground, rests upon the revolving lap, the latter will grind away the tool until its surface agrees throughout with the plane of the lap, and in consequence the end of the tool will ultimately be made perfectly flat.

As however tools for turning are required to possess a variety of forms, some square, others bevilled or pointed, others to cut at the side, and that their edges should be more or less acute, according to the material upon which they are employed, it is essential to give the socket which holds the tool two adjustments, the one vertical, the other horizontal, and both furnished with divisions and clamping screws for determining every required position to be given to the tools.

The general arrangement of the instrument will be sufficiently obvious from an inspection of fig. 1042, in which A, represents the base of the instrument on which is fixed the vertical arch-piece B, an adjustable plane C, is connected with the base by a joint at D, on which it moves, and may be fixed by the binding screw E, at any angle from 0, at the top of the arc B to 60 degrees, lower than which it is never required to be placed, the upper part of the plane C, has a circular mortise, and is graduated through an arc of 50 degrees on each side of the central line. The piece G, which serves as the bed for the tool to be ground, is bevilled on its front edge that it may not come in contact with the lap, and a pointed rectangular bar proceeds from the back of this piece to the circle of graduations on the plane C, to which the bed piece G, is united by means of a pivot a little in advance of D, consequently the bed piece is capable of being moved to the right or left, and it can be fixed at any angle on the graduated arc, by means of a capstan headed screw passing from beneath the plate C, through the circular mortise into the upper end of the bar on G.

On the upper surface of the piece G is a steel plate H, fastened by two square headed screws, i, i, this plate has a spring underneath which raises the plate to admit the tool which is to be ground. The four screws marked k are for regulating the height of the steel plate, so as to leave the same opening between the plates on the side unoccupied, as on that where the tool is fixed, the application of these screws is shown in figs. 1043 to 1045, which represent the manner in which different tools are fixed in the instrument.

A flat tool is held as in fig. 1043 the small screws 3 and 4 are each withdrawn a little below the surface of the steel plate, and the screws 1 and 2 are projected forwards for the support of the same, the screw 1 being as much in advance of the plate as the thickness of the tool at 3, and the projection of the screw 2, being equal to the thickness of the tool at 4, now therefore the steel plate will be supported equally on every side, and it will bear flat on the tool, and hold it firmly when the steel plate is clamped by the square headed screws. Without the aid of the screws for

FIGS. 1043.   1044.   1045.

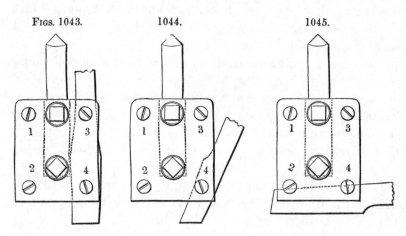

supporting the plate on the opposite side to the tool, it would only bear upon the edge of the tool and would not hold it firmly, the adjustment of the small screws however admits of the tool being firmly fixed, notwithstanding that it may be of irregular thickness.

Point tools to be ground at angles not exceeding 50 degrees, may be clamped in the same manner as flat tools, and the angular position be obtained by shifting the point of G to the required graduation on the plane C, the socket is then secured by the capstan screw. When the angle of the tool exceeds 50 degrees it is clamped in the manner next described.

Bevil tools are more conveniently fixed as in fig. 1044, in which case the screw 4 is withdrawn, and 1, 2, and 3, are advanced to equal the thickness of the tool.

Side cutting tools are held as in fig. 1045, screws 2 and 4 being withdrawn, and 1 and 3 adjusted to the thickness of the tool.

The tool having been firmly clamped, the vertical and horizontal angles are adjusted until the chamfer of the tool bears fairly upon the lap, when the two legs of the instrument rest upon the platform of the grinding machine.   To avoid the rapid deterioration of the lap, it is desirable to distribute the wear by applying the tools to different parts of the lap in succession.   For grinding the tools to definite angles, this instrument is adjusted in the same manner as the corresponding instrument for setting angular tools for ornamental turning, described on pages 1164 to 1169.

Fig. 1046, represents an instrument that is very generally employed by practical rose engine turners, for sharpening their small angular sliding rest tools, which require a considerable degree of accuracy.   This instrument is provided with two planes ointed together, upon the one of which the tool to be sharpened,

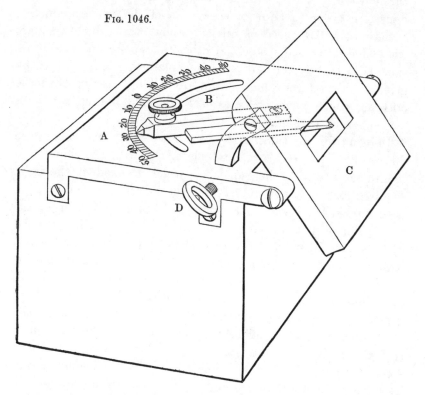

Fig. 1046.

is placed in the required position for grinding the horizontal angle of the edge, whilst the second plane serves for determining the vertical angle of the chamfer. The instrument is generally attached to the frame of the lathe, but to render it portable it is sometimes fixed to a block of wood sufficiently heavy to give it stability; the tool to be ground is held nearly stationary by the left hand, while a piece of oilstone, or other abrasive is rubbed with the right hand on the chamfer of the tool.

The instrument consists of a horizontal brass plate A fig. 1046, having a circular mortise, and a graduated arc for denoting the angle at which the central guide bar B is placed, this bar moves upon a pivot near the front edge of the plate A, and is fixed in any angular position by the clamping screw, passing through the circular mortise. The vertical plate C, is jointed near its middle to the edge of the plate A, and can be fixed at any inclination within its range, by means of the arc and clamping screw D. This plate has a central rectangular opening through which the end of the tool may project as seen in the figure, in order to allow of the action of the grinder, which is sometimes a flat piece of oilstone about three inches square embedded in a wooden stock, at other times a piece of hard brass supplied with fine flour emery or oilstone powder, is used as the grinder, this retains a level surface for a longer period than the oilstone, which must be occasionally ground flat upon a level plate charged with emery.

In using this instrument, the tool to be sharpened is laid face downwards upon the horizontal plate, and with the side of the tool in contact with the guide bar, which is fixed at the angle required for the horizontal edge of the tool, the second plate is then adjusted to give the required bevil to the chamfer of the tool. The oilstone moistened with a few drops of oil is applied with its face flat upon the vertical plate, and the tool is advanced with the fingers of the left hand, until its end touches the oilstone, which is rubbed in contact with the vertical plate in all directions by the right hand, while the end of the tool is kept gently pressing against the oilstone, this is continued until the chamfer of the tool is sufficiently sharpened. If it be an angular tool the position of the guide bar is then changed, and the second chamfer is operated upon in the same manner; and lastly the face of the tool is laid flat on the oilstone, and gently rubbed to remove any trifling burr that may have formed upon the edge. It is of course necessary that the tool should be held quite steadily in its position on the bed of the instrument, not-withstanding that it is kept constantly pressed endways against the oilstone.

Angular tools that are used for rose engine turning on curved surfaces such as those of watch cases, are generally ground with the one angle of the edge of nearly twice the length of the other, this is done to give the tool increased strength, and allow of a rubber with a rounded end being fixed near to the point of the tool, to regulate its penetration.

The various small tools with straight and angular edges, employed for eccentric and ornamental turning, are required to have very accurate, keen, and highly polished edges, in order that they may impart the same degree of excellence and finish to the work, whether executed with tools fixed in the slide rest, or with revolving cutters employed in the various apparatus that will be described in a future volume. These ornamental works, from their intricate and delicate character, scarcely admit of any polishing, and therefore the beauty and finish of their surfaces depend almost exclusively upon the perfection of the cutting edges of the tool, as the good or bad quality it may possess, is literally copied upon the work, without the possibility of subse-quent correction. It is therefore highly desirable that the edges of the tools should be formed by perfectly true planes, polished in the most careful manner, results which cannot be obtained without the assistance of suitable guides for holding the tool, and the employment of the most delicate abrasive powders.

The instrument for setting straight and angular tools for orna-mental turning shown in fig. 1047, resembles in principle and con-struction the instrument for grinding common turning tools on the revolving lap, described on page 1159, but fig. 1047, has greater range in the angles to which the tools may be set, and it is also provided with a more suitable socket for the reception of these small tools, which are made of one uniform size in their shanks or stems, in order that they may all fit the same socket of the sliding rest in which they are to be used. Fig. 1047 is employed in the reverse manner to the instrument for grinding common turning tools, as instead of the tool being held stationary upon a revolving lap, the tool when fixed in the instrument for angular tools, is rubbed first upon a stationary piece of oilstone, and subsequently set and polished in like manner upon flat plates of metal supplied with oilstone powder or crocus.

The case for containing the instrument for setting angular tools, has three slabs of mahogany, measuring about eight inches long, and six and a half inches wide, fitted as drawers; into the

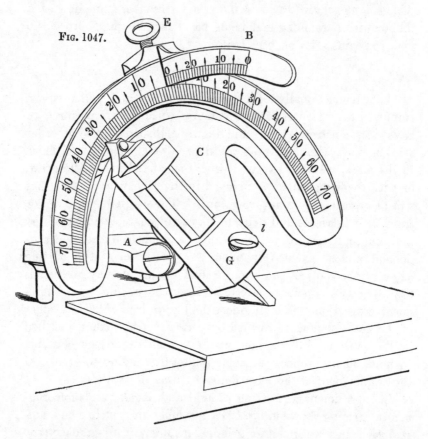

FIG. 1047.

one side of each of the drawers, and close to the edge, are inlaid respectively, a piece of oilstone, brass, and cast iron, about three and a half inches, by three inches. The upper surfaces of these plates are made quite flat, and they project slightly above the wood as shown in fig. 1047, in which the one edge of the angular tool is supposed to rest upon the metal plate, whilst the two feet of the instrument stand upon the mahogany slab, which is sufficiently large to support them whilst the tool is traversed in all directions over the metal plate.

In fig. 1047, the same letters of reference are used for corresponding parts as for fig. 1042, and the description of the latter instrument on page 1160, is equally applicable to fig. 1047, except that the graduated arc on C, is extended to 75 degrees on each side of the central line, and the socket G is made as a straight bar with two projecting pieces having rectangular openings to fit the shafts of the tools, which are fixed by the binding screw *l*.

To sharpen an angular tool of 30 degrees, the instrument is adjusted as shown in fig. 1047. The index point of the socket G, is placed at the division marked 30 on the arc C, which is then adjusted on the vertical arc B, to the angle required for the chamfer of the tool; in the drawing this is supposed to be 30 degrees, the tool is then placed in the socket G, and the distance which it should project from the socket, is determined by placing the instrument in the position shown in the figure, with its two legs upon the wood surface, and the edge of the tool resting upon the oilstone. The projection of the tool is then so regulated that the base piece A, may be parallel with the wood surface, when the tool is fixed by the binding screw *l*. Should the projection of the tool be such that the base of the instrument is inclined to the wood surface, the chamfer of the tool would not be ground to an angle of 30 degrees; the precise angle of the chamfer is however not generally very important.

The instrument having been adjusted, the next operation is to sharpen the tool upon the oilstone, which is moistened with a few drops of oil, and the tool is applied as shown in the drawing, and lightly rubbed with circular or elliptical strokes in all directions over the surface of the stone, until a keen edge is produced upon one angle of the tool. The index point of the socket G is then shifted to 30 degrees on the opposite side of the circle of graduations on the piece C, and the second edge of the tool is sharpened in the same manner.

The tool having been completely sharpened upon the oilstone, is next taken to the metallic surfaces to have its edges polished, and which is done in the following manner. Without unfixing the tool, the plate C is moved about 2 degrees higher upon the arc B, and the tool is then applied upon the brass surface, which is supplied with a very small quantity of oilstone powder and oil. The tool is rubbed upon the brass surface in the same manner as upon the oilstone, until the chamfer presents a narrow facet with a dull greyish polish; when both edges of the tool have been thus treated, the tool is very carefully wiped to remove every particle of oilstone powder, and the final polish is given by rubbing the tool upon the iron surface, which is supplied with a little crocus and oil.

The upper surface of the tool, or the flat face, should be kept in very good condition towards the cutting edges, this is effected by removing the tool from the instrument and laying its face flat upon the iron surface, upon which the tool is rubbed with the fingers until the slight burr thrown up in the sharpening is removed.

Small tools, such as the revolving cutters used in the various cutting frames employed for ornamenting the surfaces of turned works, are from necessity made too short to be held in the instrument, fig. 1047 ; in this case they are first clamped in a tool-holder having a rectangular hole suited to the size of the stem of the tool, which is clamped therein by a square-headed

Figs. 1048.

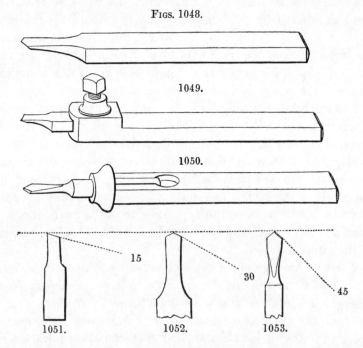

1049.

1050.

15

30

45

1051.   1052.   1053.

binding screw, as shown in fig. 1049, which represents a tool-holder adapted for revolving cutters of a medium size. The stem of the tool-holder is made to fit the socket G, of the instrument, fig. 1047, in which it is secured exactly as described for the slide rest tool, shown detached in fig. 1048.

Drills, such as fig. 1053, intended to be used in the drilling instrument for ornamental turning, are in like manner fixed in a holder, as shown in fig. 1050 ; but in this case the binding screw is not required, as the stem of the drill fits the cylindrical hole in the holder, and it is prevented from twisting round by a short projecting piece at the end, which is filed down to the diametrical line, so as to slide into the flat-bottomed recess in the holder, and also to fit the drilling instrument in which it is to be employed, as shown in fig. 489, page 555, Vol. II.

To avoid uncertainty respecting the angles of the tools used for ornamental turning, they are usually stamped with figures denoting the angles at which the tools are ground ; but it should be remembered that these numbers are measured from a line at right angles to the center of the tool, or, in other words, it is the angle which is ground away, that is estimated, and not the angle, which the edges of the tool make to each other. Thus, in the instance of the tool just described as being ground at the angle of 30 degrees, each side of the tool is ground at an angle of 30 degrees, or the edges differ to that extent from a flat tool, and the sum of these two angles being 60 degrees, it follows that the edges of the tool meet each other at an angle of 120 degrees, or the complement to the sum of the two angles at which the tool is ground.

This will be more distinctly seen in figs. 1051 to 1053, which represent the plan of three tools of different angles. Fig. 1051 shows a single bevil tool ground at an angle of 15 degrees ; and consequently the edge of this tool will meet its side at an angle of 75 degrees, or the difference between 15 degrees and 90 degrees, which latter is of course the angle formed by the edge of a flat tool with its side, when it is ground perfectly square. Fig. 1052 represents the plan of an angular tool ground on both bevils at an angle of 30 degrees, and, as just explained, its edges will meet at 120 degrees, or the difference between 60 degrees, the sum of the two angles ground away, and 180 degrees, or the straight edge of a flat tool. The drill, fig. 1053, is ground at two angles of 45 degrees, and the sum of these being 90 degrees, it follows that its edges form an angle of 90 degrees.

The vertical angle, at which the tools are sharpened, is in like manner estimated by the angle ground away; thus, when the piece C, fig. 1047, is elevated to 0 on the arc B, the tool is ground quite square, or at an angle of 90 degrees, and when placed at division 10 the chamfer of the tool differs 10 degrees from the right angle, or it forms an angle of 80 degrees with the face of the tool, and so on of other numbers.

The instrument for setting angular tools, fig. 1047, is sometimes used with the horizontal grinding machine, fig. 1039; it is then applied in exactly the same manner as the instrument for grinding ordinary turning tools.   At other times the lap is screwed upon the mandrel of a lathe, so as to revolve vertically,

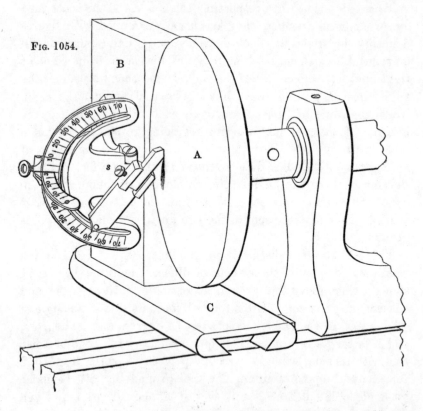

Fig. 1054.

in exactly the same manner as a surface chuck; but in this case it is necessary to provide a support for the two legs of the instrument, and which generally consists of a block of wood mounted on a base piece similar to that of a common turning rest. This arrangement is shown in fig. 1054, in which A represents the lap, B the wooden block, which measures about $4\frac{1}{2}$ inches wide and $1\frac{1}{2}$ inches thick, held by two screws to the iron base C, which is secured to the bearers by the rest bolt, not seen in the drawing, but which allows of the wooden block being adjusted, so that its side may be in a line with the face of the lap, when tested by a straight edge applied to both. The wooden block then serves the same purpose as the platform of the horizontal grinding machine, and the instrument is applied in a similar manner, except that it is held vertically, as shown in the figure, which represents the application of the instrument to setting detached angular blades for cutting the threads of screws, and adapted to tool-holders, such as fig. 608, page 630, Vol. II. For sharpening these blades a different form of socket is adopted, in order that tools of various depths and thicknesses may be securely clamped. This socket consists of a flat bar of steel with two projecting sides at the front extremity, as seen in the drawing; the tool to be sharpened is placed in the channel, and held in its position by the small side screw, s. The instrument is then adjusted to the angle required for the depth of the thread of the screw, and which has been already explained in Section IX. of the Chapter on Screws, Vol. II.

Concave tools, whose edges when seen in plan form part of a circular line, such as the bead, astragal, and quarter hollow tools, figs. 395 to 398, page 519, Vol. II., are most conveniently and accurately ground upon conical grinders fed with flour emery, or other abrasive powders, after the manner of laps; these grinders are in the form of long cones of small diameter, so that some part of their circumference may agree with the curve of the tool, which may be then ground with great accuracy to the circular form.

Bead tools, exceeding about half an inch wide, are commonly ground upon a soft iron cone, fig. 1055, about seven inches long, one inch and a half diameter at the larger end, and half an inch at the smaller. The cone is mostly furnished with a square tang at a to fit the square hole chuck of the turning lathe in which it is mounted, the smaller end of the cone being pierced in the center with a conical hole for the reception of the center point of the popit head. For tools less than about half an inch wide,

shorter cones are used, and which are fixed in a plain chuck, as
shown at fig. 1056, so as to be supported at the one end only, as

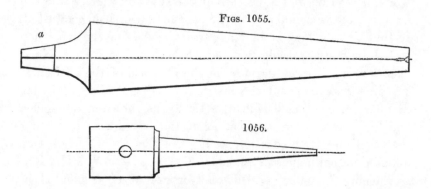

Figs. 1055.

1056.

the lesser end of the cone is too small to admit of the support of
the popit head, and which is also less required with the shorter
cone.

The cone having been turned true, and its surface slightly
roughened by drawfiling, it is then charged with flour emery and
oil, and the tool is applied to that part of the cone which fits the
curve: and with the face of the tool towards the small end of the
cone, in order that the lower side of the tool may be ground to
a larger diameter, to give the proper angle of penetration to the
chamfer of the tool at all parts of the curve.   Large tools, which
only require a moderate degree of accuracy, are finished upon a
corresponding cone of lead, or hard wood, fed in like manner
with flour emery and oil, the emery becomes embedded in the
wood, and consequently gives a higher polish to the chamfer of
the tool, the rectilinear corners of which are sharpened upon
a flat oilstone, and, lastly, the face of the tool is rubbed on
the oilstone to remove the wire edge.   Quarter hollow tools
are treated in exactly the same manner as bead tools and
astragals.

Bead tools, bead drills, and revolving cutters, less than about
one quarter of an inch wide, that are used in the various apparatus for ornamental turning, although ground in the same
manner, require to have more accurate and highly-polished
surfaces, as was explained in reference to the angular tools at
page 1164; and for these delicate tools the more suitable
arrangement is shown in fig. 1057, the instrument for setting

bead tools and drills, which consists of a miniature lathe head, mounted on a wooden table-tee, having an iron stem that fits the socket of the common lathe rest. The instrument is driven by a

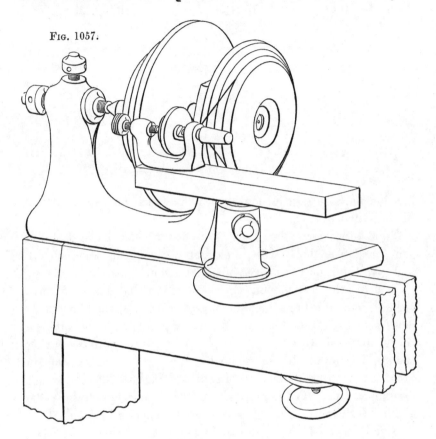

Fig. 1057.

pulley about eight inches diameter, screwed on the mandrel of the turning lathe, the band from which proceeds to the small pulley fixed in the little mandrel of the instrument, which thus admits of being driven at a considerable velocity, to compensate for the small diameter of the grinders, figs. 1058—9, which are made as a series of six brass and six iron truncated cones, each a little more than one inch long, and gradually diminishing in size from the largest, which measures about five-eighths of an inch diameter, to the smallest, which terminates in a point, so that the series serves for all sizes of tools below five-eighths of an inch wide.   The cylindrical stems of the grinders are fitted to a plain hole in the mandrel of the instrument; and to ensure their rotation, they are provided with a semicylindrical projection at the end, which slides into a corresponding notch in the mandrel in the same manner as in the drill stocks, figs. 489 and 450, Vol. II.   Indeed, fig. 1057 is used also as a drilling lathe ; and

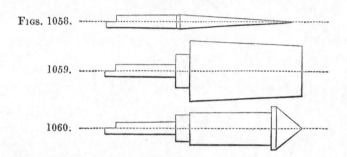

Figs. 1058.

1059.

1060.

for this purpose it is generally provided with an assortment of piercing drills for small holes.

The obtuse cone, fig. 1060 is used for bead drills that are sharpened from both sides, in order to keep the edge central, and give the required degree of penetration.

In using the instrument, the tools to be sharpened are first ground upon the brass cones, charged with a little fine emery powder and oil, and they are afterwards polished on the soft iron cones, supplied with crocus and oil.   To give steadiness during the application of the tools, the hand is rested on the wooden table-tee to which the instrument is fixed.   The cones are roughened to retain the powders, and the tools should always be applied with the face towards the smaller ends of the cones.

Figs. 1061 to 1076, represent of about twice their usual size, some of the varieties of drills used for ornamenting turned works.   The concave sweeps of figs. 1061 to 1071, are sharpened with the instrument for setting bead tools and drills, and the manner in which the tools are applied to the cones will be sufficiently obvious from an inspection of the figures.   Figs. 1061—2 is the bead drill sharpened from both sides, but all the rest are sharpened from the one side only ; and it is quite essential that the cutting edge should be exactly in a line with the center of the drilling instrument, as, should the edge be in the least degree out of the center of rotation, the drill would leave a small portion of the material projecting in the center, and which would spoil the appearance of the work : these drills therefore require in all cases to be fitted to the particular instrument in which they are to be used. The flat surface of the drill is made exactly diametrical, and unlike the screw tools and moulding tools used by hand, these drills do not admit of being sharpened by rubbing the flat face on the oilstone, as such a course would remove the edge from the line of center; the ornamental drills should therefore in all cases be sharpened upon the end only. It will also be seen that with the exception of the three first, they are made to embrace only about the one-fourth of the circle, as when the drills are sharpened with one bevel they can

Figs. 1061.   1062.   1063.   1064.   1065.   1066.   1067.

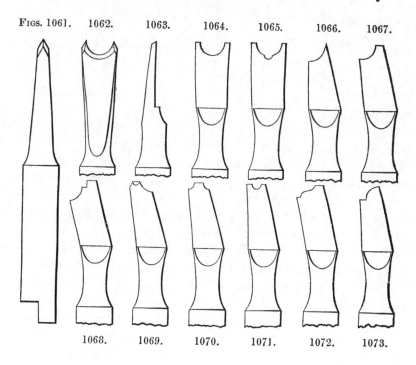

1068.   1069.   1070.   1071.   1072.   1073.

only cut on the one side of the center, and if the drills were made to embrace the half circle, the chamfer of the edge on the second side would be in the wrong direction for cutting, and consequently it could only rub against the work, and impede the action of the drill.

Figs. 1072 to 1076, which have convex and rectilinear edges do not admit of being sharpened by any of the guide instruments described; and the restoration of their edges is effected with small slips of oilstone delicately applied with the fingers, like a file. For reaching the square internal corners of figs. 1074 to 1076, the square edges of the oilstone slip are kept keen by rubbing it upon a piece of emery paper.

Small straight metal bars, charged with fine flour emery, oilstone powder, or crocus and oil, are sometimes used for sharpening tools of mixed forms, such as the above. These metal bars,

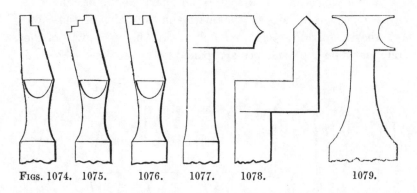

FIGS. 1074. 1075.   1076.   1077.   1078.   1079.

like the metallic laps, retain their shapes longer without deterioration than the natural oilstone ; they are generally made of soft brass, and similar in shape to small files of a square or half round section. Considerable practice is however required to sharpen the small ornamental drills and cutters of mixed forms, without losing the necessary accuracy of shape.

The side cutters, fig.1077, with two quarter hollows, are made of different radii, and used for fluting concave sweeps, such as the foot of a vase, they are ground on the conical grinders of fig. 1057. The bent cutters, fig. 1078, are also made of various radii, and are principally used for small eccentric patterns on plane or spherical surfaces, such as the top of a snuff-box, or the head of a walking stick ; but the bent cutters, although generally made with angular edges, do not admit of being ground on the instrument for angular tools, fig. 1047, but are sharpened with slips of oilstone. The tool, fig. 1079, is employed for turning rings of ivory or hardwood, the two half-round hollows are made of the same size, and exactly opposite to each other, in order that when the tool is fixed in the slide rest, the left hand edge may be used to turn a bead on the inside of a hollow tube, and which constitutes the first half of the ring, the second half is completed by applying the right hand edge of the tool to the outside of the tube, and the rectilinear action of the slide-rest ensures the beads being opposite to each other. The application of these various tools will however be treated of in a future volume.

Many tools from their complex forms or other reasons do not admit of being sharpened by the ordinary grinding processes, and it is frequently necessary to resort to the file for restoring their edges. Those tools that are left only of a moderate degree of hardness such as the saws, brace bits, and some circular cutters for wood and brass, may be filed without having been previously softened, other tools are lowered in temper just enough to admit of the action of the files, and still retain sufficient hardness to be tolerably durable when applied to their work, but such tools as cannot be ground, and yet are required to possess considerable hardness, are softened prior to the application of the file, and are subsequently rehardened, which processes have been already explained in the first volume of this work, but as there mentioned, the less frequently steel is passed through the fire the better, as its brittleness becomes thereby materially increased.

Moulding tools used in the sliding rest for turning do not admit of being sharpened on the flat surface of the tool, as this method would remove the edge below the center of the lathe, these tools must therefore be sharpened at the end only, and to do which in the most effective manner it is necessary that they should be first softened and then sharpened with files, or the revolving hob on which they were originally made. The edges of these moulding tools may be partially restored with slips of oilstone, or the small straight metal grinders fed with fine emery, or still better, with a temporary counterpart grinder, made by turning with the tool itself a circular moulding on a piece of boxwood, which may be afterwards charged with flour emery, and used as a grinder to restore the edges, by this method however the tools soon deteriorate, as at every sharpening they depart further from the original figure.

The fixed moulding cutters used in the large planing machines for wood, are frequently sharpened upon revolving laps with rounded edges. The tool is twisted about to expose all parts of the chamfer to the action of the lap, and which plan is tolerably manageable with tools for large mouldings. Sometimes a circular piece of oilstone turned to a round edge is used for this purpose, but the difficulty of obtaining the oilstone in sufficiently large pieces, and the numerous hard and soft places in the stone, prevent this from being so effective a tool as might at first be supposed. When the forms of the moulding cutters become depreciated, it is the better practice to resort to the use of the file, as for the small slide rest tools.

Figured cutting punches for cloth, leather, and paper, and also envelope cutters, are sharpened with oilstone slips. When they are worn down so as to become thickened so much as to render the sharpening very tedious, they are sometimes thinned by grinding them on rounded laps, but it is better that they should be softened and filed to their original forms. Circular cutting punches such as figs. 938 to 941, page 928, Vol. II. are softened and turned in the lathe; the edges are sometimes made a little keener by holding a piece of oilstone to the chamfer of the punch as it revolves in the lathe, and circular punches that are used in manufactories for cutting large quantities of gun wadding, are in some cases sharpened in the lathe by a lap which is made to revolve against the side of the punch, whilst the latter also revolves, so as to expose it equally to the action of the lap.

An instrument somewhat analogous to the patent knife sharpeners was invented by the late Sir John Robison for setting the edges of razors, penknives, and surgeon's instruments, and is

Figs. 1080.   1081.

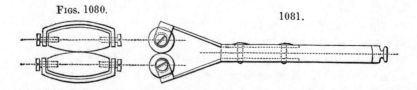

shown half size in figs. 1080 & 1081, it consisted of two barrel shaped agates mounted on pivots, free to revolve in an elastic frame of sheet brass, the surface of the agates was supplied with finely pulverized corundum, emery, or oilstone powder, the edge of the blade to be sharpened was passed with slight pressure between the two agates, which from their shape could only be in contact at the central point, so that both sides of the edge were acted on at the same time, and if too much pressure was applied, the elastic frame allowed the agates to separate, and avoid injury to the edge of the blade.

The sharpening of saws with files has been already explained in Vol. II. pages 688 to 698, and the appendix, note B. L. page 1011 of the same volume describes the application of the grindstone to the teeth of large circular saws.

CHAPTER XXXIII.

THE FIGURATION OF MATERIALS BY ABRASION.

SECT. I.—THE PRODUCTION OF PLANE SURFACES BY ABRASION.

In the figuration of materials by abrasion, the principal dependence for the correctness of form, is generally placed upon the abrasive tool, or grinder, being exactly a counterpart of the form to be produced; thus for plane surfaces a flat grinder is employed, for concave surfaces a convex grinder, and so on. In numerous cases the grinder is made as a revolving wheel, figured to the required counterpart form, either upon the edge, or upon the side, and the work is simply held to the grinder by hand, without the assistance of any mechanical guidance. In other cases the work is traversed on slides beneath revolving or reciprocating grinders; and in some few instances, where great accuracy of form is required, the principal dependence is placed upon the relative motions of the grinder and work, both usually under the control of mechanism.

The natural grindstone is in general only used for the rough preparation of the surfaces, which are afterwards more accurately figured with metal grinders supplied with abrasive powders. Within certain limits, it may be said generally, that the greater the accuracy desired in the surfaces to be produced, the harder should be the material of which the grinder is composed; while, upon the other hand, the finer the surface, or the higher the desired polish, the softer should be the material of the grinder. These opposite qualities required in the grinder, combined with other circumstances, render the attainment of very accurate, and, at the same time, highly polished surfaces, a point of considerable practical difficulty, as will be adverted to hereafter.

The principal contents of the present chapter will be divided into four sections, relating respectively to the methods of grinding and polishing plane surfaces, cylindrical surfaces, conical surfaces, and spherical surfaces.   These elementary forms may be considered to include, by their combination, nearly every figure required in the mechanical arts ; and the concluding section of the chapter, will be devoted to a brief notice of the practice of glass-cutting, in which all kinds of mixed and arbitrary forms are produced by very simple apparatus, under the guidance of the hand alone.

The present section will refer, first, to the grinding and polishing of flat surfaces in hardened steel, and the metals generally, and this will be followed by a description of the methods of working stone and marble, materials that are almost exclusively wrought by abrasion, and both the manual and machine processes will be noticed, as a general example of the production of form by abrasion.   Plate and sheet glass will be next alluded to, and the section will conclude with some account of the methods of grinding the more accurate plane surfaces required for optical purposes.

Revolving laps of metal used upon their flat sides, and supplied with emery and water, are extensively employed by mechanicians for finishing flat surfaces of small and medium size, requiring tolerable accuracy.   Sometimes the lap is employed for brass, iron, and soft steel, but more generally the flat surfaces of works in these metals, are wrought by the planing machine or file, and finished in the manner described in the catalogue of grinding processes, pages 1074 to 1076 ; and the lap is principally employed for correcting works in hardened steel, such as the broad flat surfaces of cutting tools, the faces of dies, hardened steel plates, and numerous other objects.   All these works are made nearly flat, either with the grindstone or file, prior to their being hardened, as the general accuracy of the forms may be much quicker produced by these means; and the lap is chiefly resorted to for removing those slight distortions occasioned in hardening, that are beyond the correction of the hack hammer, described at page 247, Vol. I , and also for giving a smooth and finished surface to the work.

Sometimes the laps are made of cast-iron, or copper, because these hard metal laps longer retain their forms uninjured ; but, as previously mentioned, lead hardened with a little antimony, is the metal generally used for laps by mechanicians, as the lead being yielding, allows the emery to become embedded in its surface, and consequently a smooth face can be produced upon the work with an emery, the particles of which are sufficiently large to cut rapidly. Whereas when iron or copper laps are employed, the emery can scarcely penetrate the lap, but is partially lost, and the remainder rolls over, and makes scratches in the work nearly equal in depth to the size of the emery powder.

Laps not exceeding a few inches in diameter, used by mechanicians, are generally mounted vertically, not upon the middle of long spindles, after the method of those used for cutlery, but screwed as chucks upon the mandrel of a lathe, as shown in fig. 1054. This method is adopted in order to avoid the interference of the spindle, and render the entire side of the lap available for works of a moderate size. Larger laps are mounted to revolve horizontally, somewhat after the manner shown in fig. 1039, but in much stronger frames, and generally driven by steam power, as the diameter of these horizontal laps is sometimes as much as five or six feet. The varying velocity of the surface of the lap, which continually decreases from the periphery to the center, is however very objectionable in large laps, as it renders the tool much less effective near the middle, and is besides liable to cause the lap to become conical, from being less worn near the center. To avoid these interferences as much as possible, large laps are in most cases made as annular disks, cast upon iron plates or wheels, so as to leave a central aperture of about one-third the extreme diameter of the lap.

In lapping small works the object, if thin, is held between the thumb and finger nail, and placed fairly in its position on the lap while the latter is at rest; the lap is then put in rotation, and the work is held quite steady to the face of the lap with moderate pressure, and the lap is stopped before the removal of the work, in order to examine its progress. Larger pieces that can be conveniently held in the fingers are applied to the lap while it is in rotation; the work is quickly placed in its position, and the pressure is steadily applied on the back of the work as near as convenient to its center, in order to feel when it bears uniformly upon the lap; the work is retained in its position for a few seconds, and then, in order to examine whether it has been properly placed, the work is lifted at once perpendicularly from the face of the lap, and not gradually drawn off, as the latter course would be liable to round off the edges of the work. Should it appear to have been incorrectly placed on the lap, the work is applied in another position, but the principal dependance is placed upon the sense of feeling, as with a little practice the fingers readily appreciate when the work lies fairly upon the surface of the lap.

Thin works of moderate size that are too yielding to be applied with the fingers, or those that would become too hot to be conveniently held, are temporarily fixed upon a thin piece of wood by driving two or three pins into the wood, around the edges of the work, and very small objects are sometimes cemented upon a small piece of wood. In these cases, however, the flat position of the work upon the lap cannot be so readily appreciated as when the work is held directly in the fingers. Large works may be correctly placed upon the lap without difficulty, as their size serves at once as a guide, and prevents the general accuracy given by the file being accidentally depreciated.

When the work is first commenced it may with advantage, if not very small, be slidden to different parts of the surface of the lap to equalize the wear, but towards the conclusion the work should be held in the one position, and the uniform wear of the lap may be ensured by applying the work to a different part of the lap every time that it is placed upon it.

When fresh emery is required on the lap it should be applied by preference at the commencement of lapping the article, in order that the emery may at first cut rapidly, and be gradually worn finer with the progress of the work, so as to leave a smooth surface at the conclusion.

Flat works in steel, are sometimes polished on iron laps supplied with crocus, but more generally, after being lapped with fine emery, they are smoothed with fine emery paper wrapped around a file and moistened with oil, and the works are lastly polished with small rubbers, as explained on page 1075. Flat works in brass are finished as described on page 1039.

Facets on steel jewellery, such as beads, studs, buttons, the ornaments on the hilts of dress swords, and similar objects, are ground to form on horizontal laps, such as fig. 1039, fed with fine emery, and are afterwards polished after the general method of cutlery.

The small solid beads employed in common articles are prepared from sheets of iron of suitable thickness; the plates are first punched in a fly press, with small holes of the proper size for the passage of the wire, by which the beads are strung, the pieces of metal to constitute the beads are then punched out with a circular punch a little larger than the intended diameter of the beads, and having a small central pin that fits into the hole previously punched, in order to ensure the latter being in the center of the bead. The pieces are next fixed on a pointed steel wire and rounded at each end with a file. They are then case-hardened in bone dust enclosed in sheet-iron boxes, a layer of bone dust and one of beads being placed alternately until the box is filled; the whole are then case-hardened, after the method explained, page 260, Vol. I. For cutting the facets the beads are fixed singly on pointed steel wires, and applied to the horizontal lap supplied with emery and water; no guide is employed for these common beads, but the wire is held at the proper inclination, and twisted in the fingers to cut the facets in succession at the one end, and the bead is then inverted on the steel point for its completion. The scratches left by the lap are removed either in the rumble, or by stringing them on wires, and applying them to revolving wheel brushes, fed with oil and emery of various degrees of fineness; rottenstone is next employed in a similar manner, and the beads are finally polished by rubbing them in the naked hand with putty powder or crocus.

Large hollow steel beads for the best works, are raised from either the best charcoal iron, or decarbonized cast-steel plates, after the general method explained in Chap. XIX., Vol. I. The metal is punched out in a fly press, first as a concave disk, and by alternate punching and annealing the sides are brought to the cylindrical form, the bottom is then removed, and the ends are gradually closed in with punches, leaving a small hole at each end of the hollow sphere; the beads are then roughly filed and case-hardened. The facets on the large beads of the best kind, both hollow and solid, are sometimes more exactly cut by fixing them on pointed wires inserted in wooden handles, that, instead of being cylindrical, are made as polygonal prisms of various numbers of sides, according to the numbers of facets required in the work; a horizontal wooden bar is placed at a suitable height on one side of the lap, and the flat sides of the handle are rested in succession upon the horizontal bar; this gives the correct number of facets to every bead, and the angle at which they are placed is regulated by the height of the bar and the inclination of the handle. The beads are lastly strung on wires, smoothed on wheel brushes, and polished by hand in the same manner as the small beads, but more carefully.

Round and oval studs are in like manner punched as flat or concave disks out of decarbonized sheet steel, and rounded with the file; but before they are case-hardened the shanks are attached by soldering, and covered with small lumps of clay to prevent them from being affected by the hardening process. For cutting the facets, they are held in small hand vices or pin tongs, sometimes inserted in polygonal handles, and applied to the lap in the same manner as the best beads. For polishing the studs, they are closely arranged in a flat block covered with cement, that is softened by heat to allow the shanks of the studs to penetrate. The whole surface is then smoothed with emery and water, applied with hard flat brushes rubbed in all directions either by hand or machinery; after the emery, rottenstone is employed in the same manner, and the final lustre is given with putty powder or crocus on the hand. *See* Tech. Repos. 1830, p. 275.

Facets on gold and silver, and the flat parts of jewellery generally, are cut and polished on revolving wheels after the same general method as that pursued by the lapidary for cutting facets on stones, but the gold cutters commonly use vertical laps mounted much after the fashion of fig. 1030, in order that they may use both the side and the edge of the lap for different parts of the work. The laps are made of pewter, or an alloy of tin and zinc of different degrees of hardness according to the size of the work. They are turned very true and flat on their surfaces with the sliding rest, and left quite smooth.

For cutting the facets the laps are charged with fine washed emery, smoothed with an agate or pebble burnisher, and supplied with water. The work when too small to be held in the fingers is cemented on a small wooden stick to serve as the handle, and the position of the facets is given with the fingers unassisted by any guide. If the facets have to be entirely produced by grinding, a moderate pressure is applied when the cutting is first commenced, and the lap is driven with tolerable velocity; but as the facets become developed, the pressure on the work, and the velocity of the lap, are gradually diminished.

In some cases the work is smoothed and partially polished upon tin or zinc laps fed with dry crocus, or rouge, rubbed into the face of the lap with a piece of smooth agate.   Separate laps are employed for gold and silver, and they are kept scrupulously free from dust; the fine particles of the materials removed in polishing become embedded in the surface of the finishing laps, and which is by some persons considered to assist in giving a good face to gold and silver works.

In other cases the work is taken at once from the emery lap to the buff wheel and smoothed with fine crocus, other buff wheels supplied with rouge are used for commencing the polishing, which is completed with small buff sticks, and the final black lustre is given with rouge on the naked hand, the soft skin on the side of the fingers being sometimes employed for delicate objects.

Fig. 1082 represents a Geneva tool used by watchmakers for polishing the heads and points of small screws that are required

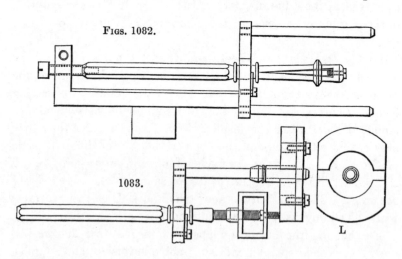

Figs. 1082.

1083.

L

to be very flat on their ends, and at the same time to be highly finished.   The instrument is made as a miniature lathe head to be fixed in the vice, the mandrel is about 3½ inches long between the bearings, and is generally made octangular, that it may be driven not with a pulley and drill bow as usual, but by the friction of the left hand laid flat upon the mandrel and passed backwards and forwards as in rolling a wire; this method is sufficiently effective for the slight purposes to which the instrument is applied. The front end of the mandrel is made as a pair of pin tongs, for grasping the screws while the heads are being polished, and several mandrels are fitted to the one instrument in order to serve for different sizes of screws. For polishing the points of the screws, other mandrels shown in fig. 1083, are employed, the end of the mandrel is made as a screw about three quarters of an inch long, upon which a square frame is fitted, having in the front end a small central hole, through which the screw is passed to expose its point, while its head is grasped between the end of the mandrel and the inside of the square frame.

To the front plate of the instrument are fixed two cylindrical pins parallel with the mandrel and about $2\frac{1}{2}$ inches long. The lower pin serves as a rest for the support of the hand grinding tools, or rubbers, made in shape like small flat files without teeth, and supplied with various polishing powders. The screw to be polished is fixed in the mandrel, which is rotated by the left hand, while the grinder supported upon the lower pin is passed to and fro with the right hand, exactly as in filing the flat head of a screw in the ordinary lathe.

The above method serves sufficiently well for screws requiring only a moderate degree of flatness, but for those in which great accuracy is required, the small lap shown at L, is employed. It consists of a plate of brass fixed to a tube that exactly fits the upper cylindrical pin of the instrument, to the inner side of the brass plate are affixed two semicircular plates of metal or laps, the surfaces of which are made quite flat, and exactly at right angles to the central line of the tube. There are generally two plates fitted to each instrument, each plate carrying two laps so as to make 4 grinders of different degrees of hardness, namely, 1 each brass and gun-metal, and 2 of iron or steel; the faces of the grinders are slightly roughened with a smooth file applied at various angles, to enable the polishing powders to be retained upon their surfaces.

The screw having been fixed in the mandrel a little of the polishing powder is rubbed on the grinder, the tube is then slid over the pin, and while the mandrel is rotated, the grinder is swung backwards and forwards in an arc of about one fourth of a circle.   The face of the grinder being quite flat, and traversed at right angles to the mandrel, the heads of the screws are ground quite flat, notwithstanding that they are polished very highly.

Sometimes instead of the mandrel being rotated by the flat hand as above described, the instrument has a pulley like a drilling lathe, and is driven with a drill bow ; in this case one mandrel only is used, and the screws are fixed in similar grasping apparatus made as small chucks, fitted to the mandrel either by a screw or a plain conical fitting.

Large flat works in cast iron for heavy machinery are in almost all cases wrought in the planing machine, and when they are smoothed it is done with files and rubbers as explained on page 1074.   Large flat works in wrought iron are frequently ground on the edges of large stones and finished with files.   The flat parts of objects of complex form are worked in the various cutting and paring machines, and the grindstone is seldom resorted to for plane surfaces requiring even moderate accuracy. Sometimes however when a large surface has to be made toler- ably level and smooth for appearance alone, the flat side of the grindstone is employed, and the work is traversed across the stone upon slides; this method of using the flat side of the stone is however liable to the objections stated on page 1135.

In a grinding machine constructed by Mr. James Nasmyth and shown in figs. 1084 and 1085,* this difficulty is removed by making the grindstone as an annulus about fifteen inches wide, composed of 12 segments of stone each fitted into a separate radial compartment in a cast iron wheel or chuck about seven feet diameter.   The machine is double or possesses two com- pound grinding stones fixed on the opposite ends of the same shaft, each of the grindstones is provided with separate slides, which are duplicates of each other, and made self-acting.   The foundation of the machine is of masonry, and pits are sunk on each side for the lower part of the stones to work in, just the same as for ordinary large grindstones.   To the masonry are firmly fixed two cast iron frames *a, a,* upon which are bolted two plummer blocks for carrying the main shaft, having at each

---

* Transcribed from plate 54 of " Buchanan's Mill Work " by Rennie, 1841.

extremity the large wheels or chucks, each made as a face plate
7 feet diameter, having on the one side 12 radial ribs about 6
inches deep, that extend from the center to the periphery where
they terminate in a ring of equal depth. A second concentric

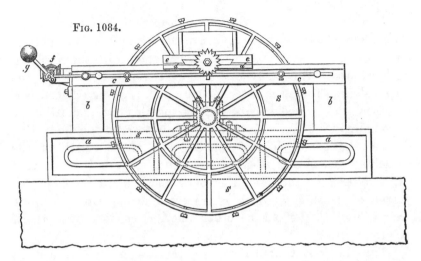

Fig. 1084.

ring about 4 feet diameter intersects the ribs, and thus divides
the entire chuck into 24 compartments, in the 12 outer of which
separate pieces of grindstone *s, s,* about 14 inches thick are fitted

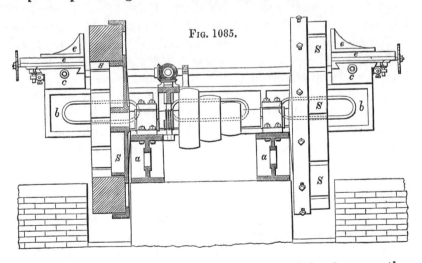

Fig. 1085.

like the stones of an arch, and each is wedged fast between the
ribs by a single set screw passing through the outer rim of the
chuck. On the top of the cross frames *a,* are fixed two longitu-

dinal frames *b, b,* for supporting the bearers *c, c,* upon which the slides *d,* are traversed across the faces of the stones. Upon the slides *d,* are mounted at right angles the slides *e,* upon which the work is fixed and advanced towards the stone as the grinding proceeds.

A self-acting motion is given to the slide *d,* by which the work being faced is gradually traversed along the bearers *c,* so as to bring the face of the work in contact with the revolving grindstones. This motion is obtained as follows. Upon the main shaft of the machine is fixed an endless screw, which drives a worm wheel fixed on an upright spindle, communicating by two pairs of bevil wheels and a short horizontal spindle, with a second horizontal spindle running the whole length of the machine, and having at each extremity a small bevil wheel, that leads alternately into two other bevil wheels fitted loosely on the screw of the slide *d,* which is traversed in opposite directions, accordingly as the one or other wheel is engaged by a central clutch seen at *f.*

The clutch is shifted for every traverse of the slide *d,* by means of a rod sliding endlong through two bearings fixed on the front of the bearers *c ;* and upon this rod two pins are fitted that admit of being adjusted to any distance from each other, according to the length of traverse required for the work in hand. A pin fixed on the slide *d,* is brought by the traverse of the machine in contact with one of the pins on the rod, and slides it endlong, so as to disengage the clutch from the one bevil wheel on the screw of the slide *d,* and cause it to take into the other and reverse the motion ; a counterpoise weight *g* is fixed on the rod to retain it steady while the clutch is being shifted. The upper slide *e,* is also provided with a screw for advancing the work towards the stone in steps, as each layer is ground off by the traverse motion.

The softer varieties of stone such as Bath, Caen, and Penswick stones, admit of being cut into slabs and smaller pieces with toothed saws, which are sometimes made of a similar form to the cross cutting saws for wood with upright teeth, shown in figs. 640 and 643, Vol. II., but the toothed saws for soft stone are generally made somewhat wider in the middle than those for wood, so as to make the blade more rounding in the direction of its length, and instead of being reciprocated backwards and forwards nearly in a horizontal line, as for cross cutting wood, the toothed saws for stone are used with a swinging stroke, so as to act upon only a moderate portion of the length of the cut at the one instant of time ; this is done to reduce the labour and give the saw teeth more penetration. Some of these very soft stones are worked with chisels and gouges similar to those of the carpenter, and they may even be worked into mouldings with planes like those used for hardwood, but this is not generally practised.

Slate as mentioned at page 165 of Vol. I. is sawn and sometimes planed with cutting tools very similar to those used for wood, except that they are stronger and are applied by machinery, the action being partly cutting, and partly forcing off the flakes of slate, as if the tools are allowed merely to scrape over the surface their edges become rapidly worn away. But the various sandstones, limestones and marbles are too compact to be thus treated, and they are consequently worked almost exclusively by the chipping chisel and various abrasive processes ; the chisel being used for such parts of the material as are in excess, as in sculptured works, and the abrasive processes being employed for dividing the blocks into slabs and small pieces, which are subsequently ground to the required forms with sand and water. In the case of marble the pieces are finally polished with abrasive powders applied on rubbers of various materials as mentioned at pages 1076 to 1078 of the present volume.

The ordinary saw used for dividing blocks of stone and marble into flat slabs, is shown in figure 1086. It consists of a parallel blade of soft iron from 5 to 10 feet long, from 4 to 5 inches wide, and from one-eighth to one-sixth of an inch thick, the blade is perforated near each end with a hole about three quarters of an inch diameter, for the reception of an iron pin, by which the saw is strained in a rectangular wooden frame. The blade is inserted in the saw kerfs in the upright sides of the frame, called the *heads*, and the pins rest in two notches near the lower extremities of the heads, which serve as the handles of the saw, and are kept distended by the wooden stretcher called the *pole*, placed about a foot from the upper ends of the heads, and rested at each end against a loose block of wood called the *bolster*.

Instead of a coil of string twisted with a short lever being employed for drawing the upper ends of the frame together, as

Fig. 1086.

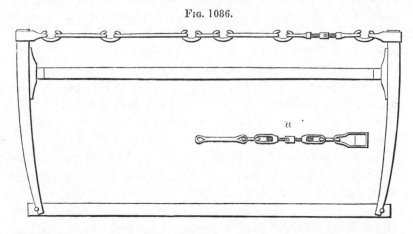

in the saws for wood, this object is effected by the use of a kind of chain made of looped iron rods, with intermediate C-shaped links, for adjusting the total length of the chain, which is furnished with iron loops that embrace the upper ends of the heads. The tension is given by a right and left hand screw fitted to two looped nuts, attached to the iron rod by C links, the double screw has holes for a lever, by which it is twisted so as to draw the upper ends of the heads of the frame together with great force, and thereby stretch the saw in a most effectual manner. The top view of the tightening apparatus is shown separately at *a*.

The depth to which the saw can penetrate, is limited by the distance from the edge of the blade to the under side of the pole, the nearer the pole is to the saw the greater is the stability of the blade, and all the parts of the frame are made detached, so as to allow of their being combined and adjusted to suit the different sizes of blocks of stone. The same pair of heads are used with poles and saws of various lengths, and the pole is placed at different heights from the blade, according to the depths of the blocks of stone. When the latter are very deep, a longer pair of heads are substituted, but long heads are avoided as much as possible, as the stability of the saw frame is thereby much reduced.

The blade of the stone-saw, like the metal-laps used for grinding generally, does not itself cut the stone, but simply serves as the vehicle for the application of the sand, which acts as the teeth of the saw, and performs the cutting process. The coarseness of the sand that is employed depends upon the hardness of the stone to be cut, for moderately soft stone a coarse sharp sand is employed, and for the harder varieties of marble a fine sand is used; the sand or grit generally employed in London for cutting stone is obtained from the scrapings of roads paved with flint. The scrapings are sifted and washed through perforated copper sieves, much the same as emery, as it is of great importance that the sand should be clean and quite free from small pieces of stone, or any other extraneous matters. Should a small piece of wood or a bit of coarse gravel by any accident get into the kerf beneath the saw blade, the little piece would roll over backwards and forwards, and materially impede the cutting of the block, and it then becomes necessary to remove the saw and wash away the obstacle, by pouring water down the saw kerf.

The cutting action of the sand is assisted by a small stream of water, supplied from a barrel placed a little above the block of stone. A small hole is made near the bottom of the barrel, to which is fitted a spigot and faucit, or more commonly a loose wooden peg grooved up the one side, which allows of the escape of a minute stream of water, that trickles down a sloping board placed so as to lead the water into the saw kerf. A little heap of sand is placed near the path of the water, and the workman is provided with a wooden stick with an iron hook at the end, or more commonly an old knife blade placed at right angles to the stick near its end. This tool is called a *drip stick*, and is used occasionally to draw forward a small quantity of sand into the running water, which thus carries down the necessary supply of sand for the cut, and the water flows away at the ends of the kerf, carrying with it the worn-out sand and the particles of stone removed in the cutting; the drip stick is also used for tapping the wooden peg, so as to increase or diminish the flow of water according to circumstances.

The weight of the saw and frame supplies the necessary pressure for causing the penetration of the sand, so that the workman has only to guide the saw, and push it backwards and forwards for the cut, and when the pressure is so great as to render the work too laborious, a counterpoise weight is hung from a pulley placed over the saw frame, to which a cord is attached, so as to reduce the pressure to the required amount. Under this arrangement the saw works more easily, but it does not cut so rapidly.

For marking upon the block of stone or marble the lines upon which it is to be sawn, as for cutting it into slabs of one or two inches thickness, the block is first shifted upon rollers into the position in which it is to be sawn ; it is then mounted upon square pieces of wood called *skids*, with that side of the block upwards which is to constitute the edges of the desired slabs, and as the blocks are frequently of very irregular forms, it is necessary to make one line around the top, and two ends of the block, to serve as the basis from which the other lines are set off, much the same as in setting out round timber described in pages 703 to 707 of Vol. II.

The position of the first line having been determined, so as to allow of the greatest number of parallel slabs being cut from the block, two marks are made on the top of the stone close to the ends, with a piece of soft black slate found amongst coal, and called *black*, a line is then drawn under the guidance of a straight edge to connect these two marks, and the line is continued down one end, also with the straight edge. An equal distance is then set off at the bottom of the opposite end, and a line is drawn to serve as a temporary guide; two straight edges, each from two to three feet longer than the depth of the block, are applied to the two end lines, and the workman looks along the line of the two straight edges, to see whether they are parallel to each other, or out of winding, in much the same manner as in the application of the winding sticks to narrow works in wood, explained at page 500 of Vol. II., except that for setting out the blocks of stone, the straight edges are placed perpendicular instead of horizontal. Should the straight edges not appear parallel to each other, the one at the second end of the stone is shifted at the bottom until the two straight edges are in one plane; the permanent line at the second end of the block is then drawn in the corrected position of the straight edge, and if the work have been correctly performed, all the three lines will be in the same plane. The thicknesses of the required slabs are then gaged off from this foundation line, and the lines on the top of the stone are *chased*, or cut in about one-eighth of an inch deep with a narrow chisel, to form a groove in which the edge of the saw is placed for the commencement of the cut. The end lines are also chased, as the water and sand would wash out the black lines.

Before commencing the sawing, the workman examines with a plumb line whether the end lines are vertical, and if not, wedges are driven under one side of the block, to bring the end lines exactly upright, the saw is then inserted in the groove, and the sawing is proceeded with, care being taken in the first entry to keep the saw quite upright, which is greatly assisted by the height of the saw frame. Should the saw make the cut a little oblique to the lines, the position of the saw is slightly twisted in the saw kerfs of the wooden heads, by blows of a hammer applied on one side of the pins which retain the blade in the frame, and which causes the saw to cut in the reverse direction. The necessity for changing the direction of the cut is, however, avoided as much as possible, as it makes the surface of the slabs irregular from the hollows thus produced, and which are called *galls*. The necessity for grinding out these galls, much increases the labour of producing a flat surface on the slabs, and the thickness of which is also lessened ; this it is sometimes an important object to avoid with valuable marbles, which are occasionally cut into veneers for inlaying, not exceeding one-eighth of an inch in thickness.

The length of the traverse of the saw is generally about 20 inches, and a saw is therefore chosen that is about 2 feet longer than the block to be cut, as the shorter the saw that can be efficiently used, the more firmly the blade is held. When two small blocks have to be cut, they are frequently placed end to end with the intended cuts in the same plane ; and to prevent the sand and water, called the *feed*, from flowing out between the stones, the interval is filled up with straw rammed in firmly between the two blocks; in the case of light-coloured marbles clean shavings are used for this purpose, as the straw would stain the surfaces, unless the slabs were washed immediately afterwards.

After the marble has been cut into slabs with the stone saw, if it is required to be reduced into smaller pieces, or narrow slips, such as shelves, or the sides of chimney-pieces, the slab is laid on a bench, having a flat surface of hard stone, or marble, called a *rubbing-bed*. The lines indicating the margins of the required pieces are marked with the straight edge, and black, and the lines are chased with a narrow chisel, as for the entry of the stone saw, but the cutting is effected with smaller blades, called *grub-saws*, shown in fig. 1087 ; they consist of plates of iron from one-twentieth to one-tenth of an inch thick, from 6 inches to 4 feet long, and 6 to 8 inches wide when new. These blades are not stretched in a frame, but are stiffened by having their upper edges clamped between two pieces of wood extending their whole length, and measuring about 2 inches wide and 1 inch thick, the

FIG. 1087.

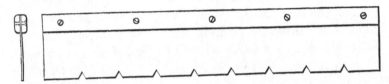

whole being held together by means of ordinary wood screws, passing through holes in the plate, so as to form a wooden back something like those of the dovetail saws, and which serves as the handle by which the grub-saw is used.

The blade should always be shorter than the length of the cut to be made, as should the blade be longer than the cut, it would be worn hollow from the greater amount of rubbing to which the middle would be exposed; but when the grub-saw is much shorter than the cut, it is liable to be worn rounding in its length. To counteract this tendency, the grub-saws are some-times filed at every 4 or 5 inches, with angular notches about $\frac{3}{4}$ of an inch deep, and which also allow the feed, or the sand and water, to reach the bottom of the cut with greater facility, and the grub-saws are consequently considered to cut rather faster for the notches.

The width of the iron blade measured to the wooden back, limits the depth of the cut to which the grub-saw can be applied, and in selecting a saw for any particular piece of stone, preference is given to as narrow a blade as can be fairly applied to that thick-ness, as when the blade is wide, it is rather feeble sideways, and it is besides more liable to be twisted from the perpendicular, when rubbed backwards and forwards in the cut, with one or both hands applied on the back of the saw near the middle of its length.

Slabs of marble or stone that are required to have flat surfaces, after having been sawn to their respective sizes are laid upon the rubbing-bed, with that side upwards which is to be ground flat, a smaller slab of stone, with a tolerably flat surface, is then selected to be used with sand and water as the grinder, the size of the grinder or, as it is called, the *runner*, depends upon the size and condition of the work to be ground; if the slab be large and moderately well sawn, as large and heavy a runner is used as the workman can conveniently push backwards and forwards; if the work be rounding in the middle, a smaller runner is employed; and if the slab be hollow in the direction of its length, a long narrow runner is used, the selection depending upon the condition of the slab, and the judgment of the workman.

The kind of stone which is used for the runner is partly dependent upon the kind of stone to be ground, but, generally speaking, the runner should be the harder stone; indeed, two soft stones, such as Portland, if ground together would hang to each other to such an extent as very materially to increase the labour of grinding. Portland stone is therefore generally ground with a runner of York stone. York stone and marble are ground with runners of the same material as the slab, but it is better that the runner should be of a harder variety.

The stone used as the runner becomes itself ground flat in the process, and advantage is taken of this circumstance to grind slabs of moderate size, by using them as runners for larger slabs, the two stones being ground flat just as readily as one.

Sometimes iron rubbers or runners are employed, and these have the advantage of retaining a much greater accuracy of form; they are far more durable, and the sand and water can be applied in a more regular manner, as the iron runners are frequently made with a raised rim around their upper surface, so as to form a kind of tray, within which the mixed sand and water is placed, and the flat surface constituting the bottom of the tray is perforated with holes, through which a constant supply of sand and water is admitted to the grinding surfaces.

Of whichsoever material the runner may consist, it is provided with a handle of sufficient length to enable the workman to traverse it over the entire surface of the slab; if the runner be large and of stone it is in general held as in fig. 1088, the end of the long handle is nailed on the upper side of a board about 1 foot long and 9 inches wide, having a slip of wood about

2 inches wide nailed on the under surface, to rest against the one end of the runner, which is retained at the other end by a loose iron ring about 1½ inch wide provided with a tail-piece. The

Fig. 1088.

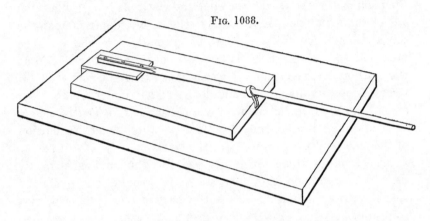

loose ring called the *hook* is slipped up the handle until the tail-piece is stopped by the stone, when from the angular position assumed by the loose ring its edges slightly penetrate the handle and prevent its return, the runner is thus securely grasped between the wooden stop and the iron tail-piece. If the runner be of iron, the handle is generally passed through two holes cast in the projecting ends of the runner, or otherwise two upright pieces are cast on the back for the reception of the handle. For small runners the handle is sometimes fixed at an angle, and sometimes vertical, as mentioned at page 1089 under the head RUBBER, Article 2.

In grinding the flat surface of a marble or stone slab, the runner plentifully supplied with sharp sand and water, is pushed backwards and forwards in all directions over the face of the slab, the flatness of which is frequently examined with a straight edge applied in all positions upon the surface of the slab, but principally upon the four margins and the two diagonals of the stone, and as the slab approaches a flat surface the sand is gradually changed for finer kinds, according to the quality of the surface required on the stone : for marble, the last process of smoothing prior to the commencement of polishing is in London effected with silver sand, which is generally obtained from the neighbourhood of Croydon. The smoothing should be continued until all the marks made by the saw and the coarser sand are entirely removed, and the slab presents a uniformly smooth surface, the last marks to be eradicated in the smoothing are generally those called *stuns*, made in sawing the marble by coarse particles of sand getting between the side of the saw blade and the saw kerf, and which are sometimes forcibly driven into the surface of the marble, and cause specks that unless removed greatly impair the appearance of the work when polished.

Single pieces of marble of a moderate size and weight, say not exceeding 18 inches square and 1 inch thick, are ground by laying them face downwards upon a slab supplied with sand and water, the marble to be ground is rubbed by the hands in all directions over the slab, but chiefly in the form of a figure of 8, to insure its being ground equally, the path in which the marble is rubbed being occasionally reversed.

When several small pieces of marble have to be ground flat, such as the squares for a tesselated pavement, it would be very tedious to grind them separately, they are therefore arranged close together and face downwards upon a large flat stone. Plaster of Paris is then poured over their upper surfaces, and a long stone a little narrower than the width of the pieces called a *liner* is laid over the whole, which thus become cemented together with all their faces level, notwithstanding that they may be of irregular thicknesses. The whole are then ground together as a runner upon a slab of marble, and the liner being narrower than the squares, allows of the two edges being ground as explained in the next paragraph.

For grinding the edges of marble, large slabs are propped upright against some temporary support, and narrow rubbers of stone or iron supplied with sand and water are applied to the edges. Narrow pieces such as shelves are placed edgeways upon flat slabs, and rubbed lengthways by one or two men.

After the smoothing with silver sand, marble works are rubbed with pieces of first and second gritstone, sometimes with pumice-stone, but which is not generally used on account of the expense, and the grounding is completed with pieces of snake-stone, as mentioned on page 1076. The pieces of gritstone and snakestone are not laid flat upon the work, but placed edgeways at an angle of about 50 degrees, and rubbed in the direction of their breadth, much the same as in sharpening a plane iron or chisel. Flat surfaces in marble are lastly polished with the *block,* or wooden rubber covered with thick felt, described on page 1089, article 3, and shown in fig. 1089. A piece of stone

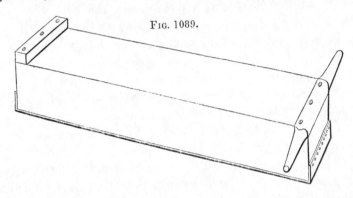

FIG. 1089.

nearly as large as the block is generally placed upon it as a weight, and the block is rubbed backwards and forwards. The proper succession of polishing powders is mentioned at page 1076, under the head MARBLE, but it should be observed that crocus is only applied upon dark-coloured marbles, as light-coloured or statuary marbles would be stained by the crocus, and for the last finish the London workmen prefer coarse linen rags.

Mouldings in stone and marble, are worked partly by the chipping chisel and partly by grinding. The drawing of the required moulding is first pricked through upon a piece of card-board, which is then cut out to the counterpart form of the moulding, and if it be small a copy is made in sheet metal, gene-rally zinc is used for the purpose, as it is easily filed, and a tolerably cheap material, these counterparts made in metal for small mouldings are called *moulds,* those counterparts made in wood for large mouldings are known as *templates,* but they are both applied in exactly the same manner.

The outline of the moulding is first scribed from the mould upon the two ends of the block of stone, and if the moulding is deep so that any considerable portions have to be removed, of either a soft stone that is easily sawn, such as Caen stone, or of any valuable marble, such as statuary marble, the large pieces are removed, either with toothed saws or grub-saws, according to the hardness of the material. If however the stone is hard and not of great value, the principal portion is chipped away in large chamfers; lines are then drawn on the face of the work, to denote the several parts of the mouldings, which parts are worked first as square fillets and small chamfers. The contour of the moulding is then formed with small straight and round-ended chipping chisels, under the guidance of the mould, and the lines on the ends of the block, the quirks of the beads and similar parts are cut in with grub-saws of suitable thicknesses.

When the mouldings have been rendered as perfect as admissible with the chisels, their surfaces are completed by grinding, which is done with stone or iron rubbers, having concave and convex edges for the curved parts, and square edges for the fillets and flat surfaces, sand of various degrees of fineness being used, according to the progress of the work.

The square iron rubbers for the fillets and square edges are made of bars of iron about 1 inch deep of various widths and from 1 to 3 feet long according to the length of the work, the bar is thinned and turned up at each end for its attachment to the wooden stock upon which it is mounted as shown in fig. 1090.

FIG. 1090.

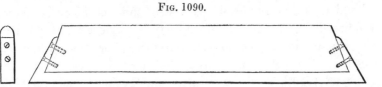

Small rubbers entirely of iron and from 2 to 10 inches long are used for these parts of mouldings which are of frequent occurrence, such as beads and astragals, but for the less frequent parts of mouldings, stone rubbers are principally employed, from motives of economy.

The mouldings are finally smoothed and polished with small slips of gritstone and snake stone, followed by putty powder applied on the ends of soft deal sticks, they are afterwards, *clouted up* or rubbed with pieces of nearly worn-out felt, removed from the blocks used for polishing flat surfaces, and the last finish is given with linen rags and putty powder.*

---

* Polished marble that has become soiled is best cleaned with a weak lye made of pearl ash and a little soft soap, and which may also be employed to clean alabaster that is only moderately soiled. This method has the advantage of not removing the polish like the more effectual method described on page 1035 of the Catalogue Article 4.

Muriatic acid is sometimes used for cleaning marble but it is ruinous to delicate

Inlaid works in coloured marbles such as mosaic and other patterns inserted in a flat surface such as a table top, are combined and ground in the following manner. The marbles are first cut into thin sheets from one-eighth to one-fourth of an inch thick, which are cut into pieces of the required forms and smoothed on the edges by filing and rubbing. Temporary slips are then fixed down to a flat surface, within which the pieces of marble to form the pattern are arranged in their proper situations, face downwards, and pressed tightly together, plaster of Paris is poured over the whole, and a slab of stone, or *liner*, is laid upon the plaster, which thus cements the whole into one mass exactly the same as the single row of squares for a tesselated pavement, previously explained. When the plaster is set, the surface of the inlaid work is ground and smoothed as a runner upon a flat slab, until it presents a level surface.

The work is now laid face upwards and a second coat of plaster of Paris, and a second liner is applied to the face of the work, which is thus cemented between the two pieces of stone, the first of which is then removed. To effect this the block is laid with the first liner upwards, a rim of clay is made on the surface of the second liner, and boiling water is poured in, which soon destroys the cohesion of the first coat of plaster, which is removed together with the liner, thus again exposing the backs of the pieces constituting the pattern, which are then cemented as one piece in the recess, previously prepared of the exact size, in the slab of marble in which the pattern is to be inserted. If the work is not intended to be exposed to the weather, plaster of Paris is used as the cement, but if the work is required to resist moisture or frost, the slab and pattern are both heated, and cemented together with the soft cement used for marble and stone which will be hereafter described.

The cement made of rosin and bees-wax is melted in a pipkin,

---

sculptured works, as it corrodes the surface and greatly depreciates the artistic character of the work.

Granite and Porphyry may be sawn and worked after the same general manner as marble, but from the greater hardness and compactness of these substances the saw cuts more rapidly when made of copper, and supplied with emery and water. The grinding is best effected with a block or rubber of lead also supplied with emery, and which is generally used like a muller for grinding paint. For further particulars on working granite and porphyry the reader is referred to Vol. I. pages 169 to 172.

poured into the recess, and the pattern is inserted bodily, so soon as the cement is set, the second liner and plaster are removed from the surface, but this time the application of the boiling water is not necessary, as the plaster can be readily detached from the smoothed surface with a chisel applied around the edges. The entire face of the slab is now ground and smoothed to make the pattern quite level with the margin, after which any imperfections that may exist in the joinings of the pieces, are corrected with the coloured shell-lac stopping or cement, to be hereafter described, and the work is finally polished as usual.

Marble has of late years been extensively worked by machinery driven by steam power, the processes are closely analogous in principle to those pursued by hand, but with various modifications of the apparatus, and it is now proposed to explain briefly some of the peculiarities of the machine processes.

In the simplest application of machinery to sawing marble, as for making one or two cuts in a large block, the construction of the ordinary stone saw, fig. 1086, is closely followed, but the frame is made much stronger, of squared timber firmly bolted together, and stayed with chains; to constitute three sides of a rectangular frame; the place of the pole and tightening chain of the saw, fig. 1086, is occupied by two fixed beams, and the saw is held and stretched by means of two clamps with screws passing through the ends of the frame, and tightened by nuts on the outside. The saw frame works between vertical guide posts to keep it upright, and it is reciprocated horizontally by a connecting rod fixed to a crank driven by the engine. The connecting rod is attached to the frame by a loop, which can be placed at various heights so as always to keep the stroke of the connecting rod nearly horizontal notwithstanding the gradual descent of the saw in the cut.

These saw frames are sometimes made as large as 16 feet long, and 10 feet high, for cutting huge blocks of marble; and to prevent the great weight of these frames from pressing on the cut, they are suspended at each end by chains or slings which vibrate with the saw, and are connected with a counterpoise weight, that is adjusted to allow of the necessary pressure for the cutting, which is effected with sand and water supplied in the same manner as for the stone saw used by hand, but the introduction of the guide principle, renders the chasing of the stone for the entry of the saw unnecessary. In some cases smaller saws of similar construction are used for cutting thick slabs into narrow slips, and sometimes several cuts are made at once by an equal number of saw blades, arranged in a rectangular frame, that is suspended horizontally by vibrating slings, and works between vertical guide posts.

In the horizontal sawing machine for marble patented by Mr. James Tulloch in 1824, the entire arrangements are combined in a very effective manner, for cutting a block of marble into a number of parallel slabs, of any thickness, at the one operation. The iron framework of the machine, shown in fig. 1091, consists of 4 vertical posts strongly connected together at

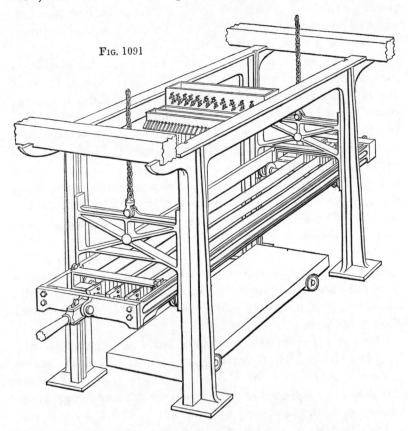

Fig. 1091

the top and bottom, to form a stationary frame from 10 to 14 feet long, 4 to 5 feet wide, and 8 to 12 feet high, within which the block of marble to be sawn is placed. The two upright posts at each end of the stationary frame have, on their insides opposite to each other, perpendicular grooves, within each pair of which slides up and down a square vertical frame ; to the lower end of each of these slides is affixed a spindle carrying two guide pulleys, or riggers, upon which the horizontal saw frame rests, and is reciprocated backwards and forwards. The saw frame is thus traversed within the fixed framing, and supported upon the four guide pulleys of the vertical slides, which latter are themselves suspended by chains coiled upon two small drums placed overhead. On the same spindle with the drums is a large wheel, to which a counterpoise weight is suspended by a chain. The weight of the counterpoise is so adjusted as to allow the saw frame to descend when left to itself, and which thus supplies the necessary pressure for causing the penetration of the saws.

The saw frame is made rectangular, and from 2 to 3 feet longer than the distance between the vertical slides, in order to permit of the horizontal traverse of the saws, which is from 18 to 20 inches.   To allow of the blades being fixed in the frame with the power of separate adjustment, every blade is secured by rivets in a clamp or buckle at each end ; the one extremity of the buckle embraces the saw, the other is made as a hook, the buckle at one end of the saw is hooked upon a horizontal bar fixed across the end of the saw frame, and the opposite end of the frame has a groove extending its entire width, through which a separate hook, provided with a vertical tightening wedge, is inserted for every saw, which thus admits of being replaced without deranging the position of the neighbouring blades.

The distances between the saws, and their parallelism with the sides of the frame, are adjusted by means of iron blocks made of the exact thickness required in the slabs of marble, the blocks and blades are placed alternately, and every blade is separately strained by its tightening wedge until it is sufficiently tense, the blocks are sustained between two transverse bars, called *gage bars*, and are allowed to remain between the blades to give them additional firmness.

The traverse of the saw frame is given by a jointed connecting rod, attached by an adjustable loop to a long vibrating pendulum, that is put in motion by a pair of connecting rods, placed one over the other, and leading from two cranks driven by the engine. All three connecting rods admit of vertical adjustment on the pendulum.   The connecting rod of the saw frame is placed intermediately between the other two, but its exact position is regulated by the height at which the saws are working, as it is suspended by a chain and counterpoise weight, which allow it to descend gradually downwards on the pendulum, with the progress of the cut, so as always to keep the connecting rod nearly horizontal.

In the London Marble Works four of these sawing machines of different sizes are grouped together, with the driving shaft and pendulums in the middle, and so arranged that each pair of saw frames reciprocate in opposite directions at the same time, in order to balance the weight, and reduce the vibration.

Another mode of traversing the saw frame sometimes adopted, is by means of a vertical frame that is reciprocated horizontally on slides, and the connecting rod instead of being jointed, is fixed rigidly to the saw frame and slides upon a vertical rod. Various other unimportant modifications in the construction of the machines are also adopted.

One of the most difficult points in the application of these machines, was found to be the supplying of the sand and water mechanically to the whole of the cuts at the same time.   This is now successfully effected by the following arrangement. Above the block of marble to be sawn, is fixed a water cistern or trough, extending across the whole width of the frame, and measuring about one foot wide and one foot deep, about 20 small cocks are arranged along each side of the cistern, and a small but constant stream from each of the cocks is received beneath in a little box, a sloping channel leads from every box across the bottom of a trough filled with sand, which mingles with the water and flows out in separate streams that are conducted to each of the saw cuts.   In the first construction of this apparatus for the feed, the sloping channels were led straight across the bottom of the sand trough, but it was then found that the water excavated little tunnels in the sand, through which it flowed without carrying the sand down.   This difficulty was overcome by leading the channels across the bottom of the trough in a curved line, when viewed in plan.   The form of the channels is shown in fig. 1092, which represents four channels cut across the middle of their length, to show their section, from which it will be seen that the channels are made as a series of gothic shaped tunnels supported only on the one side, and open on the other for the admission of the sand ; the water flows through these tunnels, and continually washing against the convex side of the channel undermines the sand, which falls into the water and is carried down ; to assist this action the attendant occasionally stirs up the sand to loosen it.   There is a sand trough and set of channels

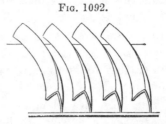

Fig. 1092.

on each side of the water cistern, so that every saw cut receives two streams of sand and water in the course of its length.

The saws having been adjusted to the proper distances for the required slabs, the saw frame is raised by means of a windlass and the suspending chains attached to the vertical frames, and the block of marble to be sawn is mounted upon a low carriage, and drawn into its position beneath the saws, and adjusted by wedges.   The saws are then lowered until they rest upon the block, the counterpoise weights are adjusted, and the mixed sand and water allowed to run upon the saw blades, which are put in motion by attaching the connecting rod to the pendulum. The sawing then proceeds mechanically until the block is divided into slabs, the weight of the saw frame and connecting rod causing them gradually to descend with the progress of the cutting.

To allow the sand and water to flow readily beneath the edges of the saw blades, it is desirable that the horizontal frame should be slightly lifted at the end of each stroke.   This is effected by making the lower edges of the frame, which bear upon the guide pulleys, straight for nearly the full length of the stroke, but with a short portion at each end made as an inclined plane, which on passing over the guide pulleys lifts the frame just sufficiently to allow the feed to flow beneath the saws.

For cutting slabs of marble into narrow pieces, such as shelves, and which is effected by hand with grub saws as explained at page 1195, a machine called a *ripping bed* is employed, in which as many cuts as may be required in the one slab are effected simultaneously, by an equal number of circular saws with smooth edges, revolving vertically, and fed as usual with sand and water.   This machine, represented in fig. 1093, consists of a bench about 12 or 14 feet long, 6 or 7 wide, and about 2 feet 6 inches high; upon the top of the bench is fixed two rails, upon which a platform mounted on pulleys is drawn slowly forward by a weight. The horizontal axis carrying the saws revolves about nine inches above the platform, and to ensure the rotation of the saws, the axis is provided with a projecting rib or feather extending its whole length. The saws are made as circular plates, about 17 inches diameter when new. The saws, or cutters, are clamped between two collars about 6 inches diameter, fitted so as to slide upon the spindle, and be retained at any part of its length by side screws.

Fig. 1093.

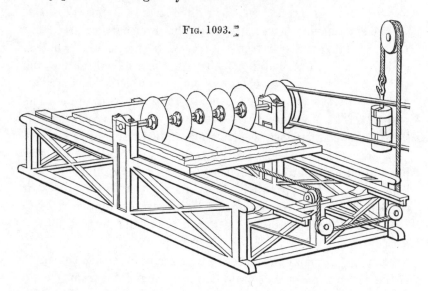

The saws having been adjusted to the required distances for the widths of the slips to be cut, and fixed by the side screws, the slab of marble is embedded in sand upon the platform, and the edge of every saw is surrounded on one side with a small heap of moist sand. The saws are then set in motion so as to cut upwards, and the platform is slowly traversed under the saws by the weight, which keeps the slab of marble constantly pressing against the edges of the revolving saws, until the slab is entirely divided into slips.

When the saws are new, they nearly reach the upper surface of the platform, and a moderate thickness of sand, just sufficient to form a bed for the slab of marble, raises it high enough to allow the saws to pass entirely through the thickness of the slab; but as the saws are reduced in diameter by wear, it becomes necessary to employ a thicker layer of sand, or to use a supplementary platform to raise the slab to the proper height. To avoid this inconvenience, an improvement has been recently introduced by mounting the axis of the saws in a vertical slide, which is adjusted by a rack and pinion, so as to allow the edges of the saw to penetrate exactly to the required depth.

Circular pieces of marble, such as the tops of round tables, and other objects, from about 6 feet diameter to the small circular dots sometimes used in tesselated pavements, are sawn to the circular form by means of revolving cylindrical cutters, constructed on much the same principle as the crown saws for wood described on page 802, Vol. II. The slab to be sawn is placed horizontally on a bench, and the axis of the machine works vertically above it in cylindrical bearings, which allow the spindle to slide through them, so as to be elevated or depressed according to circumstances. The spindle is suspended at the upper end by a swing collar attached to a connecting rod, that is jointed to the middle of a horizontal lever. The weight of the vertical rod and cutter supplies the pressure for the cutting, and the whole is raised for the admission of the work by a rope attached to the end of the lever, and passed over a pulley as shown in fig. 1094.

For circles of small diameter, the cutters are made as hollow cylinders of sheet iron of various diameters, and each attached by screws to a circular disk of cast iron, as shown in section in fig. 1096. The cutter is screwed on the lower end of the spindle, just the same as a chuck on a lathe mandrel, except that the spindle is placed vertical instead of horizontal. To ensure free access for the sand and water beneath the cutter, one or two notches, about three-quarters of an inch wide, are generally made in the lower edge.

For large circles, the apparatus is made stronger than that shown in fig. 1094, and the vertical spindle is fitted at its lower extremity with a circular plate, to which is bolted a wooden cross, shown in plan in fig. 1097, and in elevation in fig. 1098, the cross has radial grooves about 18 inches long near the outer extremities of the four arms. The cutters consist of detached plates of iron from 6 to 18 inches long, of various

widths, according to the thickness of the work. The cutters
are curved as segments of a cylinder, of the particular diameter
they are required to cut, and are each rivetted to a clamp that

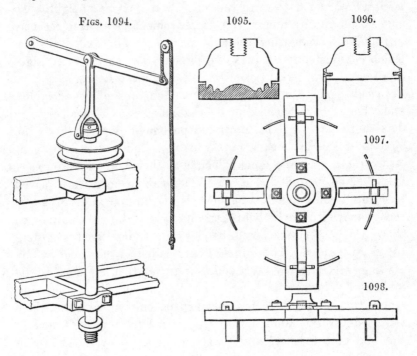

Figs. 1094.   1095.   1096.

1097.

1098.

passes through the radial groove, and is retained by a wedge. The
number and length of the cutters is solely a matter of convenience, as a single cutter, when put in rotation, would make a
circular groove, and several cutters are only employed in order
to expedite the process. But every different diameter requires a
different curve in the cutters, and which must all be placed at
exactly the proper distance from the center of rotation.

The horizontal bench upon which the marble is laid, is generally
a temporary structure, adjusted to suit the thickness of the
object to be sawn. Works of large diameter are seldom more
than one or two inches thick, but those of small diameter are
frequently much thicker, and sometimes three or four thin
pieces are cemented upon each other, and cut at one operation.
Short pillars are sometimes sawn out of an irregular block in a
similar manner, instead of being chipped and turned. And it
has been proposed that long cylinders, and tubes of stone, should

be cut with cylinders of sheet iron of corresponding length, put in rotation, and supplied with sand and water.

Marble works of small and medium size, are ground flat upon horizontal revolving laps, after the same general method as that pursued by the lapidary, but with a proportionate increase of size in the lap, which is supplied as usual with sand and water. The laps for marble works are made as circular plates of cast iron, from 6 to 14 feet diameter, and about 3 inches thick when new; they are mounted in various ways upon vertical spindles, so that their upper sides or faces may be about 2 feet 6 inches above the ground. Across the face of the lap, or as it is called the *sanding plate*, one or two strong square bars of wood, faced with iron, are fixed so that their lower sides may just avoid touching the face of the lap, and their edges present perpendicular faces, from 5 to 6 inches high, at right angles to the face of the lap. The wooden bars serve as stops to prevent the work from being carried round by the lap, and also as guides to ensure the work being ground square.

The piece of marble is laid flat upon the lap, with the face to be ground downwards, and the side of the work in contact with the guide bar. Water is allowed to drip upon the plate from a cistern fixed above, and small quantities of sand are thrown on as required. During the progress of the work the workman leans upon the marble, the position of which is shifted occasionally to expose both the work and the lap to an equal amount of wear, and prevent the formation of ridges, but which is less likely to occur with iron laps used for grinding large surfaces of marble, than when small objects are applied upon lead laps, as by the lapidary and mechanician.

The one side of the marble having been reduced to a flat surface, the work is turned over to grind the adjoining face, and the first face is held in contact with the perpendicular side of the guide bar, in order to present the second face of the work to the lap exactly at right angles to the first. When two pieces of similar size are to be ground each on the one face and two edges, as for the upright sides of a chimney-piece, the two pieces of marble are cemented together back to back with plaster of Paris, (a process that is called *lining*), and the pair are ground as one piece on all four faces; in this case the flat sides are first ground parallel to each other, or of equal thickness on the two edges, and the latter are then ground square by placing the sides in contact with the guide bar.

When the lap is of moderate size, one guide bar only is employed, and it is fixed across the diameter of the plate, which then allows of two workmen being employed on the opposite sides; but large grinding plates sometimes have two or three bars placed at equal distances across the face, and four or six workmen may then be employed at the same time upon separate pieces of marble.

The sand and water are continually thrown from the lap by the centrifugal force, and the large sizes of the works sometimes applied, prevents the use of a rim standing up above the level of the lap to catch the wet, as used by lapidaries. Every workman, therefore, stands within a kind of trough like a box, about three feet high, without a top or back; the troughs serve as a protection to the workmen, who would otherwise be exposed to a continued shower of sand and water.

The surfaces of large slabs are in some cases ground upon revolving plates; in this case the axis is placed entirely beneath the surface of the plate, somewhat as in fig. 1039, and the slab is traversed by two men over the face of the plate to grind it equally, but the machine next described is better adapted for large slabs of marble requiring tolerable accuracy.

Large slabs of marble and stone are ground very accurately in a machine patented by Mr. Tulloch, and called a grinding bed. In this machine, represented in fig. 1099, the slab to be ground is placed horizontally upon a moving bed, and the grinding is effected by sand and water, by means of a large flat plate of iron resting upon the surface of the slab. The two surfaces are traversed over each other with a compound motion, partly eccentric and partly rectilinear, so as continually to change their relative positions. The machine consists of a frame about 9 feet long, 6 feet wide, and 8 feet high; about 2 feet from the ground is mounted a platform, that is very slowly reciprocated horizontally for a distance of from 1 to 2 feet, according to the size of the slab, by means of a rack and pinion placed beneath, and worked alternately in both directions.

Above the platform are fixed vertically two revolving shafts, having at their upper extremities horizontal toothed wheels of equal diameter which are driven by means of a central toothed wheel keyed on the driving shaft. The two vertical shafts are thus made to revolve at equal velocity or turn for turn, and to

FIG. 1099.

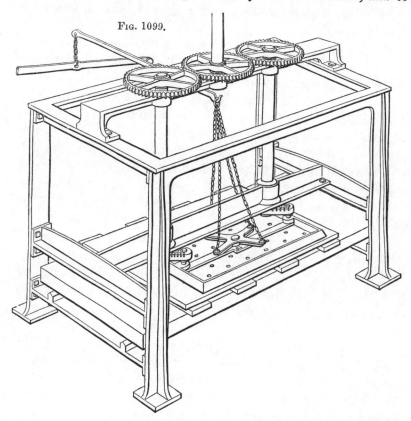

their lower ends are attached two equal cranks placed parallel to each other, the extremities of which therefore describe equal circles in the same direction. To these cranks the iron grinding plate or runner is connected by pivots fitting two sockets placed upon the central line of the plate. The cranks are made with radial grooves so that the pivots can be fixed by wedges at any distance from the center of the cranks. When the machine is put in motion the grinding plate is thus swung round bodily in a horizontal circle of the same diameter as the throw of the cranks, which is usually about 12 inches, and consequently every portion of the surface of the grinding plate would describe a circle upon the surface of the slab being ground if the latter were stationary. But by the slow rectilinear movement of the platform the slab is continually shifted beneath the plate so as to place the circles, or rather the cycloids, in a different position, and it is only after many revolutions of the cranks that the same points of the surfaces of the grinding plate and slab are a second time brought in contact.

The grinding plate is raised for the admission of the slab by means of four chains suspended from a double lever, and attached to the arms of a cross secured to the center of the upper surface of the plate, which is thus lifted almost like a scale pan. For slabs that are much thicker or thinner than usual, the principal adjustment is obtained by the removal or addition of separate beds, or loose boards, laid upon the platform to support the slab at the proper height. * Slabs that are too large to be ground over the whole surface at the one operation, are shifted once or twice during the grinding, to expose the surface equally to the action of the grinding plate.

The necessary pressure for grinding, is given by the weight of the horizontal plate, which is supported almost entirely by the work, as the pivots of the cranks merely enter the sockets, and allow the plate to descend when left to itself. For delicate works a counterpoise weight is attached to the double lever so as to regulate the pressure on the work.

The sand and water are applied to the grinding surfaces in much the same manner as in the iron runners used by hand previously described. The grinding plate is made on the upper side with a raised rim like a tray, and the bottom of the tray is perforated with numerous holes about $1\frac{1}{2}$ inch diameter arranged at equal distances apart. The sand and water are thrown into the tray at intervals in small quantities, and run through the holes and between the surfaces of the slab and grinding plate, which are thus uniformly supplied with the feed that ultimately makes its escape around the edges of the grinding plate.

Various qualities of sand may be employed according to the perfection of surface required, and very flat surfaces are produced by this machine. The *grounding* or smoothing of the best works is effected with a succession of fine emeries, with which the surfaces may be made very smooth, and almost polished; but from motives of economy, the grounding of ordinary works is more frequently completed by hand, with grit stones and snake stone before the work is finally polished on another machine, described on page 1216.

Rectilinear mouldings in marble are wrought by machinery in a manner altogether different from the hand process of working mouldings, in which, as previously described, nearly the whole of the material is removed with chipping chisels, and the surfaces of the mouldings are only smoothed by abrasion. In the machine process, on the contrary, the whole of the material is removed with revolving grinders, by which the work is reduced to the required form, and left smooth at the one operation.

The machine for working rectilinear moulding, or as it is called *the moulding bed*, closely resembles in its construction the ripping bed described at page 1207, except that the frame carrying the revolving grinders is provided with the power of vertical adjustment by a screw placed beneath, in order to raise the grinder to the proper height to suit the thickness of the marble, and that instead of the grinders, being thin circular sheets of iron, they consist of solid cylinders of cast iron turned to the counterpart forms of the required mouldings. Indeed the ordinary ripping bed is occasionally used for working mouldings on large works, and when it is provided with the vertical adjustment for elevating or depressing the axis to any required position, the ripping bed is equally suitable for working mouldings; but as the latter are in general only required on slips of marble only a few inches wide, a narrow machine is usually employed for the purpose.

The forms of some of the grinders are shown in figs. 1100 to 1102; the outline represents the grinder, and the shaded part

Figs. 1100.   1101.   1102.

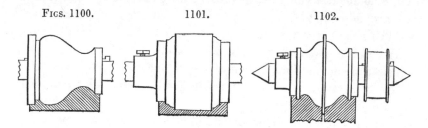

beneath, the entire compound moulding that would be produced by the same. A separate grinder is required for every different moulding, and consequently a large number of grinders have to be provided to meet the demand for variety. They are all pierced with a central hole fitted to the axis of the machine into which they are to be employed, and secured either by a wedge or a side screw, so that they admit of being readily exchanged when a different form of moulding is required.

The grinder of suitable form having been selected it is fixed on the axis of the machine, the slip of marble is cemented with plaster of Paris upon the bed, and the frame carrying the spindle is adjusted by the screws beneath to the proper position, to allow the grinders to penetrate the marble to the required depth for the production of the moulding. As in the ripping bed, the grinder is made to revolve so as to cut upwards towards the surface, and the attendant keeps a small heap of moist sand constantly in contact with the face of the grinder. The weight attached to the sliding bed by a line passing over a pulley keeps the work constantly advancing in a straight line towards the grinder as fast as it is cut, and the work finally presents a compound rectilinear moulding of exactly the counterpart form of the grinder. Mouldings on the edges of narrow slips are sometimes wrought in pairs, as in fig. 1102, the two pieces being cemented together sideways as one block, and which is placed edgeways upon the machine.

Circular mouldings in marble, such as the base of a column, a vase, or similar object, are generally wrought by turning in a lathe after the manner described in Vol. I. page 167. Small flat circular mouldings, such as are sometimes seen in the corners of chimney pieces, are ground to their forms by machinery in much the same general manner as the rectilinear mouldings, but the machine described on page 1209, for cutting out small circles of marble, is employed for grinding the small circular patterns.

The grinders are made of cast-iron turned to the counterpart form of the pattern, as shown in section in fig. 1095, and screwed upon the upright spindle of the machine the same as the circular cutters. The counterpart grinders are kept supplied with moist sand, and the grinding is continued until the circular pattern is entirely developed, the works are afterwards polished in the lathe, as described at page 1077.

The polishing of rectilinear works in marble, by machinery, closely resembles the polishing of flat slabs by hand, previously described, the chief differences being, that for large slabs, from 2 to 6 rubbers or blocks are employed, and that they are reciprocated by the machine instead of by hand. The slab of marble to be polished, is laid upon a flat bench or table about

12 feet long and 6 feet wide. At a moderate height above the bench is fixed a crank driven by the engine, a connecting rod from which leads to an iron swing frame, working as a pendulum placed 2 or 3 feet from the end. Fig. 1103 represents

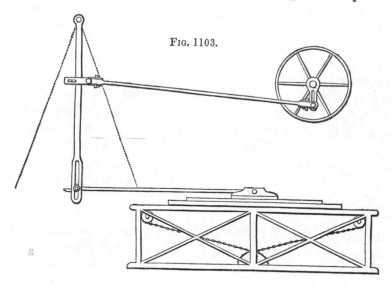

FIG. 1103.

the side view of the polishing bed; the swing frame consists simply of two rods moving upon centers above, and carrying near their lower extremities a horizontal bar extending the entire width of the bench; to this bar as many separate iron rods are attached as there are rubbers to be employed at one time, and every rod is jointed to its own rubber, which for flat surfaces consists of a block of wood about 2 feet long and 6 inches wide, covered with thick felt, as explained at page 1089, articles 3 and 4. The attachments of the connecting rods to the crank and pendulum are all capable of adjustment, so that the length of stroke can be readily changed to suit the size of the work in course of being polished, but generally the stroke is about 3 feet long.

The rubbers are used with the succession of powders explained on pages 1076 and 1077, and the weight of the blocks and rods supply the pressure. Several narrow rubbers are used instead of one wide rubber, in order to allow each rubber to adapt itself readily to any trifling irregularities in the surface of the slab. The rubbers are shifted across the width of the slab, by sliding them to another position on the horizontal bar of the pendulum frame, and the platform of the machine is traversed endways by a chain and drum, or a rack and pinion, to expose the work equally to the action of the rubbers.

Rectilinear mouldings are polished in the same manner, except that elastic rubbers are employed. These are made of coarse cloth, like sacking; generally old sugar bags are used for the purpose; they are cut into strips about six inches wide, folded lengthways, and nailed through the middle of the fold close together to a block of wood, so as to present when complete a surface 8 or 9 inches wide, composed of the edges of the cloth, the loose filaments of which penetrate into the angles of the mouldings. For polishing the edges of narrow works in marble several pieces are fixed close together edgeways in a wooden trough, and they are all polished at the same time.

The grinding and polishing of plate glass by machinery, is perhaps the largest example of the production of plane surfaces by grinding, and a brief outline of the mode of proceeding will be here offered.

In the manufacture of plate glass, the materials are first fused in melting pots made of Stourbridge clay, which measure from 30 to 40 inches diameter, and 3 to 4 feet high. The pots are made in the form of a truncated cone, being rather smaller at the bottom than the top, and are capable of containing a sufficient quantity of the melted glass to form four or five plates of the largest size. After the materials have been thoroughly fused together, a sufficient quantity of the melted glass to form a single plate, is removed by iron ladles from the large melting pot to smaller pots called *cuvettes*, which have been previously heated in another furnace. The glass now in a pasty condition is placed in the pots while they are in the furnace, which is then closed up, and kept at a considerable heat for some hours, until all the air bubbles have been expelled and the glass is sufficiently fluid to be poured.

The pot is then removed from the furnace, and carried on a truck to an iron table or bench, having a flat surface about 18 feet long and 10 feet wide, two bars of iron of equal thickness to the desired plate are laid upon the face of the table near the edges. The fluid glass is poured on the table and spread with iron or copper tools ; an iron roller about 15 inches diameter, equal in length to the width of the table, and weighing about 30 cwt. is rested upon the two iron bars and traversed over the face of the glass, to roll it out like dough to a uniform thickness. To insure the rotation of the roller in a straight line along the plate, it is provided at each end with toothed wheels that work in corresponding racks fixed on the sides of the iron table, and the roller is drawn along the table by means of two chains, coiled around the ends of the cylinder and worked by a windlass.

When the glass has been rolled flat, the cylinder is received at the end of the table upon two arms counterpoised by means of levers placed beneath, so as to allow of the heavy roller being raised or lowered by two or three men. The plate still red hot and yielding, is slid from the table upon the flat surface of a carriage which is wheeled to the annealing oven, upon the bed of which the plate is pushed and allowed to remain for several hours to cool gradually.

The plates when cold are examined as to their condition, and such plates as present defects in the glass, or irregularities in the surface that it would be tedious to grind out, are cut with the diamond into smaller pieces, but the nearly perfect plates are kept as near their full size as possible, and merely squared on the edges.

The plates of glass now measure about half-an-inch thick, and the surface is full of small irregularities, presenting a mottled appearance, the roughest side being generally that which was placed downwards upon the bed of the annealing oven, and copied all the irregularities of the bricks of which the bed of the oven is formed. The side of the glass that was uppermost in the oven, is comparatively smooth and bright from the action of the fire, although in many cases this surface is not so nearly flat as the lower. The plates have therefore to be ground flat and polished on both sides, formerly this was effected entirely by hand, but of late years the rough grinding with coarse sand, and the polishing with crocus, are almost always done by machinery, and hand labour is only resorted to for the intermediate process of smoothing with fine emery.

The grinding and polishing machines employed for plate glass differ somewhat in construction in various manufactories, but a single example of each will sufficiently explain the general method.

The grinding machines employed for the largest plate glass are arranged in pairs along the grinding room; every pair of machines is driven by one central beam, and consists of two benches of stone 15 feet long, 8 feet wide, and 18 inches high, placed about 10 feet asunder; upon each of these benches one or more plates of glass are embedded in plaster of Paris, close together, and quite level. Other plates of glass are cemented upon the lower faces of two swing tables or runners, which are traversed over the fixed beds, by a horizontal frame or beam about 30 feet long; the machinery for driving the beam is fixed in a frame about 6 feet square and 18 inches high, placed between the two grinding benches. A horizontal shaft fixed underground, extends throughout the length of the grinding room between the lines of benches, and the motion from the shaft is communicated to every pair of machines, by a pair of bevil wheels leading to a central crank that revolves horizontally, and has a radius of about 2 feet; the arm of the crank is attached by a pivot to the center of the horizontal beam. Four other cranks of the same radius are placed parallel to the central driving crank, one at each corner of the square frame, and serve to guide the traverse of the horizontal beam, which is thus swung in a circle of four feet diameter in a manner somewhat similar to the grinding bed for marble, fig. 1099. The beam is supported at various parts of its length by chains suspended from the roof of the building, which allow of the traverse of the beam, and serve for raising it by means of levers for the removal of the work.

Near each end of the beam is attached, with the power of adjustment for position, a small sliding frame carrying bearings for the reception of the central pivot of the swing table or runner, which consists of a strong frame of wood covered with boards, and measuring 8 feet long and 6 feet wide, placed face downwards upon the bench; a central pivot stands up from the back of the runner, and enters the bearing fixed on the horizontal beam, which thus communicates a circular swinging motion to the center of the runner, exactly the same as that of the driving crank; and the runner being free to revolve upon its pivot, acquires a continual rotation around its own axis. By the combination of the two movements the relative position of the fixed bench and runner are continually changing; this tends to the mutual correction of the two surfaces of the glass, and greatly assists the equal distribution of the sand and water used in grinding. The horizontal beam makes about fifty circulating strokes in a minute, and the runners revolve upon their own axes about once to every five or six strokes. The position of the runners upon the driving beam is shifted once or twice during the grinding, to distribute the action as uniformly as possible over the entire surfaces of the glass plates.

The largest plates of glass are nearly equal in size to the fixed bench, and these are imbedded singly upon the bench with the most irregular side upwards; but more generally plates of medium and small size are ground together; they are selected of uniform thickness, and arranged close together upon the bench, with the largest plates in the middle and the smallest at the ends. The runner is covered by one or two plates at most, as small pieces would be liable to be thrown off by the centrifugal force.

All the irregularities of the surfaces are first ground out with sharp river sand, that has been washed and sifted into two sizes; the sand and water are thrown on by hand occasionally, and when the plates have been ground quite flat, the finer sand is employed, and followed by emery of two finer sizes, applied as usual in succession, in order to remove the scratches made by the coarser powders. The plates of glass are thoroughly washed between every change of grinding powder, and when the one side of the glass has been ground with the finer sizes in succession, the plates are inverted, and the same routine is followed on the second side.

The grinding machines do not however admit of being employed with very fine emery, as the close approximation of large surfaces travelling over each other at a considerable velocity, causes so much friction that it would be liable to tear the surface of the glass, and, consequently, as the plates become sufficiently smooth to require the application of fine emeries, the velocity and pressure should be proportionally reduced, and a greater degree of care and management is required; it is therefore found to be preferable to effect the smoothing of plate glass by hand.

The plates are smoothed upon stone benches of suitable size, about 2 feet high, made very flat upon their surfaces, and covered with wet canvas. One large plate nearly equal to the size of the bench, and two or three plates of about half the size, are usually given out as a set of work. The large plate is laid upon the wet canvas which serves to hold it firmly, emery and water are spread over the surface, and one of the small plates is used as a grinder or runner. If the plates be large, a few flat lead weights of about 14 lbs. each are laid near the middle of the runner, to distribute the pressure uniformly, and the runner is traversed over the lower plate with a swinging stroke backwards and forwards, so as to describe nearly a semicircle around the center of the runner, which is at the same time shifted a few inches during the stroke. Every stroke follows a slightly different path from the preceding one, and the runner is also gradually twisted round as the smoothing proceeds. The combination of these movements, serves to expose every part of the surfaces of the bed plate and runner to an equal amount of grinding, and also to distribute the emery very uniformly.

Small plates are smoothed by young girls, and large plates which require greater dexterity and a proportionate increase in the amount of traverse, are smoothed by two women; who stand on opposite sides of the bench, and placing their outstretched hands flat upon the runner swing it with a stroke of five or six feet. The employment appears most masculine, but it is found that the smoothing is upon the whole executed better by women than men, as only a moderate force is required, and from the greater delicacy of touch possessed by females, they more readily appreciate when any particles of grit have become accidentally mixed with the emery.

About six sizes of carefully washed emery are used in the smoothing, and between every size, the plates, canvas, bench and hands are thoroughly washed, perfect cleanliness in the clothing is also quite essential, as a particle of coarse grit would make a scratch that would require the smoothing of the plates to be recommenced. The fine emery last employed gives a very smooth and partly polished surface, which is completed with the machine next described.

The polishing machine has a bed 15 feet long and 8 feet wide, that is mounted upon rollers, and slowly traversed sideways, a space of 4 feet to and fro, by means of a rack and pinion beneath.

A few inches above the bed are reciprocated longitudinally, 2 beams or carriages, each about 18 feet long and 9 inches wide, and consisting of two cast iron side plates connected together at intervals, and supported at each end upon two small wheels, that run upon a short railway at the end of the traversing table. The carriages are placed 4 feet asunder, and reciprocated about 2 feet by means of two cranks fixed opposite to each other on the same axis, so that the beams work in opposite directions, the one advancing as the other recedes.

The plates of glass are embedded close together, with their surfaces quite level, upon moveable platforms that are afterwards fixed upon the traversing bed, and the polishing is effected with a series of rubbers, placed 1 foot asunder and measuring 8 by 6 inches, covered with thick felt, and attached to the reciprocating carriages, which drag the rubbers backwards and forwards over the surface of the glass, while the latter is traversed beneath the rubbers, a space equal to the distance between the two lines of rubbers, to expose all parts of the glass equally to their action.

Every rubber is separately attached to one of the two carriages, to allow it to ply uniformly to the surface of the glass, this is effected as follows, between the two side plates of the beam are fixed, near the top and bottom edges, two cross pieces having square holes, through which slides vertically a square bar, the lower end of which projects about 2 inches below the beam, and is rounded semi-cylindrically. The rubber is made quite detached, with a central cavity at the back to fit the end of the upright bar, which thus forms a joint that allows the rubber to adjust itself to any trifling irregularities of the surface over which it is traversed, and the rubbers admit of being readily removed while the plates of glass are being exchanged. The pressure is given separately upon every rubber by two lead weights of about 15 lbs. each fixed one on each side of the upright bar.

The powder generally employed for polishing plate glass by machinery is the Venetian pink of the colour-man, a cheap powder which contains only a small proportion of the oxide of iron, mixed with earthy matter that renders the powder less active, and allows of the free use of water, which serves to reduce the friction and prevent the glass becoming heated by the action of the rubbers. Tripoli, crocus, or putty powder used with water, are too active to produce a high polish on glass, and therefore they are generally employed dry for the last finish of glass polished by hand. But the great amount of rubbing surface, the velocity and power employed for polishing plate glass by machinery, renders the use of dry powders inadmissible, as the surface would be torn by the friction, and the heat evolved would be liable to break the glass.

Sometimes old plate glass, that has become scratched, is re-polished; when the plates are large, and sufficiently numerous, they are repolished by machinery, just the same as new glass, but more generally old plates are repolished by hand, as the process can be then restricted principally to the scratched portions of the surface.

The polishing is commenced with tripoly on cloth rubbers of the usual form, and finished with putty powder or crocus. The pressure is generally given as in hand calendering, by attaching the rubber to the lower end of an upright pole, suspended from a long horizontal spring fixed overhead, like that of a pole lathe. The elasticity of the spring supplies the pressure, and the workman has only to push the rubber backwards and forwards, but the process is both laborious and tedious with large plates, and from the irregular action of the hand, the surfaces of glass thus polished present a wavy appearance much inferior to those polished by machinery.

Sheet glass or flattened glass, is manufactured by blowing the glass first into the form of a spherical bulb, which is afterwards elongated, by alternate heating, blowing and swinging, into a cylinder about 3 feet long and 8 inches diameter, with rounded ends, which as the last process of blowing are opened out, and the ends are cut smooth with a diamond traversed in an upright frame around the cylinder, which is then cut through on the one side longitudinally, with a diamond inserted near the extremity of a light rod, and drawn through the inside of the cylinder under the guidance of a straight edge. The cylinder is then placed with the cut upwards in a reverberatory furnace, and the heat causes the cylinder gradually to open as a sheet, which is gently flattened down on the bed of the furnace, with tools like blunt garden rakes made of iron or wood.

To improve the flatness, several sheets are afterwards laid

upon each other in a second reverberatory furnace with a leve bed, the heat of the furnace and the weight of the superincumbent mass, causes the lower sheets of glass to become sufficiently flat for ordinary use, notwithstanding that there are many little irregularities in its surface, arising from the imperfect action of the flattening process. For the best purposes these irregularities are removed by grinding and polishing, and a brief, notice of the method pursued in an extensive manufactory will be here subjoined.

The grinding room contains about 140 grinding machines, arranged in double rows of 10 each, and the annexed diagram

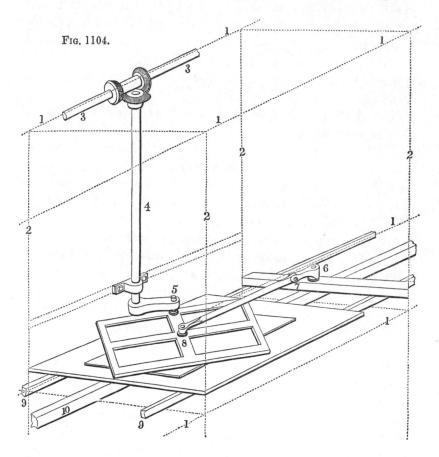

Fig. 1104.

fig. 1104, may be considered to represent roughly the moving parts of every machine, the framing being represented by the dotted lines.

The framework consists of continuous beams 1, 1, united by vertical posts 2, 2, bounding every machine, the whole firmly united. Above the framing extends an axis 3, 3, carrying for every machine one pair of bevil wheels which turn the upright shaft 4, and its crank 5, to the right or left at pleasure. The pin of the crank 5 communicates a circular motion to that point of the moving table to which it is attached, while the fixed radius bar 6, 7, 8 restrains the center of the table to describe an arc about the point 6, the two motions conjointly bring all parts of the running surface successively in opposition to nearly every part of the lower bed, which latter lies on railway bars 9, 9, and is very slowly reciprocated to and fro by the bar 10, which runs through the building, and is traversed about two feet by a crank, that is made slowly to revolve by a worm wheel and tangent screw, one screw serving for two cranks united to two lines of the machines. The whole arrangement is most massive and imposing.

The circle described by the crank 5, is about two-thirds of the length of the moving table, the lower face of which is covered with slate upon which the glass is cemented, another sheet of glass is cemented upon the lower table, and the upper table is loaded with 4 or 8 weights placed in the respective panels of the frame. When from swinging the upper table about by hand, it is judged that one of the corners bears too hard, the weights are removed from this corner. Coarse emery and water are used for the grinding, and when the machines are used with finer emeries for smoothing, the whole apparatus is carefully washed, for the convenience of which there are numerous racks and tanks between the rows of machines. In some manufactories the plates of glass are smoothed by rubbing them one upon the other by hand.

After the sheet glass has been ground flat and smoothed, it is polished in another room by the machinery rudely shown in figs. 1105 to 1107. 1, 1, is a long main shaft extending throughout the length of the building, and having for every row of the machines one double and two single cranks, which move the two long central beams, 2, 2, to the right, and the two exterior beams, 2', 2', to the left at the same instant, by the intervention of connecting rods, as usual.

The travelling beams or rods carry rubbers, 3, 3, 3, 3, about

12 by 5 inches on the face, and covered with leather; they are suspended by a joint to the loaded levers, 4, 4′, which press them on the glass. To raise them up and retain them, the piece 5 is laid down in the position 5′, which holds up the lever

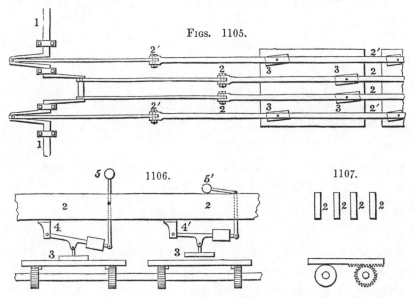

FIGS. 1105.

1106.   1107.

as at 4′, as the joint which unites 4 and 5 is situated in the mortise through the long travelling beam 2, at the part represented by the dot in the figure to the left; so that when the rubber is at work the weight 5 cannot be misplaced, and when 5 is laid down as at 5′, no shaking will allow the rubber to descend accidentally. The rubbers all assume an inclined position, from the several tables carrying the glass having a very slow transverse motion, simultaneously throughout the entire line of machines, which is effected somewhat after the manner of the annexed figure, 1108.

The main shaft 1, 1, communicates with a pair of sliding bevil wheels 6, 6; these through 7 move the tangent screw 8, and thence the worm wheel 9, which latter, by the pair of bevil wheels 10, 11, moves the long shaft carrying the line of pinions 12, 12, one or two of which are under every table, and traverse the same by aid of plain rollers 13, 13. A tumbling bob is affixed to the table nearest the cranks and gear, by which the position of the pair of bevils 6, 6, are shifted to make the tables traverse first in the one and then in the opposite direction.

The polishing machines make about 50 or 60 strokes in the minute, and the grinding machines about 20 to 30 strokes in

Fig. 1108.

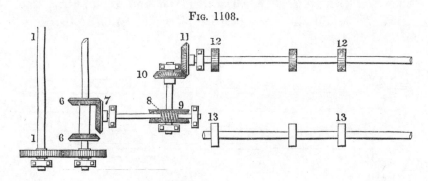

the minute, and every machine is so arranged as to admit of being readily detached from the others without impeding the movement of the principal parts.

It has been explained in the second volume, at pages 870 to 872, that the production of accurate plane surfaces by grinding is a process of great uncertainty, and that the plane surfaces of metal required in mechanical construction, are more easily and correctly produced by the methods of filing and scraping, described at pages 876, 878; but these methods are inapplicable to substances, such as glass or speculum metal, that do not admit of the application of cutting tools, and consequently when these hard materials have to be wrought into plane surfaces, it is essential to produce the necessary degree of accuracy by grinding alone. The grinding tool employed for the purpose is generally a flat surface of brass, supplied with abrasive powder moistened with water or oil. The surface is in most cases larger than the object to be ground, which is rubbed by hand upon the grinding tool with straight, circular, or elliptical strokes, applied in all directions; but these grinding tools, although they may be originally produced by the method of scraping, soon lose the required accuracy, and from the particles of the polishing powder becoming embedded in the surfaces, their restoration by the method of scraping is impracticable.

The plane surfaces of the grinding tools themselves, have therefore to be produced as nearly accurate as possible by grinding, and the method explained on page 871 is pursued with all possible care. Three surfaces, generally of brass, are operated upon at the same time, and serve for mutual correction by being rubbed one upon the other, in the succession explained at pages 877 and 878, with reference to testing the condition of planometers produced by scraping.

The two surfaces found to have the same error are rubbed together, first with large circular strokes, in order that the operator may feel at what parts of their surfaces they bear the hardest, or appear to hang together; these parts are then placed in contact and rubbed with short strokes, either straight or circular, applied longitudinally or transversely, according as they may feel to offer the greater resistance to the one or other motion, the surfaces being rubbed together in the direction, and just for the distance, that they appear to move stiffly upon each other.

Great care is required to avoid the introduction of new errors, exactly as in scraping planometers, and the surfaces must be frequently wiped clean and tried upon each other, first to feel that they bear uniformly when tried at the four diagonals, and when these larger errors are removed, the surfaces are rubbed together with short strokes, in order that they may mutually brighten the highest points of their respective surfaces. The grinding is continued under these tests until all three surfaces feel to slide smoothly and equably over each other in all directions, the final test being that when the whole of the grinding powder is removed, and they are rubbed upon each other, the surfaces should be *uniformly* covered with small bright spots close together, so as to give the surfaces a finely mottled or bronzed appearance. The degree of accuracy required to present this uniformly brightened surface, is however exceedingly difficult to attain by the process of grinding.

In the case of plane surfaces in glass required for optical purposes, as in the parallel disks employed in sextants, great accuracy is required, and in the ordinary method of grinding and polishing, much difficulty is experienced from the absence of control over the distribution of the grinding powder upon the surfaces under formation. To obviate this inconvenience, Mr. Andrew Ross, of London, was induced to investigate the causes which led to the inaccuracy of the grinding process, and he has succeeded in pointing out the principal source of error, and also the method by which it may be avoided.

Upon a careful examination of the process of grinding two surfaces upon each other, whether plane or curved, Mr. A. Ross found that the principal errors occurred in the direction in which the two surfaces were rubbed upon each other, and which arises from the unequal distribution of the grinding powder. In the act of traversing the object over the metal surface the grinding powder is pushed away by the advancing edge of the object, while near its middle an excessive quantity of the powder is accumulated, and consequently the object is ground concave near the middle, and in the return stroke it picks up, at the extreme edges, a small quantity of the new grinding powder that has not been crushed in working, and therefore acts with more energy, and rounds off the extreme edge. The combination of the two errors, makes the object that should be a plane surface, of the irregular section shown in the exaggerated diagram, fig. 1109.

For optical purposes, the rounding off at the edges is not very important, as the difficulty may be overcome, either by grinding the glass of a larger size than is ultimately required, and afterwards reducing the diameter so as to remove the rounded edges, or the edges may be covered by a ring of pasteboard or metal, so as to prevent that portion from interfering with the action of the instrument. It is therefore the concavity in the middle, that is the principal difficulty in optical glasses.

Figs. 1109.   1110.

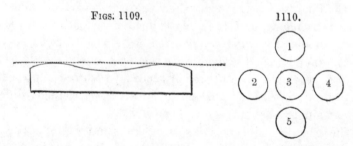

Mr. A. Ross discovered that the accumulation of the grinding powder near the middle of the glass, arose from the capillary attraction of the *moistened* powder, and that by the employment of the grinding powder in a *dry* state, the source of the most important error was removed. The grinding powder when used dry cuts less rapidly than when moistened, but from the greater exactness of the method, a much smaller amount of abrasion suffices to produce the plane surface, and consequently the dry process is but little more tedious than the wet.

In grinding and polishing the parallel disks of glass for sextants, the one surface is first ground flat, sometimes singly, but more generally from motives of economy five are ground at the same time. The disks are arranged in the order shown in the diagram, fig. 1110. The surface of the one tool having been wiped quite clean and dry, every disk is slightly moistened by breathing upon it. The disk is then placed upon the lower tool with moderate pressure ; and if the disks be tolerably flat, the capillary attraction will suffice for retaining them in position during the grinding. A small quantity of finely washed emery is then dusted upon every disk, the second tool is placed over the whole, and attached to a line leading to a pulley placed overhead, and from which a counterpoise weight is suspended to regulate the pressure upon the disks, which should be only moderate. The upper tool is then rubbed with elliptical strokes continually varied in direction, and the tools are occasionally changed end for end, in order to place the surfaces in all possible relations to each other.

The surface upon which the glass disks are attached is always the lower tool ; and the emery that is pushed off the disks falls on the lower surface, and is not picked up by the upper tool in the return stroke, which as previously mentioned, would be liable to round the extreme edges. By this arrangement it is only the tolerably uniform layer of emery that remains attached to the upper grinding tool that is employed, and the principal dependance for flatness is placed upon the condition of this tool. Water is used with the emery by most opticians, but by Mr. Ross the emery is used dry ; and, to examine the progress of the work, the upper tool is removed, and the grinding powder blown away with a pair of bellows, as wiping with a cloth would leave particles of the powder attached to the face of the disks.

When the disks have been ground flat over their whole surfaces on one side, they are removed from the lower tool, which is thoroughly cleaned ; the disks are then arranged as before, with their second faces upwards, and ground flat. But it will now happen that the two sides, although they may be plane surfaces, are not parallel to each other, and therefore the positions of the disks upon the lower tool are interchanged, 1 being placed in the position of 5, and 2 in that of 4, and the central disk is twisted round in the opposite direction. The whole are then ground in the same manner as before, until flat in their second positions, when the disks are again interchanged ; and the process is repeated until both sides of the disks are made quite parallel to each other, and they collectively present a level surface in whatever order they may be arranged upon the lower tool. The disks are lastly polished either with oxide of iron, or putty powder.

Plane mirrors, made of speculum metal, and employed in reflecting telescopes, are ground to a plane surface upon flat grinding tools prepared as above described. The grinding tool is much larger than the specula to be ground, and is supplied with a small quantity of fine washed emery. The specula are rubbed singly upon the tool, with the fingers like a muller, until they are ground perfectly flat. The principal difficulty is, however, experienced in producing the high polish required in reflecting surfaces without impairing the accuracy of the plane surface obtained in grinding. The polisher is generally of cast iron, grooved over its entire surface, so as to divide it into squares, and covered with pitch, or a resinous cement, exactly in the same manner as in the polishers used for concave specula, the methods of working which will be briefly described in the fourth section of this chapter. Great importance is attached to the sizes of the polishers relatively to those of the specula, as if the polishers are made too large, the edges of the specula will be rounded off, or made convex; and if the polishers are made too small, the specula will be wrought concave.

Small plane specula are usually polished several at the same time. They are arranged close together to make up a circle, and with their faces quite level. The polisher is also circular ; and Mr. A. Ross considers that the specula are the most accurately polished when the diameter of the polisher is about one-thirtieth greater than that of the circle of specula.

Elliptical specula, measuring above 3 inches by 2, are commonly polished singly, and Mr. Gambadella found that he succeeded the best when he employed a round polisher of the same size as the inner diameter of the oval. The Earl of Rosse found that he was enabled to polish specula of this size very perfectly with a polisher of three inches diameter applied in his machine for grinding and polishing concave specula briefly described in the fourth section of this chapter.

Speaking of polishing plane mirrors, the Earl of Rosse says :— " When the metal is polished, it is tested in the usual way by viewing an object alternately by direct and reflected vision, with a very good thirty inch achromatic, the aperture of which has been previously contracted to an inch and three quarters. If the metal is concave, it is worked with shorter strokes for about half an hour, and then tried ; it will be found to have become less concave, possibly convex ; in the latter case it is to be worked with longer strokes ; thus, with the utmost facility, a metal can be worked alternately concave and convex ; and, with a little practice, the limit between the two can be hit with such exactness, that, even with the severe test of a thirty inch achromatic, no deviation from the plane can be perceived, and the loss of light will be the only evidence that the rays have suffered reflexion before their incidence on the object glass." (Trans. Royal Society, 1840, p. 524.)

SECT. II.—THE PRODUCTION OF CYLINDRICAL SURFACES BY ABRASION.

CYLINDRICAL works in metal, of small diameter, and considerable length, such as slender rods, are difficult to be turned of strictly uniform diameter, because from their weakness they are liable to spring away from the turning tool. This liability is, to a considerable extent, counteracted by the application of supports called back stays, or sliding guides, which will be adverted to in the succeeding volume ; but, nevertheless, after slender rods have been turned as nearly uniform in diameter as possible, they still retain numerous irregularities, which, although not observable to the eye, may be readily detected by passing the rod between the fingers.

Shorter or thicker cylindrical rods, that are too rigid to spring from the tool, are nevertheless liable to slight irregularities arising from imperfections in the slides of the lathe in which they are turned, hard and soft places in the metal, and also the wear of the tool, which, although small, is quite appreciable in works of moderate length. These circumstances combined, render the attainment of a perfect cylindrical rod by turning a matter of considerable practical difficulty; and consequently, it is usual, after the work has been turned as true as possible, to reduce the minute errors by grinding, and which, at the same time, serves to give the work a more highly finished appearance. The above classes of work which only require a moderate degree of accuracy are usually ground between lead or tin grinders of counterpart form, supplied with emery and water, or oil, and fixed in iron clamps that supply the pressure, and serve as handles for the application of the grinders.

Figs. 1111, and 1112, represent in two views a grinding clamp suitable for cylindrical rods of medium size. The two halves of the clamp are connected at each end by two binding screws, *b*, and the clamps are curved in the middle, so that when they are separated about one quarter of an inch by the set screws, *s*, they may present in the center a cylindrical aperture about one inch larger in diameter than the cylinder to be ground.

Figs. 1111.

1112.

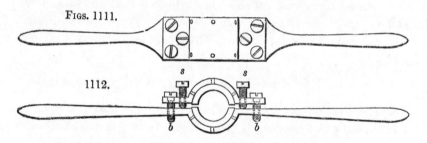

For casting the lead grinders within the iron clamps, the set screws are withdrawn, and the binding screws slackened, so as to leave an opening of about one quarter of an inch between the flat faces of the clamps, which are then placed edgeways upon a flat block, and a short cylinder or core of the same diameter as the cylinder to be ground, is placed in the center of the circular aperture, two parallel slips of wood or iron sufficiently wide to be grasped between the flat faces of the clamps, are then placed in contact with the sides of the core, so as to divide the opening into two parts, and are firmly pinched by the binding screws. Melted lead is now poured in to fill up the cavities, and form two grinders, each a little less than the semicircle, and the cylindrical faces of which are counterparts of the metal core. The inside surfaces of the clamps are left rather rough, in order that they may the better hold the lead; and, with the same view, a few radial holes are sometimes drilled in the clamps, or otherwise the edges of the opening are chamfered off, in order that the lead may be cast with a projection on each side to prevent the grinders from shifting endways.

To keep the core in the center of the clamp while the lead is being poured, a hole is sometimes bored in the block upon which the clamps are laid. At other times the grinders are cast at once upon the rod to be ground; in this case the rod is fixed vertically in a vice, and a hole is bored through a piece of wood, which is slipped on the rod, and luted with clay to make a close joint.

In grinding a long cylindrical rod the work is mounted in the lathe, and the grinder is fitted upon one part of the rod by first closing the clamps with the binding screws b, the set screws s are then advanced to partially sustain the pressure of the binding screws, and separate the clamps just sufficiently to allow the rod to revolve within the grinder, with as much friction as can be conveniently overcome by the hands applied to the extremities of the lever or handle. The lathe is then put in rotation, and the grinder is traversed backwards and forwards, throughout the length of the rod, with a screwing action somewhat as in boring a hole with an auger. If the grinder were slowly traversed straight along the rod, the latter would not be so uniformly ground, and when finished it would be marked with rings, partly owing to the emery not being equally distributed over the surface of the work. The grinder is first applied to those parts of the rod which present the greatest amount of friction, and when the resistance becomes lessened at the most prominent parts of its length, the grinding clamps are closed upon the rod, by withdrawing the set screws and tightening the binding screws. The clamps thus admit of being gradually adjusted, so as to serve almost as a gage for the parallelism of the rod, and successively reduce the parts of largest diameter, until the grinder slides smoothly and with uniform resistance from end to end of the cylinder.

The grinder should be as nearly as possible the counterpart of the desired cylinder, but in the course of work the grinder becomes irregularly enlarged, while at the same time the cylinder is gradually although slightly reduced; the closing of the clamps partially compensates for the difference of diameter, but not for the irregularity of wear, and consequently two grinders are usually required for the completion of the cylinder. The principal errors are removed with the first, and when the rod has been rendered tolerably cylindrical, and very nearly of the required diameter, a second grinder is cast for finishing the work.

When the rods are required to be of precise diameter, for sliding through bearings and similar purposes, they are turned slightly larger than the finished size, and gradually reduced by grinding, until upon trial they are found to fit with sufficient precision into the hole in which they are intended to work. Sometimes brass or gun-metal grinders made in halves, connected by screws, and bored out to the exact diameter, are employed for the final adjustment of cylindrical works required to be of definite diameter, but the method is scarcely trustworthy, as the grinders are themselves rapidly abraded, and soon become enlarged, unless they are very sparingly employed.

Short cylinders are in many cases ground by hand instead of in the lathe, the work is then fixed horizontally in the vice, and the workman stands in front of the cylinder, and twists the grinder about half way round backwards and forwards, and at the same time traverses it to and fro lengthways of the cylinder, varying the direction of the stroke as much as possible every time, and occasionally twisting the cylinder partly round in the vice, in order to expose it more equally to the action of the grinder, which is fitted upon the cylinder, and applied to reduce the high points in succession, just the same as in the lathe process.   This method is less rapid than grinding in the lathe, but is more under control, as the resistance offered by trifling irregularities, is more easily appreciated when the work is at rest, than when it is revolving, and from the constant change of the path of the grinder, the cylinder is less liable to be marked with rings.

When the cylinder terminates at the one end in a collar or projection, it is rather difficult to grind the work square in the corner, partly owing to the angle of the grinder being worn away.   In this case tin is generally used instead of lead for the grinder, which is also made narrow in order to allow of as much of the traversing or screwing action as possible, and partly avoid the liability of the grinder to become more enlarged at the ends, than in the middle.

Large cylindrical works, such as rollers, present too much surface friction to be ground between clamps, and for those purposes which only require moderate accuracy, the works are left sufficiently true from the lathe, and the surfaces are polished as explained on page 1072. Works requiring a little more accuracy are sometimes smoothed with a grinder, made by casting a lump of lead upon the cylinder to embrace about one-third of its circumference, and weighing from one to two hundred weight, a bar of iron 3 or 4 feet long is inserted in the loam mould at the time of casting, in order to serve as the handle. The roller is made to revolve in the lathe, and the grinder, mounted upon the roller, is traversed backwards and forwards by the handles, the weight of the grinder supplying the pressure.

Many cylindrical works, such as lathe mandrels, gages for the diameters of holes, flatting rollers for thin gold wire, and other similar objects, that are required to possess considerable accuracy and durability, are made of steel, and afterwards hardened, in which latter process they are liable to become distorted, as explained in Vol. I. Chap. XII. Sect. IV.

The above class of works, which require the greatest possible exactness of form, are usually ground before hardening, with the clamps, fig. 1112, but which method is not sufficiently accurate for the final correction of the best works, as the grinders have a constant tendency to wear of an oval figure, and also to become rounded in the direction of their length, from the outer edges being more rapidly worn than the middle, this partly arises from the absence of a sufficient guide to ensure the grinder being traversed parallel to the axis of the cylinder, as the shortness of the grinder allows the handles of the clamp to be imperceptibly twisted from the square position, in opposite directions with every stroke.

To avoid this liability as much as possible, in works requiring tolerable exactness, the grinder is made as long as admissible, and the handles very short, in order to reduce the leverage as much as possible, the finishing clamps being sometimes no longer than is required for the binding screws, which are only tightened so far that the grinder just touches the highest points of the cylinder, and allows of its being traversed with very moderate force, so that small inequalities may be detected by the sense of feeling, and in this manner a sufficient approach to correctness for many works is readily attained. But although with careful management the work may be made tolerably circular by this method, it is deficient of any correctional process that can be relied upon for the absolute straightness of the cylinder.

A more accurate method for the best works, is to mount the cylinder upon the lathe, and apply a fixed grinder in the sliding rest, exactly like a blunt turning tool. The grinder is made of lead, copper or iron, supplied with fine emery, and adjusted so as just to touch the highest points of the cylinder as it revolves with moderate velocity. The grinder is traversed from end to end of the cylinder by the sliding rest, and as the highest points are gradually reduced, the grinder is set forward to remove the next series of prominencies and so on. By this method the true circular form may be at once attained, and the parallelism of the cylinder will depend upon the perfection of the slide, and the accuracy with which it is adjusted. In some few instances a diamond point mounted in the sliding rest, and traversed with a very slow motion, has been similarly employed, for correcting hardened steel rollers requiring great accuracy, but the method is tedious, and scarcely better than the fixed grinder supplied with emery.

Another method very nearly as accurate and much more expeditious than the fixed grinder, is the analogous employment of a rapidly revolving lap, mounted on the sliding rest, and gradually traversed along the cylinder, which at the same time slowly revolves upon the lathe. The best lathe mandrels are frequently corrected in this manner after hardening. The iron or copper laps generally employed for this purpose measure from 6 to 9 inches diameter, and about five-eighths of an inch thick; they are driven at a velocity of about 300 to 400 revolutions per minute, and the mandrel makes about 20 revolutions in the same time.

The cylindrical rollers used in paper-making machinery, for pressing the single sheet of paper as it is produced by the machine, require that the two surfaces should fit each other with great accuracy, in order that the rollers may act uniformly upon the paper, and the surfaces at the same time are required to be very smooth, that they may impart a finished surface to the paper.

The ordinary methods of grinding cylindrical surfaces with emery, are not sufficiently exact for the production of these rollers, as the leading source of error in all grinding processes, namely, the unequal distribution of the abrading powder arising from the absence of control, allows the loose emery to accumulate upon the lowest points, and, consequently, after a certain approach to accuracy has been attained, the further continuance of the grinding leads to the depreciation of the surface by the continual introduction of new errors. The impossibility of producing by these means large cylindrical rollers, sometimes required to be as much as 6 feet long and 18 inches diameter, with sufficient accuracy to press uniformly a single sheet of the thinnest paper, has led, after numerous tedious and expensive experiments, to the final abandonment of all abrading powder, and the required accuracy of contact is attained by the simple friction of the surfaces of the rollers rubbing upon each other, plain water being plentifully supplied to lubricate the surfaces, and prevent their heating and tearing each other.

The rollers are first turned as truly cylindrical as possible in the lathe, and tested for parallelism by carefully measuring the circumference at various parts, with a thin copper wire wrapped around the cylinder, a more exact test than gaging the diameter, the journals of the cylinder are turned at the same time, in order to ensure their being concentric.

The rollers are next mounted on their own bearings, in a frame similar to that in which they are to be employed, and their surfaces are carefully adjusted to each other, the bearings of the one roller being fixed, and those of the other placed under the control of a screw adjustment, that admits of the rollers being closed upon each other so that the highest points alone just touch. The rollers are now examined to ascertain whether they fit each other tolerably well throughout their length, as when both rollers have been turned in the same lathe, they will in all probability possess the same general error, or both be either concave or convex in the direction of their length. Most generally long rollers will be turned slightly concave, from the slide of the lathe being more worn in the middle by short works, and the two rollers when placed in contact will show double the amount of error, which if considerable is sometimes reduced by grinding each roller separately, with a lead grinder supplied with emery and mounted on the end of a lever, that is used to press the grinder in contact with the surface of the cylinder, much the same as in polishing large turned works.

When the errors are so far reduced, that they cannot be detected by the line of light between the cylinders, they are put in revolution, and the one roller marked slightly with a piece of chalk applied at intervals of a few inches, the revolution of the rollers transfers the chalk lines from the one roller to the other, at those parts where they touch, which shows at a glance the highest parts. The points thus indicated are successively reduced with the grinder until the rollers fit each other sufficiently well to transfer all the lines with tolerable regularity, which indicates a moderate approach to general truth, but by no means sufficient for the purpose, as numerous minute errors will still remain that cannot be detected by the chalk lines.

The rollers are now carefully adjusted so that their highest points alone touch each other, and the rollers are driven at different velocities, by separate straps leading to pulleys fixed on the axis of the rollers, which revolve in the *same* direction, so that the two surfaces in contact meet and pass each other in *opposite* directions, and the velocities being different, the relative positions of the rollers are continually changing, and it is only after many revolutions that the same points again come in contact.

The friction of the two surfaces causes them mutually, although slowly, to abrade each other, and a constant stream of water is directed upon the rollers, to lubricate their surfaces and prevent them from heating. The latter is a point of considerable importance, as should the rollers become unequally heated from their surfaces being dry, or from too high a velocity being employed, the surfaces would not only be liable to tear, but the irregular expansion of the metal would continually introduce new errors, and the true cylindrical form could not result.

Attention is required to keep the rollers in equal contact with each other at the high points throughout their length, and as these are gradually reduced, the rollers are slightly closed upon each other to bring the next series of high points in contact. It being considered that if the rollers were firmly pressed upon each other, they would be more liable to copy their mutual irregularities, and also that the pressure would be liable to cause the one roller to follow the path of the other, or be driven by their surface contact, notwithstanding the action of the belts on the driving pulleys.

As the surfaces approach nearer to perfection, the length of contact is gradually increased, and proportionately greater care is required in the adjustment of the rollers, to prevent the friction becoming so great as to tear the surfaces, or cause increase of temperature. The process is tedious, and requires to be continued for several days, until the contact of the surfaces is as perfect as possible, throughout the length of the rollers, in every position in which they are brought, by the continual change of their relative positions.

A very smooth and polished surface is produced in this manner by the use of water alone, but for those rollers required to possess a still smoother surface, Messrs. Hopkinson and Cope, (from whose practice the foregoing particulars have been derived,) have adopted the use of oil instead of water for the last finish, and the smoothness of surface thus produced leaves little room for improvement.

A different method of carrying out the principle of grinding the rollers together with water is sometimes resorted to, in order to allow of the rollers being subjected to the same degree of pressure during grinding, that they are intended to sustain when at work, as it is occasionally found that notwithstanding the strength of the rollers, they yield slightly beneath great pressure, so as to interfere with the accuracy of contact.

To avoid this interference the bearings of the upper roller instead of being suspended over the lower, so that the high points of the two rollers alone touch, are loaded so as to press the rollers in contact with the same degree of force that is required for pressing the paper. But under this pressure the surfaces in contact do not admit of being driven in opposite directions, because it is found that the two surfaces meeting each other, cause so much friction that the rollers are almost certain to be torn even when a very slow motion is employed. The rollers are therefore driven in opposite directions at different velocities, generally in the proportion of nearly 5 to 6, so that the surfaces in contact travel in the same direction, but the velocities being different they move over each other with a sliding action.

The adjustment of the velocity depends principally upon the degree of pressure employed, and the condition of the surfaces; if driven too rapidly the surfaces are liable to heat and tear each other, which in this as in the arrangement previously described is the principal difficulty to be contended with.

The water is supplied through a perforated tube extending the length of the rollers, and should any portion of the rollers appear to be grinding too rapidly, the action may be checked by stopping up some of the holes to reduce the supply of water at that part, but which is not generally resorted to, owing to the risk of the rollers being allowed to become too dry from neglect on the part of the attendant.

The grinding action appears to be principally due to the small particles of cast iron rubbed off by the friction, and which serve as the abrading powder. The progress of the grinding may be expedited at the commencement, by using the same water repeatedly over again, in order to bring a larger quantity of the grinding powder into action, but towards the conclusion of the process when the highest finish is required, clear water is alone used.

The process appears to be partly grinding and partly burnishing, and does not admit of being indefinitely pursued, as if continued too long the surfaces crumble away, which is also liable to occur if the castings be unsound, and therefore all such places should be plugged up with cast iron of the same quality and hardness as the rollers. Wrought iron should never be used for the plugging as it is but little acted upon by the water grinding, and the wrought iron plugs would stand out beyond the general surface of the rollers.

Accuracy of surface contact is the object desired in these rollers, and their absolute straightness is a matter of secondary importance, the rollers are therefore made simply to revolve upon their axes, and are not at the same time traversed through their bearings, as this would be liable to introduce a new source of error by wearing the journals into a screw-like form. A small amount of end adjustment is however sometimes adopted, should the rollers be found to wear into rings; with this view the bearings are so far separated as to allow of a little end motion in the journals, and the insertion of washers between the collars and bearings, allows of the rollers being shifted endways a small distance when required.　This adjustment is however scarcely called for, as without it a pair of rollers may be ground so nearly straight, that the ordinary test of a straight edge would fail to detect any irregularity, and when three or more rollers are ground with their surfaces in contact, they mutually correct each other for straightness as well as circularity.

The cylindrical rims of pulleys employed for driving machinery by leather straps are usually turned to form in the lathe, and afterwards smoothed with emery applied on a stick as explained at page 1072.　But in some cases these pulleys are wrought into the cylindrical form by the ordinary grindstone, assisted by a little mechanism, after the same general method as that employed for grinding superior cylindrical works.　In the case of pulleys the grinding is resorted to not from any superiority in the method, but solely from motives of economy, the grindstone being more rapid in its action than the turning tool, when the object is merely to produce a level surface, without removing a greater bulk of the material than is necessary for that purpose, as the turning tool requires to penetrate sufficiently deep into the metal to remove the outer hard crust left in casting, as explained on page 375, Vol. I.　The action of the grindstone is however little influenced by the hard crust, and consequently a much smaller quantity of material has to to be removed by grinding to produce the cylindrical form.

In Mr. James Whitelaw's machine for grinding pulleys,* the grindstone of about 4 feet diameter is mounted in fixed bearings as usual, and revolves about 180 times per minute, the pulley to be ground is fixed upon a mandrel parallel to the axis of the grindstone, and makes about 130 revolutions in the minute in the *same* direction as the grindstone, so that when the *opposite* edges of the pulley and grindstone are brought into contact, the two surfaces rub upon each other at their combined velocities, and at the same time the pulley is reciprocated a few inches

---

* Described in a communication to the Royal Scottish Society of Arts, 1838. See Trans. Roy. Scot. Soc. of Arts., Vol. I., page 235.

backwards and forwards across the face of the grindstone, to equalise the wear of the latter, and ensure the cylindrical form of the pulley.

FIG. 1113.

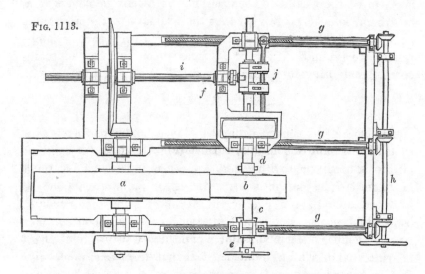

This machine is shown in plan in fig. 1113, in which *a* represents the grindstone, and *b* the pulley to be ground, the pulley is mounted upon the mandrel *c*, which for the convenience of easy removal is fitted by a key into the spindle *d*, at the one end, and works through a plummer block *e*, at the other. The spindle *d* is fitted in bearings fixed on the frame *f*, which together with the plummer block *e*, are traversed simultaneously on longitudinal slide bars *g*, by three screws of equal pitch, each communicating by a pair of bevil wheels with a transverse rod *h*, having a wheel on its end to be moved by hand. By this arrangement the pulley admits of being gradually advanced in a parallel line, to keep its edge in contact with the stone as the grinding proceeds.

The spindle upon which the pulley is mounted, is reciprocated to and fro through its bearings, by means of a crank on the end of the shaft *i*, which is driven by a bevil wheel leading to a pinion fixed on the axis of the grindstone. The pin of the crank on the shaft *i*, works in a brass that slides in a perpendicular groove in the frame *j*, which is fitted between collars on the spindle carrying the pulley, and slides upon a parallel guide rod at the back. The revolution of the crank pin traverses the frame *j*, and the pulley spindle connected with it, and as the crank pin is fitted in a groove that admits of its being placed at any distance from the center, the amount of reciprocation may be readily adjusted to suit the width of the pulley.   To allow of the crank being traversed longitudinally with the frame *f* carrying the spindle of the pulley, the crank shaft *i* is made to slide through the hollow axis of the bevil wheel, which is bored out of the proper diameter, and provided with a feather, that enters a groove extending throughout the length of the shaft, to cause its rotation.

Mr. Whitelaw also proposed another machine for grinding pulleys that are required to be rounded upon the edge instead of being cylindrical, this machine is very similar in its general arrangement to fig. 1113, but instead of the spindle carrying the pulley, being reciprocated in a straight line through the bearings, the revolving spindle is mounted in a swing frame having vertical pivots.   The frame is swung horizontally backwards and forwards by an eccentric, so that the edge of the pulley in contact with the stone describes the arc of a circle, of which the vertical pivots are the center, and as the latter are fitted into grooves in the top and bottom of the swing frame, they admit of being adjusted to give any required degree of curvature to the edge of the pulley.   The length of traverse of the swing frame is adjusted by attaching the connecting rod leading from the eccentric, at different distances from the center of motion.

In another machine for grinding cylindrical pulleys made by Messrs. Randolph Elliot & Co. of Glasgow,* the pulley to be ground is mounted on a mandrel revolving with moderate velocity in fixed bearings, and the grindstone which revolves with considerable rapidity is slowly traversed across the face of the pulley, by means of a screw passing through the hollow shaft of the grindstone, and driven by a system of differential wheels mounted on a sliding frame, that is shifted to and fro by hand, in order to reverse the motion of the screw.   The grindstone is fitted in the center with a cylindrical bearing that slides upon the shaft, and the traverse motion is communicated from the screw to the grindstone by means of a nut having two flanges, that pass through longitudinal grooves in the hollow shaft, and are firmly fixed to the cylindrical bearing of the grindstone.

---

* *See* Practical Mechanic and Engineers' Magazine, Vol. IV. p. 73.

The bearings of the spindle carrying the pulley to be ground, are attached to a frame sliding horizontally, and adjusted by a single screw to bring the edge of the pulley in contact with the stone ; and to keep the pressure uniform notwithstanding any trifling irregularities of the stone, a spring is introduced between the adjusting screw and sliding frame.   As in Mr. Whitelaw's machine the axis of the grindstone and pulley are placed parallel to each other, and are driven in the same direction, so as to combine the velocity of the two surfaces.

Internal cylindrical surfaces such as the bearings for spindles, and similar works in iron and steel, are ground with cylindrical grinders, generally of lead or tin, but sometimes for greater durability and exactness brass or iron are employed.   The grinders are in general made as solid cylinders of the required diameter, and a succession of grinders are employed each a little larger than the preceding, but sometimes the grinders are made with a small power of expansion in order to avoid the necessity for several grinders when the hole has to be materially enlarged.

Figs. 1114 to 1117 represent some of the most usual forms of grinders for internal cylinders.

FIG. 1114.

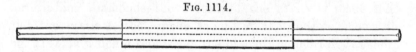

Fig. 1114 consists simply of a bar of iron, upon the middle of which a lump of lead is cast and turned to the suitable diameter. This form of grinder is the most generally employed for cylindrical holes that pass entirely through the object, the iron bar upon which the grinder is cast, is made much longer than the hole to be ground, in order that it may be traversed endways through the hole to equalize its diameter, and prevent the formation of rings.   When the hole is long and has merely to be corrected for trifling irregularities, the object is fixed horizontally in the vice, and the central rod of the grinder is grasped in a diestock or fitted with a pulley to serve as the handle.   The grinder is then charged with emery, inserted in the hole, and worked backwards and forwards with a screw-like motion, the same as in grinding an external cylinder by hand ; to facilitate the first entry of the grinder, it is made slightly taper at the front end. Small grinders soon become reduced in diameter by use, sometimes to compensate for the wear the grinder is laid upon the lathe-bearers or other support, and a few light blows of a hammer are given along one side to spread the metal out to a larger diameter. The two flat faces thus made along the sides of the grinder also serve to allow of the escape of the surplus emery, and with this view large grinders are frequently made with a few grooves along the sides.

When the hole is so short that it would not serve as a guide for the grinder, the latter is mounted to revolve in a lathe, and the work held by the hands is traversed endways on the grinder, and at intervals is allowed to be partly carried round by the friction, so as continually to place the work in different angular positions, which serve to prevent the hole from being ground either oblique, or more on one side than the other. With very short holes, care is required to traverse the work quite square on the grinder, as if it be twisted in the direction of the hole, the latter will be ground larger at the ends than in the middle.

In all cases of grinding cylindrical holes, there is great risk of enlarging the two ends, partly owing to the work being twisted, and partly to the emery cutting more keenly on its first entry into the hole, and becoming crushed before it reaches the middle. This evil is sometimes partly avoided by making the grinder much shorter than the cylinder, the grinder may then be applied to the middle of the hole for a longer period. The grinding of long holes is at all times however a process of considerable uncertainty, from the absence of any guide for the straightness of the work, and consequently, except for hardened steel, the principal reliance for accuracy is placed upon the boring and broaching tools, and a slight grinding is only occasionally resorted to for the purpose of smoothing the surfaces or fitting cylindrical works together.

Fig. 1115 is used for grinding two cylindrical holes of unequal

FIG. 1115.

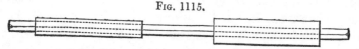

diameter on the same line, as in the case of a screw mandrel lathe head, the front bearing of which is usually made of a larger diameter than that at the back, and both are made cylindrical in order to allow of the longitudinal traverse of the mandrel through the bearings in cutting a screw. Both holes are ground at the same time, as the distance between the bearings causes them to serve as a guide to ensure the holes being ground parallel to each other. For the same reason when holes of equal diameter have to be ground for the reception of a cylindrical rod or shaft, the grinder is made sufficiently long to grind both holes at the one process ; and in a similar manner when one hole only has to be ground, advantage is taken of any hole in the same line that may be used as a guide, and the grinder is made with a cylinder to fit the second hole, which is not supplied with emery.

The grinder fig. 1116 is made in two halves to allow of the power of expansion, it consists of two semicylindrical rods of

Fig. 1116.

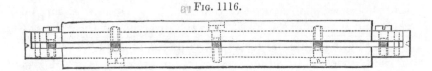

iron, fitted to each other either by steady pins, or two projections at the end of the one bar, within which the second bar is fitted. They are held together by 3 or 4 binding screws, placed at equal distances, passing freely through the one bar and tapped into the other for the purpose of closing the grinder and reducing its diameter. The bars are separated by intermediate set screws, tapped through the one bar and bearing against the opposite. The lead to constitute the grinder is cast upon the bars in much the same manner as for the grinding clamps, fig. 1112, two thin slips of wood being inserted between the bars to divide the mould in two parts.

The mould for casting cylindrical grinders is frequently a block of wood bored with a hole of the required diameter, but sometimes a temporary mould is made of a sheet of stout paper wrapped around a cylinder of suitable size, and bound with string ; the cylinder is afterwards removed. The lead should be only of a moderate heat at the time of pouring, or the casting will be liable to be honey-combed, or filled with air bubbles, even if the mould be quite dry, and if it be damp, the fluid metal may be forcibly driven out. The heat of the melted lead is therefore tested with a piece of paper thrust below the surface, and when it is cooled just sufficiently to avoid burning the paper, the lead is poured into the mould, and when cold the grinder is turned to the proper diameter.

The spring grinder, fig. 1117, is used for grinding out short holes in works that admit of being mounted in the lathe, and

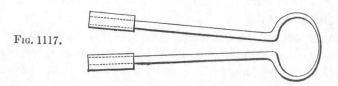

Fig. 1117.

principally for those holes that do not extend entirely through the object, and therefore do not admit of the preceding forms of grinders being employed. The two rods of the grinder when left to themselves spring open like the blades of sheep shears, and thus maintain a constant pressure upon the sides of the hole in which they are inserted. For casting this grinder the rods are tied nearly close together with a piece of string, and inserted in a smooth metal mould of the same diameter as the hole to be ground, which itself is often used as the mould, as this grinder is usually left from the casting, and not afterwards turned; the grinder is finally divided lengthways with a saw.

The angular manner in which the rods separate is rather objectionable, but nevertheless with careful management it answers moderately well for holes but little larger in diameter than itself, as the angular difference for small openings is so slight as to be scarcely appreciable. A solid grinder is sometimes used for stopped holes, but whatever form of grinder may be employed, it is difficult, with small deep holes, to grind the work cylindrical close up to the bottom of the hole, and which is also very liable to become enlarged at the open end, consequently the grinder is always required to be shorter than the depth of the hole to be ground, and to be kept towards the bottom, the amount of end traverse being only just sufficient to avoid the formation of rings.

The cylinders of steam engines are usually considered to be left sufficiently smooth from the boring machines, such as fig. 517, page 571, Vol. II.; sometimes, however, they are smoothed by grinding them with a heavy mass of lead, cast upon the middle of a long rod, to the same curve as the inside of the cylinder, which itself in most cases serves as the bottom of the mould. The cylinder is laid on its side, and the grinder supplied with emery and oil is traversed backwards and forwards by hand, the cylinder being occasionally twisted round so as to bring every portion successively beneath the grinder.

For holes of moderate length requiring considerable accuracy, the grinder of the same diameter as the required hole is in some instances mounted on the end of a revolving spindle, made to slide endways through cylindrical bearings under the control of a lever, and the object to be ground is fixed quite stationary. The bearings through which the spindle of the grinder slides, are required to be carefully adjusted so as to be quite central and parallel with the axis of the hole, or the latter will be ground either oval or oblique, and the spindle should be somewhat smaller than the grinder, to allow of the latter being traversed entirely through the hole to equalize the diameter.

Short cylindrical holes, such as ring gages for the diameters of works, admit of being very accurately ground by mounting the work to revolve rapidly in the lathe, and applying a fixed grinder of smaller diameter than the hole, held in the slide rest, and employed exactly in the counterpart manner to the fixed grinder for external cylinders described on page 1237. Sometimes the grinder is made of soft iron or copper, but a circular lump of lead cast on the end of a bar of iron usually serves as the grinder, it is mounted in the slide rest, which is carefully adjusted as for turning a cylinder, and the grinder supplied with emery is brought in contact with one side of the hole, traversed entirely through it, and gradually advanced sideways to reduce the high points in succession, and enlarge the hole exactly to the required size.

External and internal cylinders are frequently fitted together by grinding them in contact for the final adjustment. When the works are of hardened steel, they are first separately corrected for the distortion of hardening, and brought so near to the same size, that the cylinder will just enter the hole about one-eighth of an inch with stiff friction. A small quantity of the finest flour emery mixed with a little oil is then smeared over both surfaces, and the cylinder is gradually worked in, first with a circular motion only, until it is entered about half an inch, and then with a screwing action backwards and forwards, just as in grinding out the hole with a solid grinder. A pulley or a double-ended lever fixed on the end of the cylinder serves as the handle.

It is necessary to keep the surfaces plentifully supplied with emery and oil, as should they be allowed to become dry, they would be liable to heat from the friction, which then becomes so great as to tear the surfaces of the metal, and in extreme cases will even cause them to hold so firmly together that they can only be separated by blows of a hammer applied on the end of the cylinder, to the evident destruction of the cylindrical surfaces. The grinding with emery is only continued until the cylinder will just slide through the hole with uniform resistance; the surfaces are then thoroughly cleaned, and worked in the same manner for a short time with oil alone, which serves to remove the last traces of the emery and put a final polish on the work.

When one cylinder has to be ground into two holes, as for the bearings of a screw mandrel lathe, the two holes are first corrected with the grinder at the one process, as stated on page 1247, but the mandrel itself is ground into each hole separately, as a very small amount of grinding suffices to fit the two cylindrical surfaces together when properly prepared; and if the mandrel were ground into both holes at the same time, the accuracy of fitting could not be so delicately felt, and in all probability one of the holes would be ground so far larger than the cylinder as to allow of a little side play or shake in the fitting.

Emery may be employed for grinding together works of hardened steel without risk of the grinding powder becoming embedded in the surfaces of the work, as the hardness of the steel will not allow the emery to penetrate sufficiently deep to be permanently retained. With soft iron more care is required to entirely remove the last particles of emery, which if permitted to remain would convert the rubbing surfaces into grinders, and they would mutually abrade each other, to the rapid destruction of the fitting. For this reason emery is rejected for grinding together brass works, and pumice-stone powder is employed, as from its greater softness and friability it is less liable to become embedded in the metal, and may be washed away with oil. But in all cases the grinding together of soft metals should be avoided as much as possible, and when resorted to, the grinding powder should be afterwards thoroughly removed from the rubbing surfaces.

SECT. III.—THE PRODUCTION OF CONICAL SURFACES BY ABRASION.

Conical surfaces are ground after the same general methods as cylindrical surfaces, and with grinders of nearly the same general forms, the principal differences being that the grinders are made conical instead of cylindrical, and that they do not admit of being traversed through each other like cylinders to distribute and correct the errors of the grinder itself, and consequently in grinding cones the accuracy of the result depends entirely upon the truth of the grinder, which under the most favourable circumstances transfers nearly all its errors to the work.

Unlike cylindrical works, conical surfaces are not usually ground for the correction of the trifling errors of turning, partly because they are mostly short in proportion to their diameter, and therefore but little liable to spring away from the tool, the principal source of error in turning long cylinders, and partly because the ordinary methods of grinding cones are less perfect than the methods of grinding cylinders, as the conical grinders depend entirely upon the turning lathe for their accuracy, and consequently when the material is sufficiently yielding to allow of the action of cutting tools, the surfaces may be thus produced more correctly than by grinding, which in this case is principally employed for producing accuracy of contact between two cones by grinding them together, and not for improving the general truth of either.

Works in hardened steel are necessarily corrected for accuracy of form by grinding, in order to remove the distortion occasioned by hardening; but in this case the cones, whether external or internal, are prepared exactly to the angle, and only slightly larger in diameter than the required size, by turning them in the lathe while soft, so as to leave but a very trifling amount of correction to be effected by grinding. Internal cones in objects that do not admit of being conveniently chucked, are prepared with the taper broaches, or revolving cutters, described in Chap. XXV., Vol. II., which under proper management produce very accurate and smooth surfaces.

The grinding clamps for cylinders, fig. 1112, are also very generally employed for external cones; the grinder is cast in the same manner, in two halves, either upon the cone itself or upon one of the same angle and a little smaller diameter. The grinder, if cast of the same length as the cone, is liable to round off the smaller end, from this being more constantly exposed to the grinding action, and therefore the grinder is usually made a trifle shorter than the cone. The spring grinder, fig. 1118, is also much used for small cones; it is very nearly a counterpart of the grinder, fig. 1117, for internal cylinders, the principal difference being, that at the opposite extremity to the spring it is bowed out near the ends for the reception of the grinder, and beyond this enlargement a binding screw is added, for closing the grinder gradually upon the cone, and which at the same time serves to prevent the rods from springing sideways.

Figs. 1118.

1119.

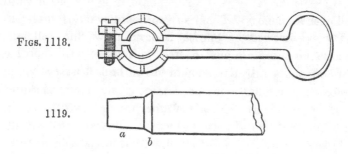

a b

In grinding the external cone the work in almost all cases revolves in the lathe, and the grinder charged with emery and water is held in the hands. The grinder is gradually twisted round to different positions, and continually traversed endways a small distance, according to the length and acuteness of the cone. The object of the short traversing motion is to distribute the emery uniformly and to keep the particles constantly shifting to different parts of the grinder, as if they were allowed to remain in the same position they would be liable to mark the work with rings. On this account much less force is applied in grinding cones than cylinders, and the grinder is lightly held in an elastic manner so as to permit the emery to roll over between the work and grinder.

At the commencement of the process the grinder should be somewhat smaller in diameter than the required cone, so as to allow for a little enlargement of the grinder, as well as the reduction of the cone, which latter should at first only enter the grinder for about three quarters to seven-eighths of its length, according to the acuteness of the cone. The abrasion of the two surfaces allows the grinder gradually to advance towards the larger end of the cone, and as this is approached the grinder is from time to time slightly closed, to compensate somewhat for the wear. As the work progresses towards completion, increased attention is required to the condition of the grinder, and when it becomes so far worn as to mark the work with rings, or that the smaller end of the cone protrudes, a new grinder is cast for the completion of the work.

In the case of two cones of different angles joining each other as in fig. 1119, a form frequently employed in lathe mandrels, the grinder cast to a counterpart form is first employed to grind both cones at the same time in order to ensure their being concentric with each other. The long and nearly cylindrical cone a, serves as a guide for applying the grinder to the short obtuse cone b, which is completed with a grinder fitting both cones, and finally the cone a is separately corrected with a single cone grinder.

By far the more accurate methods of grinding the external cone are however the employment of the end of a fixed grinder, or the edge of a revolving lap mounted in the sliding rest, while the work revolves in the lathe exactly in the manner explained on page 1237, for the production of cylindrical surfaces, except that the sliding rest is swung round to the suitable angle for the side of the cone. One of these methods is generally resorted to for works requiring the greatest accuracy, as it admits of the cone being corrected with considerable exactness, both for angle and straightness of the sides, and the circular section being derived directly from the lathe, the adjustment of the diameter is the principal object requiring attention.

The method of a fixed grinder may also be resorted to for grinding the internal cone, when the works admit of being chucked in the lathe, and the opening is of sufficient size for the admission of a rigid grinder; but conical holes are seldom so large as to admit of a revolving lap, and extreme accuracy is less frequently required in the preparation of the internal cone, as the very minute errors incidental to the ordinary process of grinding, will be partially corrected by the final grinding together of the two cones to ensure contact.

Internal cones are generally ground upon solid grinders, mostly formed of tin cast upon an iron rod and turned to the corresponding form. The best works are completed with brass grinders which from being harder retain their forms longer unimpaired and therefore leave the holes more accurate.

For short conical holes in small objects such as rings or detached collars, the grinder is mounted in the lathe, generally between centers, and the work is passed over the rod before the screw of the popit head is adjusted, but sometimes the grinder is made as a chuck to screw at once upon the lathe mandrel; this arrangement allows of the work being more readily removed. In either case the work is applied in just the same manner as for grinding the external cone. The work when small is held in the fingers, and at frequent intervals is allowed to be carried partly round by the grinder, so as continually to change its position, to compensate for any irregularity of direction in holding the work. When the hole is large and the friction is so great that the object cannot be held steadily in the hands, it is fixed in a clamp such as fig. 1112, or in the center of a pulley to serve as a handle.

Long conical holes, such as axletree boxes, are sometimes ground upon the spring grinder fig. 1120, which may be viewed as

FIG. 1120.

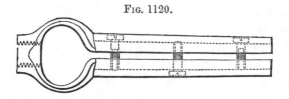

a combination of figs. 1116 and 1117, but made to screw directly upon the lathe mandrel after the manner of a chuck, and closed by two or three binding screws; the elasticity of the spring suffices for keeping the halves of the grinder distended, and the work grasped in a clamp with a double-ended lever is applied in the same manner as small objects, the workman standing in front of the grinder, the binding screws of which are gradually slackened with the progress of the work, so as to avoid the necessity for employing more than one grinder.

The conical collars of hardened steel generally employed for the bearings of lathe mandrels, as will be adverted to in the succeeding volume, are required to be made not only as accurately as possible to the same angle and diameter as the cone that is to work within the collar itself, but the axes of both bearings should also be strictly in a line with each other. In the mandrel the axes of the two cones are placed straight, almost without the possibility of error, by turning both cones in the lathe from the same centers, but a less direct mode is from necessity resorted to for ensuring the straightness of the axes of the two bearings, which are sometimes both made as detached rings, or collars of steel, fitted into cylindrical holes in the lathe head ; at other times, the mandrel works in a collar and center screw. The parallelism of the holes for the reception of the bearings is obtained by boring both holes at the one fixing, with the cutter bar described at page 569, Vol. II. The collars are turned singly in the lathe to the required cone, but a little smaller in diameter than the finished size, they are then fixed upon a mandrel revolving truly in the lathe, and the exterior turned to fit the holes in the lathe head, the steel collars are afterwards hardened and driven in. This method places the axis of the conical collar so nearly in a line with the second bearing, that the trifling correction necessary for position, is brought within the limits of the grinding necessary for fitting the mandrel into the collar, and which is effected with a grinder made nearly as a copy of the mandrel, so far as the two bearings are concerned, the one of which serves as a guide for the position of the grinder while the other bearing is being ground.

The mandrels of small lathes are usually made to work at the back end in a conical center, and at the front, through a conical collar the smaller diameter of which is outwards, and consequently in correcting the collar after it has been fixed in the lathe head, the grinder has to be inserted from the inside, between the two bearings ; the form of grinder usually employed for this purpose is represented in fig. 1121. A center screw having a cylindrical fitting in the back upright of the lathe head, is used for keeping the grinder straight, and the square end of the rod upon which the grinder is cast, passes through the conical

FIG. 1121.

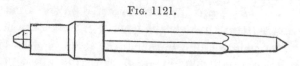

collar and is received in the square hole chuck of a lathe, by which the grinder is driven; while the end traverse for advancing the collar lengthways upon the grinder is given by the back center screw, which is supported by the popit head of the lathe employed for driving the grinder. The center screw on which the grinder revolves is screwed into a clamp, fixed on the lathe head being ground, so that the advance of this screw through its clamp traverses the lathe head upon the grinder, which revolves in one position, while the lathe head is shifted to and fro, and twisted round at all angles, to maintain a continual change in the relative positions of the grinder and work.

Sometimes instead of driving the grinder with continuous motion by the lathe, a pulley fixed on the middle of the rod of the grinder, is used to work the grinder by hand as usual; at other times a cord is wound around the pulley and led to a spring fixed overhead like a pole lathe, so as to revolve the grinder alternately backwards and forwards.

Large lathe mandrels are usually made to work through two conical collars in order to allow of wheels being fixed on the back end of the mandrel. The two conical collars are mostly ground separately in the first instance, the same as in correcting the cylindrical collars of traversing mandrels. The grinder is

FIG. 1122.

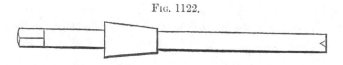

then made as in fig. 1122, with a conical grinder of tin or brass fixed upon an iron rod, the opposite end of which is turned cylindrically, and traverses through a conical plug having a central cylindrical hole that is fitted into the back collar, and serves as a guide for traversing the grinder in a straight line, while the front collar is being ground ; the back collar is afterwards ground in the same manner, a plug being fitted to the front collar as a guide.

The principal errors having been removed with the single cone grinders, the collars are further corrected in the same manner with a grinder having two brass cones, made exactly as a counterpart of the mandrel, and supplied with flour emery and water. Finally the mandrel itself is ground into the collars, first with very fine emery and oil, and lastly with oil alone for the final polish.

When the works are so large as not to be perfectly under control in the horizontal position, or that the weight of the grinder would be liable to cause the lower side of the collars to be ground in excess, the lathe head is placed vertically, and a cord attached to the grinder is passed over a pulley above and led to a counterpoise, to sustain the principal weight of the grinder. By this arrangement the irregularities of fitting in the cones can be more readily appreciated by the sense of feeling, which is principally depended upon for the condition of the work.

SECT. IV.—THE PRODUCTION OF SPHERICAL SURFACES BY ABRASION.

The grinding and polishing of spheres in hardened steel, glass, and other hard substances, after the method invented by the late Mr. Henry Guy, (at that time a workman in the employ of Holtzapffel & Co.,) is perhaps one of the most unexceptionable examples of the production of form by abrasion, as the principle being almost mathematically correct, the true spherical form is certain to be produced under proper management.

The mode is based upon the section of a perfect sphere being at every part a true circle, and if the ball be previously prepared nearly of the spherical shape, and placed within a circular grinding tool or ring of smaller diameter, so as to bear only on a narrow circular ring, upon putting the ball in rotation equally in every direction, the most prominent points of the ball will be successively reduced, until the section at all points is made truly circular, when the perfect sphere will result.

The method of fulfilling these conditions ultimately arrived at by Mr. Guy was as follows. The grinder was formed of a bar of iron or brass, equal in thickness to about one-third the diameter of the ball, and near the end of the grinder was made a conical hole, the sides of which formed an angle of about 25 degrees, and sufficiently large to allow about one-fourth of the diameter of the ball to project through the smaller side. The universal rotation of the ball within the grinding tool, upon which the whole method depends, will be explained by the diagram fig. 1123 in which A represents a large circular disk sup-

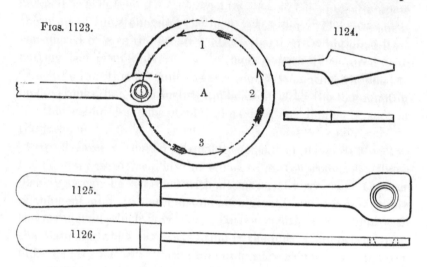

FIGS. 1123.   1124.

1125.

1126.

posed to be revolving in the direction of the arrows. If the ball be placed within the grinder, and carried round in contact with the face of the revolving disk, on the dotted line or thereabouts, the arrows will in every case represent the direction of the rotation of the ball, caused by the revolution of the disk. At 1, the ball will revolve towards the handle, at 2 perpendicularly upwards, at 3, horizontally from the handle, and so on, in fact in every position the axis of rotation of the ball will be the radius of the large disk A, and as the ball is slowly traversed around the disk, the axis of rotation will at every instant be changing in regular succession.

Two such disks are employed to rotate the ball, the interval between them being so regulated as to be exactly equal to the diameter of the ball, and they are made to travel at equal velocities in opposite directions. The disks therefore nip the ball tight, and by their simultaneous action on opposite sides they cause its rotation, notwithstanding the resistance of the grinder.

The two disks are made as wooden surface chucks about 10 inches diameter, turned quite true on the face, and fixed on two lathe heads that are mounted face to face upon the same frame or bearers, so as to bring the axes of both lathe heads in exactly the same line, with the faces of the disks parallel to each other, and at such a distance asunder as will suffice to press the ball sufficiently firm to cause its rotation. To allow of the ball being firmly held with moderate pressure, the wooden disks are required to be slightly yielding, so as to permit the ball to be somewhat embedded in the surfaces of the disks to give a better hold. Boxwood is too hard for this purpose, and beechwood answers much better when cut transversely out of large blocks, so that the end grain of the wood constitutes the sides of the disks. For polishing the balls, the disks are covered with buff leather.

The edges of the disks are turned with grooves of equal diameter for the reception of a catgut band, and in order to ensure the tension being alike upon each, it is better to employ only one band leading from two grooves on the driving-wheel to the two disks, the band being crossed on its path to the one disk and open on the other, so as to give them equal but opposite revolutions. The more rapidly the disks revolve the quicker the process will be effected, and for grinding metal balls the velocity should not be less than about 400 revolutions in the minute.

Mr. Guy proposed that one of the lathe mandrels employed should have the power of sliding endways through cylindrical bearings, like a screw mandrel lathe, in order that the disks might be kept constantly pressed against each other with uniform force, by means of a spring, or a lever and weight; but upon trial this was not found to answer, as the balls were not held sufficiently firm, and it is better to effect the required adjustment by slackening the holding-down bolt of one of the lathe heads, and advancing it bodily by slight blows of a hammer.

The grinder shown one-quarter size in figs. 1125 and 1126 is made about 15 inches long, the shaft is of iron, and small rings of brass are inserted in the square enlargement at the end, to constitute the conical grinding surface, which is broached out to the angle of about 25 degrees with the broach fig. 1124.

The cone of the grinder requires to be frequently restored

during use, as much of the truth of the result depends upon the narrowness of the surface contact of the grinder, which should be able to adapt itself readily to the curvature of the ball, notwithstanding that both the ball and grinder are continually changing in curvature, and that the ball grinds a narrow spherical seat in the grinder.

For a sphere of about one inch diameter, the bearing surface should never exceed about one-sixteenth of an inch wide. Indeed in the first attempts at grinding a sphere by this method, the process failed from a jointed grinder in halves being employed, that embraced too large a portion of the sphere, so that perfection could not be attained until the bearing surface was very much reduced.

Balls of hardened steel, to be ground truly spherical and of definite diameter, are turned while in the soft state, as nearly as possible to the spherical form under the test of a ring gage, and are left slightly larger than the finished size. The balls are afterwards hardened by inclosing them in sheet iron boxes filled with parings of horses' hoofs, or bone dust, and luted with moist clay. The whole are then heated to a cherry red, either in an open fire or closed furnace, on removal from the fire the lid of the box is knocked off, and its contents thrown bodily into cold water; the balls are not afterwards tempered.

In grinding the balls, they are placed singly within the conical hole of the grinder, a small quantity of oil and emery is then put into the space between the larger side of the cone and the ball, and the disks being put in rapid revolution, the ball and grinder are slipped in between them, while they are in motion. The grinder is held horizontally by the handle, and pressed sideways against the ball to keep the conical grinding surface equally in contact with the ball, which is at the same time slowly but uniformly traversed by the grinder around the disks, within about one inch of their edges, as of course the further the ball is kept from the center of the disks, the more rapidly it will be rotated.

After a few revolutions of the ball around the disks, the latter become slightly indented with circular grooves, which serve as guides for the path in which the ball is traversed. Care is required to keep the disks pressing against the ball sufficiently tight to cause its rotation within the grinder, or otherwise from the surfaces of the disks becoming charged with emery they will act as laps and grind facets upon the ball.

It is quite necessary that the ball should be constantly traversed around the disks with uniform motion, as should it be permitted to linger for a longer time at one part of the circle than another, the ball would be more ground at that part, and become oval. The necessary supply of emery and oil is given without removing the ball from between the disks, by keeping up the circular motion with the one hand, while a little oil is dropped upon the ball as it revolves, and the emery may be sprinkled upon it in like manner.

The grinding is continued until the ball is made truly spherical, and so near to the required size that upon trial it will barely enter the ring gage, previously prepared of the exact diameter. The final adjustment for size is given in the polishing process, which is effected with dry crocus, sometimes applied on a conical tool of boxwood of exactly the same form as the brass grinder, the revolving disks being covered with leather or cloth to prevent the ball from being scratched. But where great accuracy of size is required, this method is almost too active for the final adjustment, and the method more completely under control, is to polish the balls by rubbing them in all directions with the fingers, within a conical brass tool supplied with dry crocus. This removes the circular marks given between the disks, produces a good lustre, and allows of the adjustment for size being effected with almost any required degree of exactness.

Spheres in glass, agate or other hard substances that do not admit of being turned with cutting tools, are prepared as nearly as admissible of the spherical form by grinding them by hand after the method of the lapidary. The balls are completed by grinding them between the revolving disks, with a brass or iron grinder just the same as the hardened steel balls, except that water is employed with the emery instead of oil, partly with the view of reducing the heat occasioned by the friction, which in the case of grinding glass spheres is liable to cause them to become cracked, and therefore in grinding glass balls the velocity of the disks should be only moderate, and water should be supplied in sufficient quantity to keep the balls tolerably cool.

The glass balls are lastly polished with putty powder, applied on a wooden polishing tool, the conical surface of which is covered with wash leather, by passing the latter through the hole, and securing it around the margins with a few tacks.

The method of grinding marbles for children is described in the catalogue of grinding processes page 1078.

The spherical surfaces of lenses, are produced by grinding them in counterpart tools, or disks of metal, prepared to the same curvatures as required in the lenses, and employed as the medium for the application of the grinding and polishing powders. The tools are made in pairs, concave and convex, and are first employed mutually to correct each other's errors; as the accuracy of the surfaces of the lenses is principally dependent on the tool upon which they are ground, being accurately formed to the counterpart figure.

For the formation of the grinding tools, a concave and a convex template are first made to the radius of the curvature of the required lens. The templates of large radius, are sometimes cut out of crown glass by cementing it upon a bench, and mounting a glazier's diamond upon the end of a light radius bar, sometimes only a rod of wood, with a brad awl stuck through the rod into the bench, the distance from the diamond to the awl being the radius of the curve. The glass having been cut with the diamond, is separated, the one cut forming the concave and convex edges, which are afterwards ground together with a little emery and water, for this purpose the templates are laid upon the bench and rubbed edge to edge; one of the pieces is occasionally turned end for end to verify the curves. See Tech. Repos. 1822 page 365.

More generally however templates of large and medium radii are made out of sheet brass, the templates of long radii are cut with a strong radius bar and cutter, and those of only a few inches radii are cut in the turning lathe. The brass concave and convex gages are cut at separate operations, as it is necessary to adjust the radius to compensate for the thickness of the cutter, and the brass templates are not usually corrected by grinding, as practically it is found more convenient to fit the tools themselves together.

The templates having been made of the required radius, are used for the preparation of the grinding and polishing tools, which for convex lenses consist of a concave rough grinding tool of cast iron, called a *shell*, shown in section in fig. 1127, the wooden pattern of which is turned to the curve of the template, and the shell is left from the casting; a similar shell, turned to a radius of about three-eighths of an inch larger than the template, serves as the foundation of the polisher, the preparation of which is described in page 1267. For common glasses, that are ground several together, a convex tool of cast iron, called a *runner*, of about half an inch less radius than the templates, is also required, as the basis upon which the lenses are cemented, as shown in fig. 1129.

The most important part of the apparatus is however a pair of brass *tools*, one concave, and the other convex, made exactly to the curvature of the templates, and to fit each other as accurately as possible. The concave tool is used as the grinder for correcting the curvature of the lenses, after they have been roughly figured in the concave shell. And the convex tool is employed for producing and maintaining the true form of the concave grinding tool itself, and also that of the polisher. The pair of brass tools are represented in section in fig. 1128.

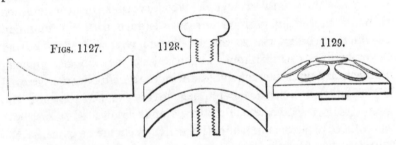

Figs. 1127.   1128.   1129.

The backs of the tools are provided with a screw exactly the same as an ordinary chuck, by which they may be fitted on the lathe mandrel, to be turned to the curvature of the templates, and by which they may also be attached to the top of a perpendicular post or pedestal, about three feet high, strongly fixed to the floor of the workshop, and carrying at the top an iron block having a vertical screw, exactly a copy of that upon the lathe mandrel.

The pair of brass tools having been turned to the curvature of the templates, they are next corrected by grinding them together; for this purpose the convex tool is fixed by its screw upon the perpendicular post, and the screw at the back of the concave tool is fitted with a wooden handle of a bulbous form, and sufficiently large to be grasped by the two hands.

The concave tool is placed upon the convex, and the two are rubbed together, first without any grinding powder, to denote by the parts brightened where they bear the hardest, as the manner in which they are ground together depends in some respects upon the nature of the general error to be corrected. Should the tools not fit each other tolerably well, the principal errors are reduced by turning until they agree nearly uniformly throughout their surfaces and touch about equally at the center and margins of the tools, the minute errors are then removed by grinding, which is usually done with emery and water, but as previously explained at page 1229, with respect to the grinding of flat tools for the parallel disks for sextants, Mr. Andrew Ross found that greater accuracy was obtained by using the emery dry. But whether wet or dry grinding be resorted to for the correction of the tools, the emery should be as uniformly distributed as possible, by rubbing it level with a piece of glass of corresponding curvature, and any excess of emery around the margin of the tool is wiped off, as there should be rather a deficiency than otherwise near the edges.

The concave tool is now placed upon the convex, and worked with a circular swinging stroke, somewhat as in rubbing the hand over the upper surface of a large ball, but instead of the motion being given by the arms alone, the body should at the same time be swung round, also in a circular path, so as to give a free bold stroke to the tool, but continually varied a little in extent and direction. Between every few strokes the operator moves a little way around the post, so as to continually change the position in which he stands, and gradually travel round the post. In every position he twists the upper tool partly round in his hands, so as by the combination of the various movements to bring the two surfaces in contact in every possible position, and rub them upon each other at all angles.

If either at the commencement, or during the process of grinding, the tools should be found to bear the hardest near the middle of the curve, the strokes are made short, and occasionally varied from the circular path to that of a narrow ellipsis, and the pressure is principally applied vertically; but if the tools bear the hardest near the edges of the curve, long bold circular strokes are taken, with the pressure principally sideways. In extreme cases the concave tool is fixed on the post, and the convex tool held in the hands is worked within it, with a swinging stroke, so as to grind the tools at the sides only; but as a general rule, the convex tool is fixed on the post in all cases, as the spherical figure may be more conveniently ground in this position.

The determining of the length and direction of the stroke, and also whether it should be circular or elliptical, are points that must be left principally to the judgment of the operator, guided in great measure by the sense of feeling; but, speaking generally, it may be said that large circular strokes increase the radius of curvature of the concave tool, from the margins being more acted upon than the center; while short elliptical strokes have the contrary effect. The curvature of the convex tool undergoes much less change, from the two modes of working, and therefore when it is desired to alter the curvature, the convex tool is first employed to alter the concave tool, and the convex is then fitted to it. The principal object aimed at is to make the tools of the true spherical figure, and to fit each other exactly, a small departure from the intended radius being in general less important than the correctness of the figure.

The glass for the lenses having been selected of suitable quality they are brought to the circular form with flat pliers called *shanks*, the jaws of which are made of soft iron that they may the more readily embed themselves upon the glass and take a firm hold; if the jaws were made of hardened steel they would be liable to slip. The pressure of the pliers applied near the edges of the glass causes it to crumble away in small fragments, and the process which is called *shanking* or *nibbling* is continued until the glasses are made circular, and of a little larger diameter than the finished size of the lenses.

They are next coated on one side with a layer of cement about half an inch thick to form a handle, by pouring the melted cement from a ladle upon the glass in small quantities, as much as will lay on the glass without running off, and as soon as it is set, a further supply is added until the cement forms a hemispherical mass, sufficiently thick to be readily grasped in the fingers.

The cement is made by mixing sifted wood ashes with melted

pitch, the essential oil of which is absorbed by the wood ashes, and the adhesiveness of the pitch is thereby reduced. The proportions are somewhat dependent on the temperature of the weather, and the quality of the pitch ; but generally about 4lbs. of wood ashes to 14lbs. of pitch are employed, and the cement if too hard and brittle is softened with hog's lard, or tallow.

The glasses are in all cases rough ground separately within the shell, fig. 1127, either with river sand and water, or coarse emery and water, until the surfaces are brought nearly to the curve of the shell. The glasses are rubbed with large circular strokes, and the shell is usually placed within a shallow tray, to catch the loose sand or emery thrown off in the grinding. The second side is rough ground in the same manner, the glass being warmed for the removal of the cement handle, which is transferred to the other side. The parallelism of the two sides is obtained by observing that the edge of the glass is left of equal thickness all round.

So far the lenses whether large or small, and of the best or common quality, are treated alike, but for grinding the glasses to the correct form in the brass tool, and also for polishing, they are operated upon either singly or several together, according to the size and degree of accuracy required in the lenses. The best lenses for the object glasses of telescopes being ground and polished singly, while on the other hand as many as four dozen of common spectacle glasses are sometimes cemented upon a runner and ground and polished at the same time. When several lenses are to be ground and polished together, the number must be such as admits of being arranged symmetrically around a central lens, as 7, 13 or 21, at other times a group of four forms the nucleus, and the numbers run 4, 14, 30. Lenses of medium quality and size are however generally ground true and polished seven at a time.

The cement at the back of the lenses is first flattened with a heated iron, and the seven lenses are then arranged with the cemented sides upwards in the concave brass tool, one lens being placed in the center, and the other six at equal distances around it, very near together but without touching. The cast iron runner is then heated just sufficiently to melt the cement, and carefully placed upon the cemented backs of the lenses. As soon as the cement is sufficiently softened to adhere firmly to the runner, the latter is cooled with a wet sponge, as the cement must be only so far fused as to fill up the spaces nearly, but not quite, level with the surface of the lenses.

The block of lenses, shown in fig. 1129, is now mounted upon the post, and ground with the concave brass tool, fig. 1128, in exactly the same manner as explained for correcting the forms of the tools themselves. About six sizes of washed emery progressively finer are employed for grinding the lenses to the true figure, or as it is called *trueing* the lens, the last size of emery being the fine powder collected after one hour's subsidence as explained at page 1055-6, and which leaves so smooth a surface, that when the lens is held between the eye and the light, it shows a semi-polish.

Of course the grinding is continued with every size of emery until all the marks made with the previous size are removed, and between every change, the brass tool, hands and block of lenses, are thoroughly washed, and wiped first with damp and afterwards with dry cloths, to remove every particle of the previous emery, which without the greatest possible care would be especially liable to lodge in the spaces between the lenses, and might near the conclusion of the work become detached, and make a scratch that would render it necessary to recommence the grinding.

The lenses have next to be polished, for ordinary lenses of medium size, the polisher is made by warming a cast iron shell, and coating it uniformly about one quarter of an inch thick with melted cement. A piece of thick woollen cloth, such as was formerly used for watchmen's coats, is cut to the size of the polisher, and unless the cloth is old and the nap worn off, it is seared with a heated iron. The cloth is placed on the cement in the polisher, and pressed into form by working the brass convex tool within it; the pores of the cloth are then filled up with putty powder prepared as explained on page 1088. The putty powder is mostly sifted through lawn, and enclosed in a box having a lid perforated with small holes. The putty powder is shook uniformly over the cloth, and moistened by sprinkling a few drops of water over it; the powder is then worked into the pores of the cloth with the brass convex tool, additional powder being applied until the surface is made quite level, and it is worked quite smooth with the tool; from two to three hours being generally required for making up a polisher of 8 or 9 inches diameter. Kerseymere is sometimes used for small lenses instead of the thick cloth, principally because the face of the cloth being finer it is sooner filled up with the putty powder.

The polisher when completed is placed upon the block of lenses, still fixed on the post, and worked with wide and narrow elliptical strokes, the operator continually walking around the post the same as for grinding. The point requiring the principal attention is the degree of moisture of the putty powder, which should be only moderate; if too wet the putty is apt to run loose upon the polisher, which produces a curdled surface so difficult to remove that when once produced it is generally necessary to return to the fine grinding. If upon the other hand the polisher is allowed to become too dry, it is indicated by the edges of the lenses cutting up the surface of the putty powder, which then works with an unpleasant scratching action that will be immediately detected.

The proper degree of moisture of the putty powder, is indicated by its being in a rather stiff saponaceous state, and during the principal portion of the polishing, the surface should present a partially glazed appearance. When the surface becomes almost entirely glazed, a little more water is sprinkled on it; but towards the conclusion of the polishing less moisture is used, and the polisher is allowed to become as nearly dry as is consistent with safety, the glazed appearance then covers almost the whole surface.

During the polishing the pressure should be very moderate, or the lenses will partially sink into the surface of the polishing tool, and become rounded at those parts of the edges which are unsupported by the neighbouring lenses. This evil may be partially remedied by cutting off a portion of the circumference in the manner alluded to on page 1229. But in order to avoid the rounding as much as possible, the more accurate the lenses are required to be, the less the pressure that is employed in rubbing them on the cloth polisher.

The edges of the lenses are finally ground circular, and of course the axes of the lenses should when put into the tubes of the instruments, be perfectly parallel with the axis of the tubes; to attain this they are cemented upon a chuck in the lathe, and before the cement has set the lathe is put in revolution, and the reflection of any fixed object such as a candle, or a bar of the window, is watched, and the lens is adjusted until the image appears strictly stationary, notwithstanding the revolution of the lens, and which shows the axis of the lens and that of the mandrel of the lathe to be in agreement. The edge is then ground circular with a piece of brass supplied with emery and water. The piece of brass being placed beneath the lens, and gradually elevated by a screw tapped through one end, while the other rests upon any convenient prop on the lathe bearers.

Concave lenses are ground and polished in the same manner as convex lenses, except that they are fixed in the concave tools and ground upon the convex, which as before mentioned is always the lower tool, when several glasses are operated upon together.

In Mr. C. Varley's lathe for grinding and polishing lenses and specula,* instead of the lower tools being mounted upon a fixed post, they are mounted upon a revolving axis, placed vertically. This considerably expedites the process, which is conducted in exactly the same manner in all other respects, but the necessity for walking around the lower tool is removed. It is however generally considered that the method of grinding lenses of medium and large sizes, with a tool mounted on a rapidly revolving axis, is less accurate than when the tool is fixed; and that when circular motion is given to the tool, it should be so slow as only to give change of position, leaving the abrasion to be effected principally by the elliptical or circular strokes.

In manufactories where large quantities of common lenses are ground and polished, these operations are principally effected by machinery. The block of lenses is mounted upon a slowly revolving axis, placed vertically, and the upper tool has an eccentric motion given to it, by means of a small crank fixed on the lower end of a second vertical axis, that is placed a little on one side of the central line of the lower axis. A pin, fixed in the center of the back of the upper grinding tool, enters a socket in the crank, and the revolution of the latter causes the upper tool to describe small circles, which, combined with the slow revolution of the block of lenses, causes every point of the grinder

---

* Described in a communication to the Society of Arts. See Trans., Vol. XLIX., page 91.

to describe epicycloids upon the surface of the lenses, much the same as in the circular strokes employed in grinding lenses by hand. The radius of the crank admits of adjustment to give various degrees of eccentricity to the upper tool, and the pressure is regulated either by a spring, or by adjusting the weight of the grinder.

As previously mentioned, the best lenses for object glasses of telescopes are ground and polished singly by hand; in this case the lens whether concave or convex is kept in the hand, and the grinding tool is fixed. The glass if small is held by a cement handle, and if large is cemented to a metal handle, as wood is liable to swell with the moisture.

The grinding is performed in exactly the same manner as when several lenses are ground together, but greater care is taken with every successive step, and these lenses are in general polished upon a piece of thick silk, the kind known as lutestring being preferred.

The silk cut to the width of about seven eighths the diameter of the lens, is stretched across the middle of the brass tool, and the lens is rubbed backwards and forwards in straight lines along the silk, and instead of the operator walking around the post, the lens is continually twisted round in the hand, and at the same time traversed gradually sideways until the center of the lens is brought to the edge of the silk, when the direction of the traverse is reversed. The single thickness of silk stretched across the tool assumes the form more correctly than the cloth polisher, and the lens is traversed partly off the silk in order that the center may be acted upon equally with the margin.

The putty powder and water with which the silk polisher is supplied, are kept ready mixed in a corked bottle to avoid the contamination of dust, and at the time of application the bottle is shaken up, and its contents allowed to subside for a few seconds, a small quantity of the water is then taken out with a clean stick and thrown upon the polisher, and thus only the suspended portions of the putty powder are used. The most carefully finished lenses are polished on a pitch tool prepared in the same manner as for polishing specula.

It has been stated at page 1265, that with ordinary lenses accuracy of spherical form is of much greater importance than the radius of curvature, but in making the object glasses of achromatic telescopes it is requisite to be enabled to measure accurately the radii of curvature of the lenses, which are first tried experimentally, and afterwards made as nearly as possible to the radii obtained by calculation, in order to correct the chromatic and spherical aberration.

In 1841 Mr. Andrew Ross, (from whose practice most of the foregoing particulars on grinding and polishing lenses have been derived,) received the silver medal from the Society of Arts for his instrument, called a spherometer, for measuring the curvature of the grinding tools. The instrument is shown in fig. 1130, and the following description by Mr. Ross is extracted from Vol. 53 of the Transactions of the Society:—

"During a series of experiments instituted many years since by Professor Barlow for verifying his methods of computing the curvatures of an achromatic object glass, in which I was practically engaged, it became necessary to ascertain with considerable accuracy the radii of curvature of the tools on which the lenses were ground. The method then adopted was that of grinding in the tool the edge of a plate of glass, till the edge accurately fitted the tool, and formed what is called a template. This was laid upon a board in which two pins were inserted, and the template, guided by the pins, was made to describe an arc of great extent. The chord and versed sine of this large arc being carefully drawn and measured afforded data for calculating the radius, by the well-known formula $2 R = \dfrac{(\frac{c}{2})^2}{v} + v$,

where R is the radius, c the chord, and v, the versed sine. This, though obviously not a very precise method, was sufficiently correct for verifying the theoretical deductions, and it was as accurate as the processes then employed in working the glasses for telescopes."

"With the view of improving these processes, and rendering their results more certain, I have, for more than two years, been carrying on a course of experiments to discover the causes of the discrepancies which were known to exist between theory and practice in this branch of optics. Every improvement in the processes rendered it indispensable to determine more correctly slight variations in the radii of curvature, to accomplish which I was led to invent the instrument which I now offer to the notice of the Society.

"Its principle and general features are explained in the accompanying sketch, where T, T, represents a portion of the convex tool to be measured ; and as the tools are of necessity made

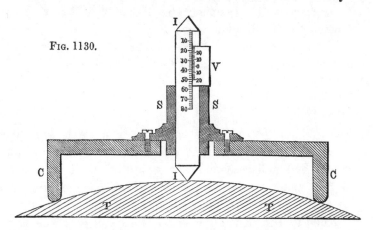

Fig. 1130.

in pairs we require to measure only one of each. A short cylinder C, C, nearly closed at one end has its edges very accurately turned and ground to a portion of a circle whose radius is known. In the cylinder is attached a carefully made square socket S, S, in which fits and moves the square index bar I, I, the extremities of which are finished with hard steel cones. Upon these conical terminations as centers the circular edge of the cylinder C, C, is ultimately turned and ground, so that all errors of workmanship in fitting and fixing the socket to the cylinder are completely obviated. The index bar I, I, is divided on one face to $\frac{1}{50}$th of an inch, and a vernier V, is secured to the socket by which it may be read to $\frac{1}{1000}$th of an inch, or, by estimation, to $\frac{1}{2000}$th.

"If the edge of the cylinder had been made square instead of circular, then the clear diameter of the cylinder would have been in all cases the value of the chord ; but the difficulty of preserving a square angular edge perfectly true, and the different manner in which such a form would lie on spheres of small and large radii, induced me to adopt the circular edge, by which of course the value of the measured chord varies with every change of curvature in the tool." To obtain the value of the radius without determining the value of the varying chord Mr. A. Ross devised the formula $R = \dfrac{v^2 + a^2}{2v} - r.$

a = The known semidiameter, or half the distance between the centers of the small circles which form the edge (which is determined by gently rubbing the cylinder on a perfectly flat surface and measuring the diameter of the ring thus marked on the circular edge).

v = The apparent versed sine as indicated by the vernier.

r = The known radius of the edge of the spherometer.

R = The radius of the tool sought.

Diminutive microscopic lenses, whose diameter is sometimes as small as from one quarter, to one twentieth of an inch, are also ground and polished singly, as the radius of curvature is in general too small to allow of several being grouped together. The templates are made as small disks of steel, with slender stems turned in the lathe; for lenses, the radii of whose curvature are 5, 10 or 20 hundredths of an inch the diameters of the disks are 10, 20 or 40 hundredths. They are made with square edges and when hardened are applied diametrically as the finishing tools for turning the small metal cups or concave grinding tools. For measuring the diameters of the disks they are applied either in the sector gage, or one of the sliding gages often used for measuring the diameter of wire, and graduated decimally for reading the width of the opening to the hundredth or thousandth of an inch.

The cups when turned are charged with emery, and put in rapid revolution in the lathe, which for these minute lenses is in general very small, and worked with the drill bow. The lens is cemented with shell-lac upon a small wooden stick, and held against the grinding tool with a continual change of angle, the end of the stick being moved in the arc of a circle, while it is at the same time twisted on its axis.

The same succession of emeries is used as for grinding the larger lenses, but the polishing is usually done with bees-wax hardened with fine crocus, the wax is melted, and a sufficient quantity of the crocus stirred in to make it so hard that when cold the finger nail will only just indent it. The smaller the lenses the harder the wax is made, as it should be of such a consistence that with moderate pressure the wax will yield sufficiently to assume the form of the lens, and at the same time be so hard as to retain the figure during the polishing. This composition has also been recommended for larger lenses, but is found to be less suitable than the pitch polisher, as when sufficiently hard to retain its figure, the adhesion is too great to be completely under the control of the fingers.

The brass cups for the polishing tools of small lenses, are turned in the lathe of a little larger radius than the grinding tool, and the surface is roughened that it may the better hold the wax, the tool is then heated, and the melted wax poured in, and when cold is either moulded to the form with a convex tool, or turned in the lathe, first with a thin scraping tool, and afterwards finished with a circular disk, just as in turning the grinding tool. In polishing the lens the surface of the wax is kept constantly wet with fine crocus and water, applied with a feather, and the lens is held in the same manner as for grinding. To separate the lenses from the runner or handle, they are warmed sufficiently to soften the shell-lac, and to prevent scratching the lenses in removing the last particles of cement, the latter is dissolved in spirits of wine.

The grinding and polishing of specula for reflecting telescopes requires the greatest possible amount of accuracy and care, and is by far the most difficult of all the processes of grinding and polishing for the production of form. The perfection of the refracting telescope is in great measure limited by the difficulty of grinding and polishing the lenses to the correct spherical figure, but an amount of error that would be quite passable in the best lenses, would be altogether inadmissible in the specula of large reflecting telescopes, consequently a very high degree of accuracy of form is essential, and at the same time a high polish is of necessity required to produce a reflecting surface. The ordinary difficulties of producing very accurate and highly finished surfaces are also increased by the untractable nature of the alloy of which speculums are formed.

Some remarks on the composition of speculum metal have been offered at page 270 of the first volume of this work, and other particulars on the method of casting specula are given in the foot note, pages 371-2, and also in the Appendix, note F, page 462. This interesting subject will be here followed up by some observations on the mode by which the castings, whether of small or large size, are ground and polished to adapt them to the telescope.

The process of grinding and polishing specula of small size by hand will be first described, and the application of machinery to the figuration of specula of large and medium sizes, will be afterwards adverted to. The hand process is subject to small variations in the practice of different individuals, but these variations are made principally in matters of detail that do not affect the general method, or materially influence the result, and are therefore omitted from the description to avoid unnecessary complication.

In grinding specula by hand, the same general method of manipulation is adopted as for grinding the best concave lenses, that is convex tools formed of the same curvature as the required specula are fixed upon a vertical post, and the work is rubbed upon the tool with circular and elliptical strokes in all directions, while the operator continually walks around the post to change the angle of the strokes.

The speculum after having been carefully annealed, is attached by the cement made of pitch and wood-ashes to a metal back, to support it during the working, and serve for the attachment of the wooden handle. The back is made from two-thirds to three-fourths of the diameter of the speculum, and its face is made concave to exactly fit the convex side of the speculum. The back has in the center a screw by which it can be mounted on a lathe to make the edge of the speculum circular, first by holding a fine file to the revolving edge, and afterwards either a metal grinder supplied with emery, or a piece of blue polishing stone.

A pair of brass templates are prepared to the exact radius required in the speculum, in the same manner as for lenses; but they are more carefully fitted together. The rough face of the speculum left from casting is sometimes removed on a common grindstone, turned as described on page 1108-9, nearly to fit the concave template. At other times the speculum is rough ground with coarse emery, on an iron or pewter tool fixed on the post. This grinding is continued until any holes in the surface of the casting are removed, and the face is made quite bright.

The smooth grinding is next effected with fine emery upon a convex pewter tool, turned exactly to fit the template. This tool is usually made circular and slightly larger than the speculum. But the Rev. J. Edwards recommends that the form should be elliptical, in order that the same tool may serve for the foundation of the polisher; this is however not very important. The smooth grinding is continued with fine emery until the face of the speculum is brought very nearly to the true curve. But however fine the emery may be, it is very liable to break up the surface of speculum metal into small holes, notwithstanding the greatest care, and therefore as soon as the speculum has been brought to a nearly true figure, the smooth grinding is discontinued, to avoid the risk of depreciating the surface.

The face of the speculum is next very carefully ground to a fine surface, and as true a figure as possible, upon a bed of hones which is made of small pieces of either blue polishing stone, or Water-of-Ayr stone, cemented upon a pewter tool with pitch and wood ashes. The stones should be carefully selected as homogeneous as possible, and sawn into blocks about three quarters of an inch cube, the tool is warmed to ensure the hold of the cement, which is then melted and spread uniformly over the surface, the stone cubes are carefully arranged upon the tool in straight lines about one-eighth of an inch asunder, and if the stones are of unequal hardness, it is necessary to scatter the hard and soft pieces as equally as possible, in order that the bed of hones may wear uniformly, the stones should not however differ materially either in hardness or grain, otherwise the correct figure of the speculum will not be attained.

After the stones are arranged in their places and slightly pressed into the cement, the interstices are filled with melted cement to within about a quarter of an inch of the face. The general surface of the bed of hones is then turned very carefully to the curve of the template; to avoid accident it may be roughed out with the ordinary sliding rest into the form of a shallow cone, as the convexity required is very slight.

The bed of hones is used with very little water, and cuts smoothly, so that the roughness left by the emery may be entirely removed, and the speculum brought to a very good surface. At the first commencement it appears to act very slowly, but after the principal prominences are reduced it acts more quickly. Great importance in the figuration of the speculum is attached to the proper management of the bed of hones, which is applied with circular and elliptical strokes, exactly the same as the other tools. The Rev. Mr. Edwards says, the bed of hones should be of a circular figure, and but very little larger than the metal intended to be figured upon it. "If the tool is made considerably larger than the metal, it will grind the metal perpetually into a larger sphere, and by no means of a good figure, if the metal and tool are of the same size exactly, the metal will work truly spherical, but it is apt to shorten its focus less and less, unless the metal and tool are worked alternately upwards, it had therefore better be made about one-twentieth part larger than the mirror, when it will not alter its focus."

The smoothing with the bed of hones is continued until the face of the speculum is brought to a very true and fine surface, uniformly bright, it is then put into the tube of the telescope, and tried as to sphericity and reflection, and any errors of figure that may be thus detected are removed by returning to the use of the bed of hones as often as may be requisite. The surface is made as perfect as possible with the hones, in order to leave but very little to be effected with the polisher, as should the polishing be long continued it is liable to depreciate the figure of the speculum.

Specula are polished on metal blocks coated with pitch, or a combination of pitch and resin, materials that are employed on account of their inelasticity.

The degree of hardness of the pitch, and its perfect freedom from all impurities, are matters of primary importance. For removing the impurities, the pitch is carefully washed with water and when melted, strained through linen. It is then thickened by boiling it slowly, until it is of such a consistence that when cold it will just admit of being slightly indented with the finger nail. Sometimes the pitch is hardened by the addition of about an equal quantity of resin, and this compound has the advantage of being less brittle than when pitch of equal hardness is used, and is therefore less liable to chip in the polishing. Should the pitch be made too hard, it may be softened with a little tallow.

The Earl of Rosse employed resin, melted and mixed with about one-fifth its weight of spirits of turpentine to soften it, this was adopted on account of the difficulty of obtaining the pitch free from gritty particles. But whether pitch or resin be employed, the hardness requires to be adjusted with great care.

If the pitch is too hard it will not readily take the figure of the speculum, and if too soft it will not sufficiently retain the figure.

In consequence of the different qualities of various samples of pitch and resin, no regular proportions can be adopted, and the degree of hardness must be decided experimentally in every case.

The form of the polisher is also a matter of considerable importance, the face of the speculum should be polished, not strictly spherical, but slightly parabolical. Mr. Mudge obtained an approximation to the parabolical form by first polishing the speculum as truly spherical as possible, and at the last finish giving the speculum a few large circular strokes upon the round polisher, so as to increase the radius of curvature near the margin. *See* Trans. Royal Soc., Vol. LXVII.

The elliptical polisher introduced by the Rev. John Edwards, and first described in the "Nautical Almanack" for 1787, will however give a much nearer approach to the parabolical form, without any other than straight or elliptical strokes in all directions. Mr. Edwards speaking of the proportions of the ellipse says, "for common foci and apertures, viz. from two-and-a-half to nine-and-a-half focus or 3·8 inches in diameter to eighteen inches focus the diameters should be as ten to nine. The shortest diameter of the ellipse being accurately the same as the diameter of the metal, and the longest diameter of the ellipse to the shortest diameter as ten to nine." Mr. Edwards also recommends that for speculums having a hole through the center, the polisher should also have a hole through it, of the same size or somewhat less than the hole in the speculum, and he adds, " I have always found that small mirrors without any hole in the middle, will polish much better and the figure will be more correct, if the polisher has a hole in the middle of it."

The Earl of Rosse, among his numerous experiments on the grinding and polishing of specula, tried this form of polisher, and expresses himself as follows :—" The experiments to which I have alluded were made with the elliptic polisher of Mr. Edwards, a contrivance in my opinion possessing more merit than has usually been ascribed to it. I found that a speculum of four inches aperture and eighteen inches radius, after having been polished by hand as truly spherical as I could make it, was invariably improved by working it on the elliptic polisher."

The polisher, generally made of pewter or lead, is turned on the face to the true curve of the speculum, but left rough in order to hold the cement. It is then warmed, and the melted pitch or resin is very uniformly spread over its surface about one-eighth of an inch in thickness, and when the pitch is sufficiently cooled to retain the impression of the finger, the speculum is dipped in water and pressed firmly upon the pitch as in taking the impression of a seal. Owing to the slow conducting power of the pitch, there will be no danger of the speculum being cracked by the heat, if the temperature of the pitch dees not exceed about 80 degrees, although a slight difference in the temperature of any quickly conducting substance, if placed directly upon the speculum, would be almost certain to cause a crack.

When the polisher has been moulded to the form of the speculum, the rough edges are pared away from the margin, and also around the central hole, if the polisher have one. The surface of the pitch is then divided into small squares by making grooves quite through its thickness with a heated knife, to allow of the polisher more readily adapting itself to the surface of the speculum.

The thickness of the coat of pitch is partly dependent on the size of the speculum, and partly on the hardness of the pitch: the hardness and thickness of the pitch requiring to be so adjusted, that the polisher will always yield to the surface of the speculum, so as exactly to fit it during the whole process. If the layer of pitch is too thin, it cannot expand laterally to enable it to ply to the surface of the speculum ; and if too thick, it will expand so readily as not to retain the figure.

Oxide of iron, prepared as explained on page 1082, is in general employed for the polishing of specula. Sometimes the oxide of tin is used ; but it is considered to give a whiter polish, that is less reflecting. The powder is kept mixed with water in a vial, and applied in the same manner as the polishing powder for lenses; but it is better to employ at the commencement as much of the polishing powder as is necessary for the completion of the polish, and if a further quantity is required, it should be applied as sparingly as possible.

The speculum is worked on the polisher with straight or elliptical strokes, the operator continually moving around the post to change the angle. Sufficient pressure must be uniformly applied, to keep the polisher fitted to the face of the speculum. After the rubbing has been continued some time, the polisher and speculum both become slightly warmed by the friction; and if the pitch was originally rather too hard to copy the figure of the speculum perfectly, the increased warmth will soften the pitch, which will then ply well to the speculum, and the polishing will go on satisfactorily; but if the pitch becomes too soft, the figure of the speculum will be depreciated, and consequently great care is required to maintain the temperature of the polisher as uniform as possible, and just sufficient to keep the pitch in good working condition. Sometimes the polisher is very slightly warmed before applying it to the speculum.

The method of grinding and polishing specula by hand is at all times very difficult, and the results very uncertain, even with those of four or five inches diameter; as although it is comparatively easy to figure the specula so accurately to the general form that no errors can be detected by mechanical means, yet, when tried in the telescope, it frequently happens that so many minute errors are presented in the speculum, that the reflection appears quite undefined, and of course, in this condition, the speculum is unfit for its intended purpose.

The principal sources of error apparently inseparable from hand-polishing are, the absence of exact control in regulating the lengths and directions of the strokes, irregular increase of temperature in the speculum and polisher, unavoidably caused by the friction; and also the unequal pressure of the hand. All these difficulties rapidly increase with an enlargement of size; and a speculum of six or eight inches diameter is perhaps as large as can, with the utmost care, be produced by hand with the required accuracy. Larger specula have occasionally been polished by hand; but in the majority of instances it has ultimately proved that the increased incorrectness of defining power, has to a considerable extent counterbalanced the advantages derived from an increase of diameter.

With the view of avoiding the uncertainties of the hand-process, the Earl of Rosse constructed a machine for grinding and polishing specula, in which the different motions were susceptible of separate adjustments, and were all under complete control. A sketch of this machine was published in Sir D. Brewster's Journal for October, 1828. The machine was subsequently improved and enlarged, so as to be capable of working a speculum of three feet diameter; and from an experience of many years, during which specula were polished with it many hundred times with great accuracy, it was found perfectly successful in producing large specula with a degree of precision quite unattainable by hand, even by accident.

The machine is shown in fig. 1132, copied from his Lordship's paper on the reflecting telescope, published in the Philosophical Transactions of the Royal Society for 1840, from which the

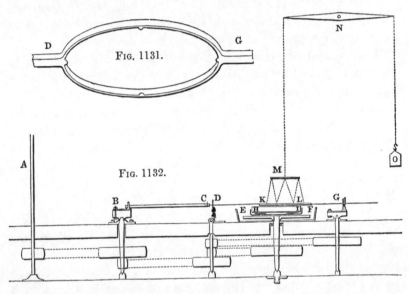

Fig. 1131.

Fig. 1132.

annexed description is also extracted:—" A is a shaft connected with a steam-engine; B, an eccentric, adjustable by a screwbolt, to give any length of stroke from 0 to 18 inches; C, a joint; D, a guide; E F, a cistern for water, in which the speculum revolves; G, another eccentric, adjustable, like the first, to any length of stroke from 0 to 18 inches. The bar D G passes through a slit, and therefore the pin at G necessarily turns on its axis in the same time as the eccentric. H I is the speculum in its box, immersed in water to within one inch of its surface; and K L, the polisher, which is of cast iron, and weighs about two and a half hundred weight. M is a round disk of wood, connected with the polisher by strings hooked to it in six places, each two-thirds of the radius from the centre. At M there is a swivel and hook, to which a rope is attached connecting the whole with the lever N, so that the polisher presses upon the speculum with a force equal to the difference between its own weight and that of the counterpoise O. For a speculum three feet diameter I make the counterpoise ten pounds lighter than the polisher. The bar D G fits the polisher nicely, but without tightness, so that the polisher turns freely round, usually about once for every fifteen or twenty revolutions of the speculum, and it is prevented by four guards from accidentally touching the speculum, and from pressing upon the polisher by the two guides through which its extremities pass. In fig. 1131 this bar is on a larger scale. I have used a variety of contrivances for connecting the machinery with the polisher; but the one I have described is by far the best. The wheel B makes, when polishing a three-feet speculum, sixteen revolutions in a minute; to polish a smaller speculum, the velocity is increased by changing the pulley on the the shaft A. The machine is in a room at the bottom of a high tower, and doors can be opened in the successive floors, so that a dial-plate of a watch placed perpendicularly over the speculum can be examined at any moment. The dial-plate is attached to a mast, so as to be much higher than the tower, and about ninety feet from the speculum; and a small flat metal and eye-piece, with its proper adjustments, completes the arrangements for a Newtonian telescope."

The machine is driven by flat leather bands, as shown in the figure, an inspection of which will readily explain the action of the machine. The cast iron polisher is used first with emery and water for the grinding, and is afterwards coated with resinous cement for polishing, the intermediate process of the bed of hones not being required with the machine. No material difficulty was experienced in grinding the speculum to the spherical form; but some adjustments are required for obtaining the parabolical figure. The elliptical polisher of Mr. Edwards, although so valuable for figuring small specula by hand, was found to fail with large specula, from the radius of curvature being increased too rapidly near the edge. Speaking of this adjustment, the Earl of Rosse says:—

"Having observed that when the extent of the motions of the polishing machine were in certain proportions to the diameter of the speculum, its focal length gradually and regularly increased, that fact suggested another mode of working an approximate parabolical figure. If we suppose a spherical surface, under the operation of grinding and polishing, gradually to change into one of longer radius, it is very evident that, during the change, at no one instant of time will it be actually spherical, and the abrasion of the metal will be more rapid at each point as it is more distant from the center of the *face*. When, however, the focal length neither increases nor diminishes, the abrasion will become uniform over the whole surface, producing a spherical figure. According, however, as the focal length (the actual amount of abrasion during a given time being given) increases more or less rapidly, the nature of the curve will vary, and we might conceive it possible, having it in our power completely to control the rate at which the focal length increases, so to proportion the rate of increase as to produce a surface approximating to that of the paraboloid. Of course, the chances against obtaining an exact paraboloid are infinitely great, as an infinite number of curves may pass between the parabola and its circle of curvature, and it is vain to look for a guide in searching for the proper one in calculations founded on the principles of exact science, as the effect of friction in polishing is not conformable to any known law; still from a number of experiments it might be possible to deduce an empirical formula practically valuable: this I have endeavoured to accomplish."

" The weight of the polisher was constant, being the least possible consistent with its working properly, viz., ten pounds for a speculum three feet diameter.

" The distance of the counterpoising lever would obviously influence the curve; that I have regarded as constant also, viz. twelve feet; as also, in all my most recent experiments the length of stroke of the first eccentric B, which was one-third of the diameter of the speculum; the only variable quantity was therefore the stroke of the second eccentric G.   Under these circumstances, the most accurate determination at which I have been enabled to arrive is, that when the stroke of the second eccentric G is such as to communicate a lateral motion to the polisher equal to about ·27 of the diameter of the speculum, the curve will be nearly parabolic." The figure of the speculum is tested during the grinding and polishing, by observing the reflection of the watch-dial, and the adjustment of the length of stroke admits of being made with such accuracy, that the three feet speculum

" with its whole aperture, is thrown perceptibly out of focus by a motion of the eye-piece, amounting to less than the thirtieth of an inch : and even with a single lens of an eighth of an inch focus, giving a power of 2592, the dots on a watch-dial are still in some degree defined."

Much difficulty was experienced in the management of the resinous composition for the surface of the polisher, the necessity for increasing the thickness of the composition in proportion to the size of the speculum was in itself sufficient to prevent great accuracy being attained. This was first endeavoured to be overcome by dividing the surface of the composition with a heated iron into squares, but although this greatly improved the figure of the speculum by allowing of the lateral expansion of a thin layer of the resinous composition, it was found that the spaces soon filled up, and the same difficulty then returned. This defect was entirely remedied by dividing the iron disk itself instead of the cement. Several polishers were made on this construction, in which the arrangement and dimensions of the grooves were varied, but the form ultimately preferred is shown in figs. 1133 and 1134, which represent the face and

FIG. 1133.   FIG. 1134.

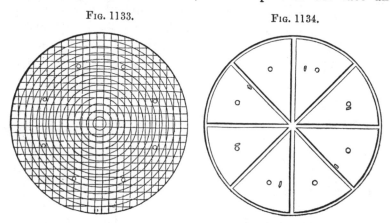

back views of the polisher. " The circular grooves were turned with the slide rest, and are three-eighths of an inch deep and one quarter wide, leaving bands of continuous surface one quarter of an inch wide. The grooves at right angles are about one inch and a quarter distant, one quarter of an inch wide and half an inch deep, cut with the circular saw. The speculum was of course truly ground with the polisher first, and then

s 2

the layer of resinous composition applied, the grooves remaining empty.

There was still a difficulty with respect to the hardness of the resinous composition; on the one hand it is essential to the truth of the general figure that the composition should be soft enough to expand laterally to enable it to fit the speculum, on the other hand the composition is required to be as hard as is consistent with the polishing powder being able to embed itself in its surface, in order that the face of the speculum may be equally acted upon by the polisher, notwithstanding minute differences in the texture of the metal at different parts. The Earl of Rosse found that the two properties apparently inconsistent with each other, could be imparted to the polisher at the same time, simply by using the resinous composition of two degrees of hardness, so as to form two very thin strata, the outer one being the harder.

For the preparation of the composition " common resin is melted, and when nearly boiling, spirit of turpentine is added to it, perhaps about one-fifth of its weight; but resin varies so much in quality, that there is no guide except trial. When the mixture has been incorporated by stirring, a cold piece of iron is to be immersed in it, and then placed for some minutes in a vessel of water, at a temperature of $55°$; if then a moderate pressure of the nail makes a decided impression without splintering, it is of a proper hardness for the first layer on the polisher, and only requires to be strained through canvass."

" For the second layer, it is mixed with one fourth of wheat flour, which by increasing its tenacity and diminishing its adhesiveness, prevents that accident so much complained of by practical men, viz., the separation of minute particles of pitch from the polisher, which afterwards run loose between the polisher and the speculum. It is to be boiled till the water of the flour has been expelled, and the mixture becomes clear, and the boiling further continued till some of the turpentine has been driven off, and the mixture has become so hard, that at a temperature of $55°$, a very strong pressure of the nail makes but a slight impression: it is still too soft, and I then add to it an equal weight of resin; it will then be hard enough to produce a very true surface and at the same time, soft enough to suffer the particles of polishing powder to embed themselves, and consequently to produce a very fine black polish. Whenever the resinous mixture is remelted, I suspend the vessel to the beam of a scale, counterpoise it, and take care to apply the heat so gradually as not to drive off any of the turpentine, which is immediately perceptible by the disturbance of the equilibrium."

" To apply the resin, the polisher is first heated to about 150° and the soft mixture laid on with a large flat brush, to about the thickness of about one-thirtieth, or one twenty-fifth of an inch ; it is then suffered to cool to about 100°, and the hard mixture applied in the same way and to about the same thickness. When the temperature has sunk to 80°, the polisher is placed on the speculum previously covered with peroxide of iron and water, of about the consistence of thin cream."

The Earl of Rosse found that the quality of the polish which yields the maximum of defining power is that technically called a black polish, provided a very fine grain is perceptible when the speculum is placed near a window. A speculum may be polished so that its surface appears without grain like quicksilver, but it is necessary for this purpose to employ a softer resinous cement than appears consistent with a very true surface, and the Earl of Rosse considers the best chance of improving the polish would be to search for some polishing substance consisting of smaller particles than the fine peroxide of iron, so as to produce a grain not exceeding the magnitude which theory has assigned as that of an undulation of light.

As shown in fig. 1132, the speculum revolves face upwards within the water cistern E, F, and this cistern being nearly filled with water kept at a temperature of 55° no unequal expansion of the speculum from increase of temperature can take place, and the pitch being also maintained at the same temperature as that at which it was first adjusted, does not become softened during the polishing as in the hand process.

In grinding and polishing the gigantic speculum of 6 feet diameter, the Earl of Rosse employed the same general arrangement of apparatus as that used for the 3 feet speculum; but from the increased dimensions, some modifications were required, the most important of which were noticed in a lecture on large reflecting telescopes, delivered by the Astronomer Royal before the Astronomical Society, and the substance of which was published in their Memoirs for March, 1849. From this, it appears that, in figuring the 6 feet speculum, the circular grooves in the cast-iron polisher were omitted, and the straight grooves at right angles were made about 1 inch deep, and 2 inches asunder, so as to divide the surface into squares. The weight of the polisher was uniformly supported at twelve points, the piece M, fig. 1132, being made triangular, with a pulley at each corner; a cord was passed over every pulley, and each end of the cord supported the middle of a straight lever, the ends of which were attached to the polisher.

In the rough grinding, the great weight of the iron disk, and the brittle nature of the speculum metal, rendered the placing of the grinder upon the mirror highly dangerous, as the slightest jar of the grinder upon the speculum would have been liable to break the latter. To avoid this risk, a number of thin wooden wedges were placed upon the margin of the speculum; the polisher was slowly lowered upon the wedges, and then, by degrees, they were gently withdrawn.

In the machine shown in fig. 1132, the bar, D G, passing through the fixed guide, D, at one end, and through the revolving guide, G, at the other, communicates a slow lateral motion to the grinder, alternately to the right and left. " But as, in the ordinary crank motion, the duration of the strokes at the extreme right and left would be too great, the wheel on the spindle of this grinding crank is elliptical, the proportion of its axes being about three to one; its angular motion is, therefore, unequal; and the strokes are thus made to dwell a shorter time near the extreme right and left, and a longer time near the center."

In polishing the speculum, it was found that not only should the temperature of the air in the polishing room be maintained nearly uniform during the process, in order to prevent the irregular expansion of the speculum, but also that it was essential that the degree of moisture in the air should be such, that the wet polishing powder should gradually dry at the proper rate. The polishing is therefore not attempted when the air in the room is too damp, and should the air be too dry, it is moistened by a jet of steam. After the process had been continued about eight hours, the polisher is removed, and a fresh application is made of the polishing powder mixed with " ammonia soap," a substance formed by treating common soap with ammonia. This dries more rapidly than the powder mixed with water alone, and the polishing is continued until the surface of the metal is very nearly dry, the process is then considered to be completed, and the polisher is taken off the speculum to allow of its inspection.

In the figuration of small specula by hand, the metal is usually attached by cement to a temporary back, which serves as the support during the grinding and polishing, and is removed before the speculum is placed in the telescope, but even with small specula there is always some risk of distorting or breaking the speculum in the act of detaching the back, and it is therefore at all times the better practice, to form the back in such a manner, that it may remain permanently attached to the speculum, and constitute its bed in the telescope. Larger specula, unless uniformly supported at all times, are liable to flexure, which would destroy the accuracy of figure given by grinding; it is therefore of the first importance that the larger specula should be ground and polished in the same bed that is to be employed in the telescope.

To prevent flexure in specula of moderate dimensions, the Earl of Rosse found it quite sufficient to support them in their box, on three strong iron plates, each plate being one-third part of a circular area, the same size as the speculum, and a sector of it; the plates rest at their centers of gravity, on points fixed at the bottom of the box of the speculum, and therefore no flexure of the box can affect the speculum. In supporting the speculum of 3 feet diameter, Lord Rosse attached nine plates to the speculum, every group of three being supported at their centers of gravity upon a triangle, having three points to sustain the pressure, and the center of every triangle is supported upon one of three points in the bottom of the box. The 6 foot speculum is supported in a similar manner, upon twenty-seven cast-iron plates, sustained upon a series of nine triangles, that are again supported upon three triangles, the centers of which rest upon three points. The twenty-seven plates were originally attached to the speculum by felt and pitch, but when the telescope was placed at different inclinations, it was found that the reflection was distorted, owing to the speculum having a slight motion edgeways, which threw some of the points of bearing partially out of contact. This difficulty has been overcome by removing

the layer of pitch and felt, by which the plates were attached to
the speculum, and substituting sheets of tin, which allow the
speculum to slide a small distance upon the plates.

A very valuable machine, of a different construction, for
polishing specula, has been contrived by Mr. William Lassell,
of Starfield, near Liverpool. The attention of this gentleman
has been for many years devoted to the construction of reflecting
telescopes, and his success in figuring by hand specula of all
sizes, up to 9 inch diameter and 9 feet focal length, led him to
conceive the idea of constructing a telescope with a speculum of
2 feet diameter, and 20 feet focal length.

As a preliminary step to the construction of the speculum,
Mr. Lassell inspected Lord Rosse's laboratory, and the per-
formance of the machinery for grinding and polishing specula
appeared so satisfactory, that Mr. Lassell determined to employ
a similar machine for polishing his 2 foot speculum. " But
finding, after many months' trial, that he could not succeed in
obtaining a satisfactory figure, he was led to contrive a machine
for imitating as closely as possible those evolutions of the hand
by which he had been accustomed to produce perfect surfaces on
smaller specula."   The idea of the machine was communicated
by Mr. Lassell to his friend Mr. James Nasmyth, of Patricroft,
near Manchester, by whom the mechanical details were designed,
and the machine constructed on the beautiful arrangement shown
in fig. 1135, which is copied from a drawing kindly supplied by
Mr. Nasmyth, and we are also indebted to the same gentleman
for the annexed description, which he has obligingly written for
these pages.

" The power is conveyed, in the first instance, by a band or
belt, to the pulley A, which conveys motion by the endless screw
B, to the wheel C. The spindle of the wheel C, viz., D, has
made fast to it, a crank, or arm, E, which carries a pinion F,
and causes the pinion to revolve round the toothed circumference of the wheel G, which wheel G being fixed to the bracket
H, causes the pinion F to revolve with as many turns as its
circumference is less than that of the wheel G, viz., 5 to 1.

" As the spindle of the pinion F, has a wheel K, fixed to it at

FIG. 1135.

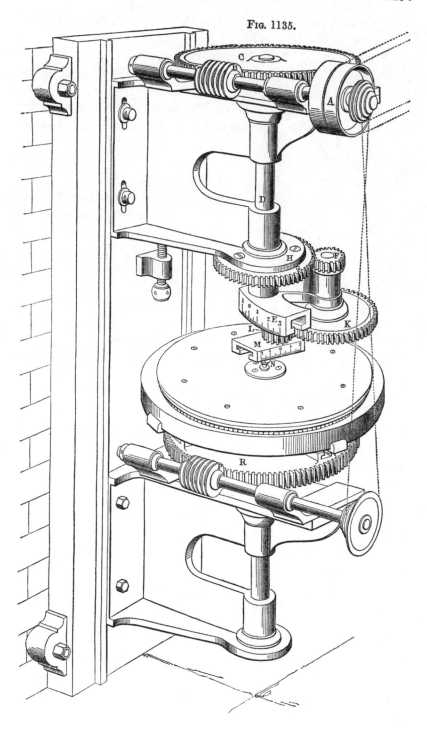

its lower end, this wheel K will, in like manner, convey motion
to the pinion L, which works on an adjustable center pin, and as
the T groove in which the center pin of L works, is radial to the
center of the wheel K, this pinion may be set to any degree of
eccentricity, and yet be in gear with K.

"It will also be seen that the pinion L has a cross crank, M,
attached to its under side, which, having its crank pin, N, also sliding in a T groove, it may be set to,
and fixed at, any degree of eccentricity, so that we have by these two
eccentric movements the means of
giving to the pin N, any compound
motion we require.

Fig. 1136.

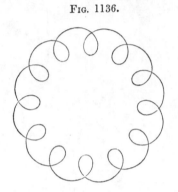

"The polisher is of wood, or
other suitable material coated
with pitch, and divided into
squares. This polisher is free to
move upon the pin N, while N
causes the polisher to slide over
the surface of the speculum with a motion somewhat like that
shown in fig. 1136.

"In order to cause every part of the surface of the speculum
to continually change its situation with respect to the movements of the polisher, it has also a slow revolving motion given
by an endless screw, P, pitched or working into the teeth of the
wheel R, which forms the base on which the speculum rests,
while receiving the action of the polisher.

"The speculum rests on nine equilibrium points so that each
ninth of its body is made to rest on a point or surface placed
under the center of gravity of each ninth of the speculum surface,
and so avoid all risk of distortion. It is the best practice to
polish the speculum while resting in the cell in which it is to be
when actually in the telescope, so as no risk of distortion may
occur, as would be the case were it removed, after polishing, into
another cell or bed.

"By means of this admirable machine, a speculum having a
decidedly hyperbolic figure may be corrected and brought to a
perfect parabola, or to a spherical curve, or the same may be
done in the reverse order at pleasure. A stronger proof of the
perfect capabilities of Mr. Lassell's machine could not be given."

From the foregoing description it will be seen that the essential difference between the machines contrived by Lord Rosse and Mr. Lassell, is that in the former, the polisher is traversed over the speculum with reciprocating longitudinal motion, and in the latter, the polisher has a continuous epitrochoidal motion, the path of which is dependent upon the adjustments of L and M. Mr. Lassell's polisher was made of two thicknesses of pine wood, with the grain crossed; this, from its lightness, did not require to be counterpoised, and apparently from its being sufficiently yielding to accommodate itself somewhat to the form of the speculum, a single coating of pitch was found sufficient, and the polishing was completed with wet powder.

Very complete evidence of the perfection of the speculum polished in this machine is afforded by the circumstance, that with the telescope to which it was fitted, Mr. Lassell discovered the satellite of Neptune, the eighth satellite of Saturn, and re-observed the satellites of Uranus, which latter, since their announcement by Sir W. Herschel had been seen by no other observer. These results have already arisen from the employment of Mr. Lassell's admirable contrivance and dexterity in the management of his polishing machine, and his excellent skill as an observer, in conjunction with a very perfect and powerful instrument, which has resulted principally from his own skilful exertions. The high value attached to these contributions to science, is evidenced by the circumstance that the Royal Astronomical Society awarded their gold medal for 1848 to Mr. Lassell.

Since the Earl of Rosse has shown that contrary to the previous general opinion, specula may be successfully polished by mechanical means, other machines have been constructed for the same purpose, but have not been applied to specula of such large dimensions. In Dr. R. Greene's machine for grinding and polishing specula and lenses, rewarded by the Society of Arts in 1834 (See Trans., Vol. L., p. 140), the polisher is mounted on a very slowly revolving axis, and the speculum also revolving slowly, but at a different rate, is traversed over the polisher by means of a central pin, joined to the extremities of two horizontal connecting rods at right angles to each other, actuated by two cranks, the relative velocities, length of stroke, and angular positions of which all admit of adjustment, and consequently the mirror can be traversed over the polisher in an infinite variety of curves.

A very simple machine for grinding and polishing specula of small size has been contrived by the Rev. William Hodgson, M.A., of Brathay, who has followed the general principles introduced by Lord Rosse, but has arranged the machine on the foundation of an ordinary turning lathe, driven by a foot-wheel, which, with the common overhead motion, and a part of the horizontal grinding machine shown in fig. 1039, page 1157, forms the principal portion of his polishing machine for specula. This contrivance, therefore, possesses the recommendation of being composed, in great measure, of the ordinary apparatus possessed by most amateurs, and may be readily fitted up for an occasional purpose, in those cases which would scarcely be considered of sufficient importance to call for the construction of the more elaborate machines of Lord Rosse or Mr. Lassell.

Fig. 1137 represents a modification of the arrangement of Mr. Hodgson's machine; the cast-iron frame, *a*, carrying the

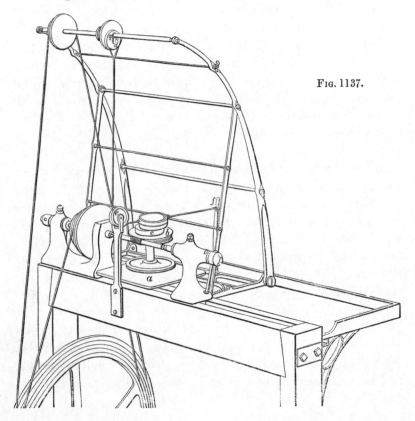

Fig. 1137.

vertical mandrel of the horizontal grinding machine, is fixed at the back of the lathe-bearers, either by a bolt passing through the bearer; or a short supplementary bearer is fixed at the back, and the frame is held by a wedge beneath, as shown in fig. 1039. The speculum is mounted on a chuck, *b*, fixed on the screw of the vertical mandrel, in the usual manner, and the edge of the chuck is cut as a screw-wheel, which is driven by a tangent screw, mounted between the mandrel and popit-head of the lathe, and by which a slow rotatory motion is given to the speculum, *c*. The polisher, which is placed upon the speculum, is encircled by a loose ring, precisely similar to that employed in Lord Rosse's machine, and a reciprocating motion is given to the ring, which allows of the very slow rotation of the polisher, exactly as in Lord Rosse's arrangement.

The reciprocating motion of the polisher across the face of the speculum is obtained after the method adopted by Professor Willis for giving a reciprocating motion to his vertical sawing machine, shown in fig. 729, Vol. II., the only changes being those required in the alteration of the motion from the vertical to the horizontal position. For this purpose the spindle of the over-head motion is fitted with an adjustable eccentric, shown at *d*, a loop encircles the eccentric, and terminates in a catgut band that passes under the guide pulley *e*, and is connected to the front of the ring embracing the polisher. A second band proceeds from the back of the ring, and is connected to a vertical steel spring, *f*, fixed at the back of the lathe.

Motion is communicated to the lathe mandrel, by the band leading to the foot wheel in the ordinary manner, and a second band is led to the over-head motion, either from the foot wheel, as shown in the figure, or from the pulley of the mandrel. The relative velocities of the polisher and speculum, may be readily adjusted by shifting the bands to different grooves on the driving pulleys, and the length of stroke of the polisher is adjusted by shifting the position of the eccentric, which, as seen in the figure, is fixed on the front of a plain pulley by two clamping screws. The height of the guide pulley *e*, and the spring *f*, are of course required to be adjusted to the level of the polisher.

With this arrangement of apparatus, Mr. Hodgson succeeded without material difficulty in grinding and polishing specula, one of which is $3\frac{1}{2}$ inches aperture, with a focal length of 33 inches; this has a tolerably good figure, and performs very well.

In figuring this speculum an elliptical polisher was used, the proportions of which were the same as those recommended by Mr. Edwards (see page 1278). To allow of the free rotation of the polisher, which was made of a mixture of lead and tin, the upper part was finished as a cylinder, to fit loosely in the ring, and the length of traverse of the center of the polisher across that of the speculum, was rather more than one inch.

Mr. Hodgson suggests that should it be considered desirable, a second guide pulley may be placed at the back, instead of the steel spring, and a second eccentric on the spindle of the overhead motion would, no doubt, answer quite as well to produce the back stroke; but the plan which he followed appeared in his own case to be more easily executed.

A machine employed at the Vauxhall pottery works, for grinding the spherical stoppers of air-tight earthenware jars, is represented in the diagram, fig. 1138. The stoppers and jars

FIG. 1138.

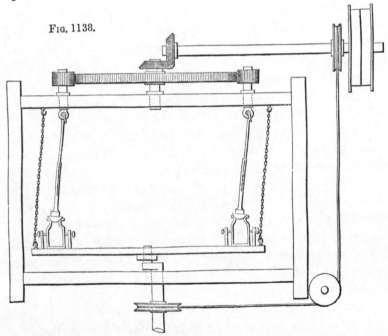

were ground together in the state in which they left the kiln, without separate preparation. About a dozen jars were fixed by clamping apparatus around the margin of a circular table, that was suspended by swing chains from the upper part of the frame of the machine. The circular table was swung bodily in a circle of about three inches diameter, by a slowly revolving eccentric placed beneath, and every stopper was made to revolve with considerable rapidity within the spherical fitting of the jar by the following arrangement.

A large toothed wheel fixed horizontally in the center of the upper part of the frame, communicated by a pair of bevil wheels with a horizontal shaft driven by a strap from the engine. Around the central wheel about a dozen small pinions were mounted in separate bearings at equal distances, so as to be all driven at the same time by the central wheel. The axis of every pinion passed through its bearing, and terminated beneath in an eye to which a hooked rod was suspended. To allow of variation in the length, this rod was fitted within a piece of gas-tube with a slit down the side for a pin to ensure the rotation of the tube, which terminated at its lower extremity in a chuck for the attachment of the stopper.

The rapid revolution of the stoppers gave the grinding motion, and the slow circular swinging of the table derived from the eccentric beneath, gave the continual change of position required for the true spherical form. The weight of the tube and chuck supplied the pressure for the grinding, which was begun with sand and water, and completed with emery, the time occupied in grinding a dozen jars being about one hour. This machine was perfectly successful in producing the true spherical fitting, but is now little used, as it is found more economical to grind the stoppers and jars together in the lathe by hand, the true spherical form not being considered by manufacturers of sufficient importance to justify the additional expense of the machine.

SECT. V.—GLASS-CUTTING.

Glass cutting, or the grinding and polishing of cut glass for household and other purposes, is effected with revolving wheels of iron, stone, or wood, mounted on horizontal spindles, after the same general method as the grindstones and buff-wheels of the cutler; but the grinding of glass requires a plentiful supply of water, which mostly runs in a small stream, from either a hopper-shaped box, or a can, placed above the revolving wheel; the water is led by a sloping channel to the upper edge of the wheel, and a small piece of wood is placed nearly upright and in contact with the wheel, a little in advance of the point at which the water is delivered, in order to distribute it equally over the edge. A splash-board is fixed behind the wheel, to catch the water thrown off, by centrifugal force, and lead it to the trough placed beneath; a second splash-board is sometimes fixed in front, to protect the operator from the wet.

Figs. 1139 and 1140 represent, in two views, the general arrangement of the apparatus employed in large manufactories,

FIG. 1139.   FIG. 1140.

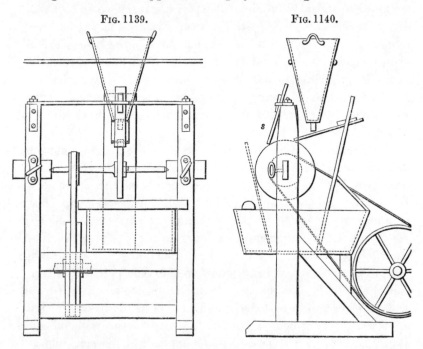

where the spindles are usually driven by steam power, but in small workshops, and for occasional purposes, the foot-wheel and treadle are employed, in much the same manner as in the small grinding machine shown in fig. 1030, except that the spindles are placed a few inches higher.

The wheels, whether of iron, stone, or wood, are generally made from about 6 to 20 inches diameter, and about 1 to 1½ in thickness; a considerable variety is required of all the three kinds, with flat, angular, rounded, or concave edges, to suit the different forms in which the glass is to be cut; the wheels are mounted upon separate spindles, and are exchanged in exactly the same manner as those used by cutlers.

The majority of the hollow works in cut glass, such as wine glasses and decanters, are blown to the circular form, and the ornament is entirely produced by grinding and polishing; some few of the hollow works are blown in figured moulds, and the general forms thus produced are finished by cutting. Small solid objects, such as the prisms and drops for chandeliers, are mostly *pinched*, or the glass, while red hot, is pressed into the cavities of metal moulds, something like those for casting bullets, but formed with the required facets; and for chandelier drops the moulds are provided with steel wires, that pierce the apertures for the brass wires, by which the glass drops are united to form the chandelier.

The first process in glass-cutting, or the rough grinding, is performed with cast-iron wheels, called *mills*, turned truly circular, and of the required figure, on their own spindles; the mills are supplied with fine sand, that has been previously washed and sifted, to free it from dirt, or coarse particles of grit. The sand is placed in the hopper, which is filled up with water, and the opening at the bottom adjusted by a plug, so as to allow a stream of the mixed sand and water, of about one quarter of an inch diameter, to flow through.

The glass to be ground is applied either above or below the center of the mill, according to the convenience of the operator. If the object be large, and much has to be ground away, the work is generally applied above the center, as this position is less fatiguing for the arms; and hollow objects are in general sufficiently transparent to allow of the operator looking *through* the article to see the progress of the work. Small solid objects, and such as are not transparent, are mostly applied below the center, to enable the workman to watch the progress of the cutting; in this case a wooden bar is laid across the water trough, upon which the arms are rested, partly to avoid fatigue, and partly to give greater steadiness.

When the object to be ground is large, and is required to have several faces, or *flutes*, the circumference is divided with a pair of compasses into the required number of parts for the principal circle, and the divisions are roughly scratched with an old triangular file, ground like a triangular turning tool; the height of the flutes is also marked on the best works. These divisions assist the workman in cutting the first circle of flutes of uniform size, and which serves as the basis for all the other circles of flutes, which are mostly placed intermediate with the adjacent circle, and are successively produced under the guidance of the eye alone. Small articles, such as wine-glasses, are not generally divided with the compasses, unless for the best works, as, from constant habit, the glass-cutters attain considerable dexterity in grinding any regular number of faces upon a circular object.

Generally the edge of the mill is alone employed for cutting, and the faces produced, therefore, partake of the curvature of the mill, and are ground concave instead of flat, and which has the advantage of making the intersections of the edges appear sharper; when, however, the surfaces are required to be quite flat, the side of the mill is employed in the same manner as for lapping the metals.

For cutting long straight faces, the work is held parallel with the axis of the mill, and gradually traversed from end to end, over a flat-edged mill. For curved surfaces, such as the neck of a claret jug, a mill with a slightly rounded edge is used, and the work is traversed in a curved path. For angular grooves, or splits, up the side of a decanter, or similar object, a mill with an angular edge is employed, and the decanter is held upright, or at right angles, to the axis of the mill, the same position is also employed for convex ribs, called pillars, for which a concave mill is used. In rough grinding, the work is applied with considerable pressure, and large deeply-cut flutes sometimes require as much as one horse power to drive the mill. When the supply of water in the hopper is exhausted, it is ladled back from the trough, the same supply of water serving for several days' use, or until it becomes dirty.

The second process in glass-cutting is the smooth grinding of the flutes; this is done upon fine grit-stones, known either as York or Warrington stones. These varieties of grit-stones are chosen because they are fine and compact in the grain, and are capable of retaining sharp angular edges. The York stones are the harder, and are usually selected from the finest grained pieces of Yorkshire paving slabs.

The stones are ground very true to the circular form, by means of a stationary bar of iron supported on the water trough, and supplied with sand and water; the stones are afterwards smoothed—first, with a piece of stone of the same quality, held in the hand; and, lastly, with a piece of flint, similarly applied: this leaves the surfaces of the stones quite smooth, and almost polished. If the stones were left with a rough surface, the glass would not hang to the stones, but would slip away, and be quite unmanageable. A smaller stream of water is required with the stones than with the cast-iron mill, and a straw frequently serves as the channel for leading the water from the can to the stone. A piece of sponge is often attached to the sloping board s, in front of the straw, to moisten the stone uniformly, as the stone must be kept tolerably wet, or it will generate so much heat as to break the glass.

More care is required in the smoothing than in the roughing, as the smooth grinding gives the finished form to the glass, and at the same time a very smooth surface. If the smoothing is carried on too vigorously, the stone is liable to *jar* the glass or put it in vibration, this causes the glass to *squeak*, or make a noise like a dry cart wheel, and frequently the glass breaks immediately afterwards, unless it be applied to the stone with reduced pressure, and also more firmly held in order to prevent the glass from vibrating. In smoothing the slender neck of a bottle, a cork is sometimes inserted to check the vibration, which never occurs in the rough grinding with loose sand, and is less frequent in smoothing with Warrington stones than with the harder York stones.

The work is applied to the stone for smoothing in exactly the same manner as upon the mill for roughing, but the work is more frequently held below the center of the stone, and in finishing straight flutes they are often applied upright, or at right angles to the axis of the stone, as in this position they may be made somewhat straighter, and smoothed rather more expeditiously. The stones used for this purpose are sometimes as much as three inches in thickness.

After the smooth grinding the glass is polished on wheels of willow, cut transversely out of round timber, and turned true and smooth. The wooden wheels are charged with pumice stone powder, mixed with water, and applied with a brush; sometimes rotten stone is mixed with the pumice stone. As in the cutting process the edges of the wheels are principally used, but the work is almost always applied on the top of the wheel, when the latter are driven by power, and instead of the glass being held in one position and traversed endways, it is twisted about in all directions, to remove the marks made by the stone in smoothing. The final lustre is given with wet putty powder applied also on willow wheels.

Wheel brushes of about 8 or 10 inches diameter, supplied with pumice stone, rotten stone, or putty powder, are also used as an expeditious means of polishing those parts of cut glass in which the sharpness of the angles is not considered to be of great importance, but the use of the wheel brushes is avoided as much as possible in polishing the best works.

In fitting the conical stoppers into glass bottles, the hollow cone of the bottle is ground by means of a solid cone of iron, sometimes roughened like a steel for sharpening knives. The cone is chucked on a lathe mandrel, and fed with emery and water. The stoppers are fixed in a hollow wood chuck by slight blows of a mallet, and are ground also with emery and water, applied on a grinder made of a piece of sheet iron, hammered around a cone of the same angle, and left with two flaps or ears, by which the grinder is held and compressed upon the revolving glass stopper.

The cones are ground separately until the stopper will enter the bottle, to within about one-sixteenth of an inch of the intended position, the two are then slightly ground together for the exact fitting. The stoppers of the best works are afterwards polished on the edge of the willow wheels, in the same manner as cut glass. The internal cone is polished on a small willow cone revolving in the lathe.

The large stoppers for medical bottles are sometimes rough ground with sand, on the flat side of a mill made of stout sheet iron, and which also serves for grinding the bottom of the bottle flat.

Glass drops for chandeliers are cut upon the flat faces of wheels, which sometimes revolve horizontally, and are almost entirely concealed within wooden cases to catch the dirt, only a small opening being left for applying the drops. They are roughed with sand and water on iron mills, smoothed on stones, and polished on lead laps supplied with rotten stone and water; the lead is considered to produce a black polish that reflects the prismatic colours in a higher degree than when wood is employed as the material for the polisher.

CHAPTER XXXIV.

LAPIDARY WORK.

SECT. I. — SLITTING, CUTTING, AND POLISHING FLAT AND ROUNDED WORKS.

ALTHOUGH the term lapidary work, may seem to be applicable to all the various modes of working or finishing stones, it is restricted to the cutting, grinding, and polishing of gems and small stones, and some other materials, principally for jewellery, or mineralogical specimens.

The lapidary never employs abrasive materials in that which may be called their natural or unprepared state, in the manner that the grindstone or oilstone are employed for restoring the edges of tools; but he uses the several abrasive materials in a pulverized form, and upon revolving disks of metal and other materials by way of vehicles, thus constituting artificial grinders, which he denominates as *mills;* thus we have the slitting mill, the roughing mill, the smoothing mill, and the polishing mill, all generally of metal; but for soft stones the smoothing mill is sometimes a plain disk of willow wood or mahogany. The polishing mill is sometimes composed of a spiral coil of list placed on edge like the leaves of a book; sometimes of bristles like a brush, or of wood covered with buff leather, which several apparatus are fully described under the head WHEELS, in the Catalogue of Abrasive Processes at the commencement of this volume.

The general succession in which these mills are employed by the lapidary for substances of different degrees of hardness, is also briefly explained in the catalogue under the three heads, ALABASTER, CARNELIAN, and SAPPHIRE, stones that differ considerably in hardness, and have therefore been selected as general examples; under each head is appended a list of such gems and other substances as are worked by the lapidary in a similar manner.   The principal peculiarities in the methods of working other stones, are also mentioned in the catalogue under their respective names, as Agate, Amber, Avanturine, &c.

The general remarks offered under these heads, have greatly abridged the observations to be submitted in the present chapter, which will be confined principally to a description of the apparatus, and the details of manipulation, which are nearly alike in working corresponding forms in either hard or soft stones ; the principal difference being that the polishing mills are composed of hard or soft materials, according to the degree of hardness of the substances to be polished.

The apparatus commonly employed by the practical lapidary will be first described, followed by some account of the methods of producing the more usual forms met with in lapidary work, and the modifications in the apparatus generally employed by amateurs for similar purposes will be subsequently adverted to.

All the mills of the lapidary revolve upon vertical spindles or axes, so that the disks travel horizontally, which is just the reverse of the position employed by the cutler, and also by the glass and gold cutters, although the two latter classes of artizans are in the frequent habit of working analogous forms, and in some few instances, as in the case of cutting facets on amber beads, the gold cutters are considered to excel the ordinary lapidary.

Flat and rectilinear works are, in all their stages, ground and polished upon the broad flat surfaces of the lapidary mills, which revolve with moderate velocity, and the work is held almost stationary, much the same as in lapping flat works in metal.

Convex works are roughened on the ordinary flat roughing mill; but they require to be continually rolled about to bring every part in quick succession into contact with the mill or disk, as holding the stone at rest would inevitably wear down a flat place.   Convex works in soft substances are in general smoothed on a wooden disk, which, from its elasticity, and also from its surface wearing slightly rough, or fibrous, yields a little to the stone, and does not meet it so rigidly upon one mathematical line as the unyielding metal disk. The list mill, from its pliancy, is also very well adapted to convex works, and is commonly used for glass; the leather and brush mills are also occasionally employed for rounded works.

Concave works necessarily require mills that will penetrate into their cavities; the rounded edge of the disk is in this case used somewhat as a glass-cutter would grind a transverse flute, except that the work is held at an angle instead of parallel to the axis. But when the cavity is required to be spherical, or curvilinear in two directions, the grinder is required to be of a bulbous form, and of the suitable diameter for the required curvatures, and the grinding and polishing tools must be all turned to the same diameter.

In Germany and other parts of the Continent, where large quantities of common lapidary works, such as seal handles, are executed, water-power is generally employed for driving the mills, which for these works are, in some cases, mounted upon horizontal spindles, and the edges of the mills are then principally used. The cutting of diamonds has been slightly noticed in vol. i., page 176; as there mentioned, the facets are cut by cementing two diamonds upon the ends of two sticks, and rubbing them together. The facets are afterwards polished upon an iron skive or mill, charged with diamond powder; considerable pressure is exerted upon the stone, and in Holland, where the greatest quantity of diamonds are cut and polished, horse power is generally employed, or the mills are driven by one or two men. In the latter case the driving-wheel is about 6 feet diameter, and instead of being mounted vertically, and driven by a winch handle, as usual in this country for similar purposes, the driving wheel is mounted to revolve horizontally, upon a vertical spindle, having a crank of small radius, to which the motion is communicated by a connecting rod leading to a wooden frame, that swings horizontally upon pivots at the one end, like an ordinary gate, and has at the other end two upright handles, by which it is pushed alternately backwards and forwards.

The stones worked in this country by lapidaries are in general small, and but little pressure is exerted upon the stone, the power of an assistant is therefore not required; but the lapidary mostly gives motion to the wheel with his left hand, while the stone is applied to the mill with his right. The details of the apparatus are somewhat varied in unimportant particulars, but fig. 1141 may be considered to represent the general arrangement of apparatus employed by working lapidaries.

The lapidary's bench consists of a stout plank, about 3 feet 6 inches long, and 1 foot 9 inches wide, supported upon a frame about

FIG. 1141.

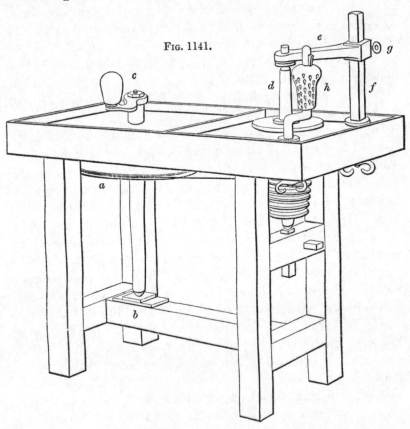

2 feet 6 inches high; the top is divided into two unequal compartments, and the whole is surrounded by a rim of about 2 inches above the face of the bench, intended to catch the waste emery and water thrown off by the centrifugal force. The compartment to the left hand is about 2 feet long, and has a central hole fitted with a collar, through which passes the vertical spindle of the driving wheel a, the lower end of the spindle is made conical, and fits into a corresponding center b, fixed in the longitudinal rail of the frame. The driving wheel, about 18 inches diameter, is fitted on the spindle between flanges, and

works just beneath the under surface of the bench top, which nearly conceals it, and a horizontal handle c, of about 6 inches radius, is fitted on the upper end of the spindle. The distance between the spindle of the driving wheel, and that of the lap or mill, should not exceed about 1 foot 9 inches, in order that the arms may not be inconveniently extended, when the hands are respectively applied to the wheel and mill.

The right hand compartment of the bench is about 16 inches wide, and through a hole in the center is passed the spindle d, that carries the mill; this latter is usually about 8 or 9 inches diameter, and revolves about 1 inch above the surface of the bench. The spindle is about 18 inches long, and the mill is held between a flange and screwed nut, about 12 inches from the lower end, which is made conical, and received in a corresponding center, capable of adjustment for height, in order to compensate for irregularities in the lengths of the spindles, and also to allow of the mill being more or less elevated above the face of the bench, according as the edge or side of the mill may be employed at the time. In the bench represented in the figure, this center consists of a square wooden rod, passing through a mortise in the transverse rail of the frame, and retained at any desired height by a side wedge; but frequently the center is supported upon the middle of a transverse bar moving at the one end on a pivot in the back upright of the frame, and supported in the front by a wedge.

The upper end of the spindle is also made conical, and likewise works in a wooden center, which is screwed into a hole near the extremity of a horizontal iron arm e, that slides upon a perpendicular bar f, fixed behind the mill; the height of the horizontal bar is adjusted to suit the height of the spindle, and is retained in the proper position by the binding screw g. The pulley, about four inches diameter, is fixed on the spindle to work just below the bench top, the hole through which is sufficiently large to allow the pulley to be passed through, either in exchanging the mills, or when they are required to be elevated.

The support shown at h, placed a little to the right and in advance of the lap, is called a *gim peg* or *germ peg*; it is about 8 inches high, and made of a round rod of iron bent into a crank form, and fitted with a flange that bears upon the surface of the bench; the lower end of the rod passes through a hole or mortise in the bench, and is fixed by a wing nut beneath, in order to allow of the gim peg being twisted round to different positions, according to the distance it is required to be placed from the mill.

The gim peg serves as a support for the arm of the workman in grinding the edges of small stones, but its principal use is to serve as a guide for the vertical angle in cutting facets; for this purpose a wooden socket, of the form shown in the figure, is slipped over the upper part of the rod, and retained in its position by a wedge driven in between the iron stem and the hole in the wooden socket. Several series of holes, or rather notches, one above the other, are arranged around the sides of the socket, and which serve to determine the inclination of the stick upon which the stones are cemented, as will be hereafter explained.

In producing a plane surface upon an irregular piece of stone, as in the case of smoothing a mineralogical specimen, if the natural surface is so nearly flat that but little has to be removed, the stone may be at once applied to the flat surface of the roughing mill; and if the stone be soft, such as a piece of potstone, the flat surface will be quickly attained; but if the natural surface be irregular, and the stone be hard, such as a piece of bloodstone, or even an ordinary pebble, the reduction of the stone to a flat surface by grinding would be very tedious, if much of the material had to be removed. Splitting or cleavage is seldom resorted to, as few of the stones wrought by the lapidary have a sufficiently lamellar structure to allow of nearly plane surfaces being thus produced, and the surfaces would be also liable to interferences from flaws or veins in the stone. In the majority of cases, therefore, even in polishing mineralogical specimens, the level surface is produced by cutting off a thin slice of the stone with the slitting-mill or slicer, which is a revolving disk of thin sheet iron, charged on the edge with diamond powder, and used as a circular saw for dividing all stones inferior in hardness to the diamond.

Notwithstanding the apparent expence of the diamond powder, it is very generally employed, and is used for cutting nearly every Turkey oilstone that is sold; and although for this and some of the softer stones, emery, or in some cases even sand, might be successfully employed, the diamond powder is almost exclusively used, as it is found to be the most economical, when the time occupied in the cutting is taken into account. The diamond powder cuts more rapidly than emery, and is very much more enduring; it also admits of being employed with very thin plates, and consequently the progress is also more expeditious on this account, and comparatively only a small thickness of material is wasted in the cutting. This is sometimes an important object with valuable stones, and the slicer is then made of small diameter, in order that it may be as thin as possible, and still retain the required degree of stiffness.

The slicer is made of a disk of sheet iron, usually about eight or nine inches diameter, and two hundredths of an inch in thickness. It is of course necessary that the edge of the slicer should run exactly in one plane; it is therefore planished or hammered in the manner explained in vol. i., pp. 414 to 422. But if so thin a plate were made perfectly flat, like a circular saw, it would be very feeble sideways, and would be readily distorted by the resistance of the work, and therefore, to give greater rigidity, the slicer is hammered into a slightly arched or dished form, the concavity being about one-sixth of an inch in the entire diameter. This trifling concavity materially increases the stiffness of the slicer, and does not interfere with its use for cutting straight sections; as when the slicer is properly hammered and turned true, the extreme edge runs exactly in one plane for the commencement of the cut; and when the slicer has penetrated a small depth, the trifling curvature of the plate gives way, and it is flattened by the groove it has itself cut, and in which it is compelled to run.

The slicer is further stiffened by being firmly clamped, like a circular saw, between two flanges on its spindle, which is made of such a length that the edge of the slicer may be about 3 inches above the level of the bench, in order to allow room for the hand, and also for large stones.

The preparation of the diamond powder for charging the slicer has been already described on page 1052, under the head DIAMOND, Article 1; but it may be added that the usual criterion for the fineness of the diamond powder used by lapidaries, is that the particles should be so small that no sparkling is perceptible when the diamond powder is exposed to the light. Slight differences are made in the forms of mortars for crushing diamonds, but that represented in fig. 1142 is the more generally preferred. The mortar *a*, has a deep cylindrical hole

Figs. 1142.   1143.   1144.

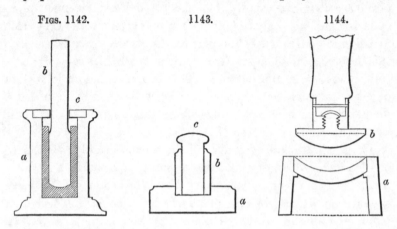

terminating at the bottom in a spherical cavity of hardened steel, embracing from about one-third to one-sixth of a circle, into which the pestle *b*, is accurately fitted by grinding. The long cylindrical fitting serves as a guide for keeping the pestle upright, and also prevents any of the valuable particles from flying about when the pestle is struck with the hammer; the cover *c*, is also added for the latter purpose. In some mortars for crushing diamonds, the bottom of the cavity is made flat, and the pestle is then made square at the end, as shown in fig. 1143, in which *a* represents the base of the mortar, *b*, a short cylindrical tube fitted into a shallow cavity in the base, and *c*, the pestle, which is fitted within the tube. But this form of mortar is seldom employed by working lapidaries.

Sometimes, when the diamond has not been crushed sufficiently fine in the mortar, the lapidaries grind the diamond powder; for this purpose they commonly mix it with a little olive oil or the oil of brick, and spread it upon a flat piece of iron, generally an old laundry iron, and any small piece of iron is used as a muller. The mortar represented in fig. 1144 is, however, greatly preferable for grinding the diamond powder. The base *a* of the mortar has a spherical cavity, of hardened steel and about two inches radius, to which is fitted the pestle *b*, which is also made of hardened steel and fixed in a wooden handle. The diamond powder is placed in the center of the cavity, and a few drops of oil are added; the diamond is then ground as fine as required by rubbing the pestle within the mortar with moderate pressure.

In applying the diamond powder to a new slicer, or as it is called *seasoning the slicer*, it is mounted in the machine, and the edge is turned quite true and smooth, with a graver supported upon the rest *h*, fig. 1141 ; or in some cases it is afterwards smoothed with a fine file, as it is of importance that the edge of the slicer should be quite true, and free from even minute notches, or otherwise the irregularities would be liable to catch the stone, and throw it out of the hand, or if the stone were firmly held, the slicer would become distorted.

A small quantity of diamond powder, mixed with the oil of brick, is then taken out of the cup with a small piece of stick, or a better practice is to employ a piece of an ordinary quill about 1 inch long, prepared by splitting the barrel of a quill length-ways into three or four pieces, and rounding the ends. The quill is dipped in the cup, and a little of the diamond powder, or rather paste, is taken on the concave side of the quill, which is then held vertically against the edge of the slicer, so that the curvature of the slicer may nearly agree with that of the quill; the latter is then held steady while the slicer is moved slowly round, in order to distribute the diamond uniformly on the extreme edge of the slicer. To fix the particles therein, a smooth piece of any hard stone, such as agate or flint, from half an inch to an inch wide, is immediately applied with gentle pressure against the edge of the slicer.

In order that both hands may be at liberty for charging the slicer, the wheel is sometimes turned by an assistant, and the lapidary supplies the diamond powder with one hand while he holds the charging stone to the edge of the slicer with the other. As soon as the diamond begins to cut the stone, the latter is shifted to another position, as, if the slicer were permitted to cut a groove in the charging stone, the diamond powder would become fixed in the sides of the slicer, which must of course be avoided. As soon as the small quantity of diamond resting on the edge of the slicer has been pressed into it, the margin of the slicer is carefully wiped on both sides with the forefinger, in order to remove any small portions of the diamond that may have become accidentally lodged on the sides, and these particles are pushed to the edge of the slicer, and pressed in with the charging stone. When the whole of the diamond powder has been pressed in to the extreme edge, a second quantity is applied in the same manner, and which is generally sufficient for charging or *seasoning* a new slicer. After the edge of the slicer has been once fairly charged with the diamond powder, a single application is generally sufficient for restoring the cutting edge, and under the hands of the practical lapidary, a single seasoning will endure several hours' work.

The stone to be sliced is first washed clean and dried, the line of the intended section may then be marked in ink as a guide, and the slicer is plentifully lubricated with the oil of brick, a thin oil that is used on account of its limpidity, and not being liable to become thickened by exposure to the atmosphere. Stones of small or moderate size are held in the hand, while the arm is rested upon the edge of the bench to steady it. The stone is then lightly pressed against the edge of the slicer, which is driven with only moderate velocity, or the friction would be liable to heat the stone, and cause it to crack. Care should be taken in the commencement of the cut to present a tolerably smooth surface to the slicer, as if a sharp corner were first advanced, it would be liable to scrape the diamond off the edge ; and the diamond may also be torn off the edge if a smooth stone is pressed too forcibly against the slicer with the view of expediting the process. During the slitting the slicer should be kept plentifully supplied with the oil of brick, and the stone should be held steadily, and cautiously managed to keep the cut in a straight line, as from the concave form of the slicer it is rather liable to cut upwards. The principal attention is however required at the first commencement of the cut, and if this be correctly performed, the groove will serve in a great measure as a guide for the completion of the cut.

When the stone to be sliced is too large and heavy to be conveniently held in the hand, it is mounted on the *crane*, as shown in fig. 1145. The crane consists of an upright rod, mounted between centers, just in front of the perpendicular bar *f*, and upon this rod slides vertically a horizontal arm *j*, about 20 inches long, provided with a binding screw, by which it may be fixed to the rod at any height. The stone to be sliced is fixed to the middle of the arm and opposite the slicer, by means of a clamping piece and two binding screws, as seen in the figure, and the whole is drawn forward by a weight k, attached to a line leading from the extremity of the horizontal arm, over a pulley

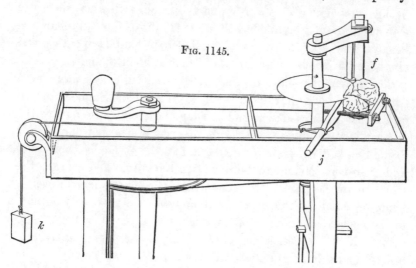

FIG. 1145.

fixed to the end of the bench. The stone to be sliced is carefully clamped, so that the line of the intended division is exactly horizontal, and the precise height is adjusted by sliding the horizontal arm upon the vertical rod, until the line of division just meets the edge of the slicer. The weight then suffices to keep the stone continually pressing against the edge of the slicer, and the operator has merely to keep the latter in motion, and supply the oil.

For cutting parallel slices, it is only requisite between every cut, to shift the horizontal arm upwards upon the vertical rod. This simple contrivance entirely removes all difficulty in holding the stone, but is very seldom resorted to by practical lapidaries, except for large stones. A modification of this instrument to adapt it to the use of amateurs for cutting small stones will be hereafter adverted to.

To remove the marks made by the slitting mill, the flat surfaces of the stones are ground upon the roughing mill, or lead lap, supplied with coarse emery and water, by means of a brush. If the stone be large and thick, it is held directly in the fingers, but more generally the stones are too thin to be thus held, and it then becomes necessary to cement them to a wooden stick to serve as a handle. Large thin stones would also be liable to be broken in working if left unsupported, such stones are therefore cemented upon a handle made as a flat disk of wood, nearly as large in diameter, as the width of the stone, and having a central stem 4 or 5 inches long, and about half an inch diameter.

The cement is made of rosin, tempered with bees-wax and a little tallow, and hardened with red ochre, or Spanish brown and whiting, the smaller and harder the stones, the harder the cement is made by an increased quantity of the powders. For sapphires and other hard gems, a little shell-lac is sometimes added to the cement to increase its tenacity. To cement the stone upon the stick, the wooden disk is first warmed over a lamp, or candle, the cement is then heated, and evenly applied to the surface and edges of the disk, the layer of cement being made sufficiently thick to allow of the stone being fairly embedded, and it is then worked with the fingers nearly to the form of the stone, which is next warmed just sufficiently to cause the cement to adhere, without making it so hot as to be liable to burn the fingers; the surface of the cement is then melted over the lamp, and the warm stone is immediately pressed upon it. Care should be taken to place the stone quite central with the stick, which should also be exactly at right angles with the flat surface of the stone. The cement around the edges of the disk is then worked with the fingers into the angle around the stone, to support it uniformly near the edges.

In charging the lap with emery, a small brush dipped in water is generally applied to the lap to moisten it, and the dry emery is then sprinkled over its surface, and rubbed in with a flat piece of emery stone, or a piece of sheet iron; but some lapidaries prefer to dip the moistened brush in dry emery, and then apply it to the lap. In whichsoever way the emery be applied, it is desirable that as much emery should be supplied at the commencement of the roughing, as it is judged will suffice for the removal of the marks made by the slicer, and should more emery be required as the work progresses, the coarser particles remaining of the emery first supplied are partially crushed, either with a smooth lump of emery stone, or with a piece of soft sheet iron about 1 inch wide and 8 inches long, and the work is completed with a finer size of emery, so as gradually to reduce the coarseness of the grinding powder as the flat surface is approached.

As mentioned at page 1034, under the head ALABASTER, Article 3, many lapidaries employ the same lead mill, both for roughing and smoothing the surface of the stones ; some lapidaries however employ two benches for these purposes, so that the work may be taken from the roughing mill to the smoothing mill, without the loss of time incurred in crushing the coarser emery quite fine, but when one bench only is used for the roughing and smoothing, the same lap is made to serve both purposes. For large stones, the roughing is generally commenced with grinding emery, and finished with flour emery ; but for small stones, superfine grinding emery is sufficiently coarse for the commencement, and fine flour emery is used for the smoothing.

In applying the stone to the mill, it is placed flat on the surface, and firmly pressed with the ends of the fingers and thumb applied on the back of the wooden disk, the upright stem passing between the fore and middle fingers. If the stone be large, it may, with advantage, at the commencement, be rubbed upon the flat face of the revolving mill with small circular strokes, and at the same time the stone may be slowly twisted round with the fingers, in order to expose it equally to the action of the mill. If the stone be small it must be held quite steady throughout the process, but in order to wear the lap uniformly, the stone is placed in a different position every time that it is rested on the mill.

The velocity of the mill employed in grinding should be only moderate, so as just to avoid throwing off much of the grinding powder with the centrifugal force ; the progress of the work may be expedited by using a higher velocity, but the emery and water are then thrown off so abundantly as to be very objectionable, and the condition of the work can be less delicately felt. The stone should also be pressed upon the mill with only moderate force, as great pressure is liable to cause the stone to push away the loose particles of grinding powder, and also to wear the mill irregularly, whereas moderate pressure allows the loose particles of emery to roll over between the mill and stone, and the work then progresses more rapidly, and the mill is less injured.

The stone having been made as smooth as practicable with

U

the emery, the polishing is proceeded with in the same manner, upon a mill of appropriate material, generally pewter, hacked, or jarred, as explained under the head CARNELIAN, page 1044, and supplied with rottenstone and water. This completes the one side of the stone, and it is then detached by heat from the cement stick; and the same routine is followed with the second side.

If the stone is required to be wrought to a definite shape, as for example an oval, the edge is ground to the oval form before the sides are flattened. For this purpose a corresponding oval is cut out of card to the exact dimensions, and laid upon the stone; the oval is then marked with ink upon the stone, which is brought very nearly to the shape by means of *nippers*, or flat pliers of soft iron, like those employed for rounding disks of glass preparatory to grinding them into lenses, see page 1265; the nippers are firmly compressed upon the stone, and then twisted sideways to break off small particles. The hardest stones, such as sapphires, will yield to the action of the nippers, although they are scarcely ever used with valuable gems; but if the stones are smooth and rounded like the natural surface of a pebble, the nippers will slide off, and therefore such stones are first slightly roughened to give a hold to the nippers.

The stone having been nipped of the required shape, and nearly to the size, it is cemented upon a stick, the edge being left exposed, and this is then ground square by holding the stick horizontally, and continually twisting it round between the fingers to avoid grinding flat places; when the stone has been thus figured to the required shape, the flat face is ground and polished.

If the stone is required to have a bevelled edge, or chamfer around the face, the stone is first nipped to the form, then fixed on the cement stick, with the side outwards that is to form the back of the stone; the edge is ground square and the back flattened and polished if necessary. The stone is then re-cemented upon the stick with the face side outwards; the face is flattened, and the bevelled edge is then ground by holding the stick at an angle, and continually twisting the stone round to grind the chamfer uniformly. The thickness of the narrow square edge left on the stone, serves as a sufficient guide for practised lapidaries to ensure the uniformity of the bevel, but the amateur will probably find it desirable to mark a line on the edge, and also the face of the stone, to show how far the chamfer should extend.

If the stone is to have a rounded edge, it is first prepared with a bevelled edge exactly as above, and the angle is removed by a rocking motion of the stone upon the flat mill. For this purpose the stick is held underhand, being grasped between the fingers as near to the bottom as admissible, and the stick is continually traversed from nearly the perpendicular position to the angle, at which the chamfer was ground. The wrist or elbow being the center of motion according to the curvature required, and at the same time the stick is twisted round in the fingers, in order to round the edge uniformly.

If the stone is to be considerably rounded over the entire face, the preparatory step of grinding the face flat may be omitted, as the stone will be left sufficiently level by the slicer, and the principal bulk of the material is removed by the chamfer, which serves as the basis or guide for keeping the rounding uniform, assisted during the principal portion of the work by the central part of the stone, not reached by the rounding until near the conclusion of the rough grinding.

If the stone to be rounded on the face be circular, it is rolled upon the flat mill with circular strokes; between every few strokes it is shifted to another part of the mill, and the stick is continually twisted round in the fingers. If the stone be of a short elliptical shape, it is treated in the same manner, except that it is traversed in an elliptical path. In the case of very long ellipses, the two sides of the ellipsis are first ground separately with a rocking motion, and the stick is slightly twisted in the fingers between every few strokes. The ends of the ellipsis are rounded in the same manner, and, lastly, it is smoothed with long, semi-elliptical strokes. The principal guide for the degree of rolling is obtained from an inspection of the progress, but the sense of feeling is also greatly trusted to by working lapidaries. Stones that are flat on the back, and much rounded on the front, are called *tallow tops*, from their resemblance to a drop of tallow.

Stones that are rounded to a cylindrical or conical form, such as a drop for an earring, are cemented sideways upon a stick, and the one-half ground to the semi-circular section; they are then detached from the stick, and cemented with the other side outwards, and this is similarly wrought. Of course, some care is required to grind the two semi-circular sections exactly opposite to each other; and when this has been done as nearly as possible, the stone is successively cemented in two other positions at right angles to the first two, in order to expose the junctures of the two curved surfaces first produced, and which are then corrected.

Stones that are to be ground into spheres, for beads or the heads of pins, are, in like manner, required to be cemented in at least four positions before they can be brought sufficiently near to the required form. The method of grinding spheres perfectly true has been already explained in sect. iv. of the foregoing chapter; but, of course, this amount of accuracy is not required for lapidary purposes, as, generally, the form is only required to be sufficiently correct to satisfy the eye. With the view of expediting the process of grinding stones that are much rounded, and also to preserve the lap used for flat surfaces, one lap is generally set aside, to be used only for rounded works, and, from constant use, the side of this lap becomes worn into numerous hollows, of different sizes, some of which are generally found to nearly fit the curve of the stone being ground. This materially lessens the difficulty of producing spherical surfaces, and the edge of the same lap is, in general, rounded off, to serve for concave works.

In grinding a pebble to the shape of a heart with rounded sides, the pebble, if much thicker than the intended heart, is first cut to the suitable thickness with the slicer; it is then marked from a card pattern, and nipped nearly to the form and size. The edges are then squared, the square angle of the lap being employed for making the indentation at the top of the heart. So far, the stone is generally held in the fingers; and when the outline has been thus produced, the stone is cemented on a stick, the edges are chamfered all round, and the stone is rough-ground to the rounded form, smoothed, and polished; the second side is then treated in the same manner.

Small stones cut in the form of a shield, as for a signet ring, are, in the same manner, first wrought to the outline of the shield while held in the fingers, although these stones are often not more than one quarter of an inch in height. In holding such small stones, some care is, of course, required to avoid bringing the fingers in contact with the lap, which would be likely to grind through the skin even before the operator was fairly aware that they touched the lap, the grinding action being almost insensible until the outer coat of the skin is worn through.

Stones that are semi-transparent, such as garnets, are frequently left round on the face, or cut *en cabochon;* but such stones, if left of the full thickness, would be too opake to display much brilliancy ; and, therefore, with the view of increasing the transparency, garnets cut en cabochon, and called carbuncles, are generally hollowed on the under side, to make them thinner. The hollow on the under side is ground upon small spherical grinders of lead, called balls, made of various thicknesses and diameters, but mostly about the size of bullets. The balls are mounted upon a small conical spindle, that is fitted to the ordinary lapidary's bench ; the hole through the balls is also made slightly conical, so that they may be retained upon the spindle by the plain fitting, and allow of being readily detached for the substitution of other balls of different sizes. Similar balls, made of pewter, are employed for polishing ; and it is, of course, necessary that the grinding and polishing balls should be, as nearly as possible, of the same size.

For cutting small mouldings, or hollows, in the edges or sides of stones, the lapidary employs little lead mills, not exceeding about three inches diameter; they are generally held by a plain fitting, upon the same spindle that carries the ordinary mills, and which is made somewhat conical for the purpose. The edges of these mills are principally used, and they are made of various shapes and thicknesses, but mostly with rounded or angular edges, in order to penetrate the cavities of hollow mouldings, and the rounded parts are chiefly produced by rolling the work over the edges. The small diameter of these mills allows of delicate works being better seen, and, from the velocity being less at the edge of the mill, the position and progress of the work is also more readily appreciated by the sense of feeling.

In cutting a seal-handle, with an octagonal section, and a rounded top, such as fig. 1146, the stone is first sliced into the pyramidal form indicated by the dotted lines; the sides are then flattened and the angles removed upon the ordinary roughing mill, to bring the stone to the octagonal section, and the top is

rounded.   The indentations at *a a* are then cut upon the angle
of a mill having a square edge.   The curved portion at *b* is

FIGS. 1146.   1147.

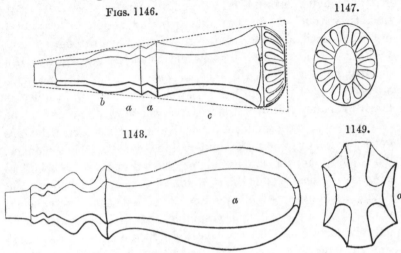

1148.   1149.

cut upon a mill with a slightly rounded edge, which also serves
for removing the principal portion of the material from the
large hollows at *c*; and these are afterwards corrected either
by applying the stone transversely upon a lap with a rounded
edge, turned to the required curvature, or by applying the stone
longitudinally upon a square-edged mill, of about two inches
diameter, the curvature of which would correspond with the
hollows in the figure.   The small flutes in the rounded top are
cut with a mill of small diameter, having a narrow rounded edge.

In cutting the handle, figs. 1148 and 1149, the stone is roughed
out to the general contour upon mills with rounded edges of appropriate thicknesses.   The stone is first wrought of an elliptical
section throughout, by continually twisting it round in the fingers.
The two longest sides are then flattened by holding the stone
firmly in the fingers, and traversing it backwards and forwards
a small distance upon the edge of the mill; the four angles are
removed in the same manner, and the two narrow ends of the
irregular octagon are formed by portions of the original ellipsis,
the curvature being scarcely perceptible in the lower part of the
handle.   The two large flutes, *a*, are cut by traversing the stone
over a mill of about two inches diameter, with a rounded edge;
and the four small flutes are cut upon a similar mill, of smaller
diameter.

In all these cases, no guide whatever is employed for producing the form, the perfection of which depends entirely upon the figure of the edge of the mill, and the dexterity of the workman. Sharp internal angles are not often attempted, as it is difficult to maintain the sharp angle of the grinder.

The minute cutting on the surfaces of small works, such as coral drops for ear-rings, and similar objects, is performed by another class of artizans, who mount small angular, flat, or rounded grinders, upon horizontal spindles in the ordinary lathe, and apply the work beneath the grinders, in much the same manner as the glass-cutters; indeed, the coral cutting may be considered to form a link between glass-cutting, and seal engraving, described respectively in sect. v., chap. xxxiii., and sect. iii., chap. xxxv.

For perforating very small holes through beads and similar objects, the lapidary employs as a drill a small steel or iron wire, such as fig. 67, page 178, Vol. I. The wire is mounted in a chuck, to revolve horizontally upon an ordinary lathe mandrel, and is charged with diamond powder in the same manner as the slicer. For holes more than about the twentieth ‘of an inch diameter, tubular drills are used, such as fig. 71, made of thin sheet iron, bent around a small central wire. These drills remove a small solid core, which breaks when the tube has penetrated some little distance, and the core is pushed out of the tube by passing a fine needle through a hole in the side.

Larger tubes are employed in the same manner for cutting out the circular holes sometimes made in large brooches for the insertion of another stone, or a locket. If the hole is required to be oval, two circular holes of suitable size are made to constitute the two ends of the oval, and the little angular pieces left between the two circles are removed with a small conical grinder. Small tubes are soldered upon the metal wires, but those exceeding about half an inch in diameter are, by the lapidary, generally attached by cement to a wooden chuck. These annular drills are sometimes made as large as from one to two inches diameter, and thus the lapidary's tubular drills are carried up to the size of the smallest circular cutters or grinders used for similar purposes in marble, as alluded to in page 1208 of the present volume.

SECTION II.—CUTTING FACETS.

THE surfaces of gems, pastes, and most other substances worked by the lapidary, are, as is well known, cut into facets to improve their brilliancy, by multiplying the number of reflecting surfaces, in order that the play of light may be proportionally increased. Facets are principally cut upon transparent and semi-transparent stones, but sometimes also upon opake stones, such as carnelian; and speaking generally, it may be said that the greater the natural brilliancy of the stone, the fewer facets are necessary to produce the required play of light; and with valuable gems it is always desirable to produce the brilliancy with as few facets as possible, in order to avoid confusion in the rays of light.

Opake stones are cut on the face only, and the stone is in general thin, and flat on the back; but transparent stones are, if possible, left thick, and so cut as to make the back, or lower part of the stone that is enclosed in the setting, of about double the thickness of the front or face that is exposed. The back of the stone is cut into facets or squares that exactly correspond in plan with the position of the principal facets on the front of the stone; and the angles which the squares at the back make with the axis of the stone, are required to be such, that all the light reflected from their surfaces, may fall within the central flat surface on the front of the stone, called the *table*.

The facets are arranged upon the stones in a great variety of methods, but they may nearly all be considered as modifications of three principal varieties, namely, the *trap cut*, the *brilliant cut*, and the *rose cut*, one of the two latter forms being always employed for diamonds.

The trap cut, or trapping, as it is called by lapidaries, consists of parallel planes nearly rectangular, arranged round the contour of the stone, as shown in figs. 1151 to 1156. This cut is always used for emeralds, and sometimes also for the fronts of other gems, but it is principally employed for the backs of stones, the fronts of which are cut in one of the modifications of the brilliant cut.

The brilliant cut consists of lozenge-shaped facets alternated with triangles, as shown in figs. 1157 to 1167, and is used for the fronts of most transparent stones that are sufficiently thick to allow of being cut into facets on both the front and back. The different modifications of this form of facetting, are known as the half brilliant, or single cut; the full brilliant; the split brilliant, or trap brilliant; and the double brilliant, or Lisbon cut; according to the arrangement of the principal facets.

The rose cut consists of triangular facets arranged upon and around a central hexagon, as in figs. 1169 to 1173. This cut is employed upon such stones as are thin, and large on the surface, or, as it is called, much *spread*, as the rose cut is applied only on the front of the stone, and the back is left flat. The rose cut is considered to give the greatest lustre that can be obtained from cutting the front only, as the surface is entirely covered with facets, and on this account the rose cut is sometimes applied to opake stones, but its principal application is to the diamond, or to other colourless gems employed as fictitious diamonds, such as the jargoon.

In all cases of cutting valuable gems, the principal object of the lapidary is to fashion the stone so as to produce as much display as can be attained without materially reducing the size of the gem, and this circumstance in great measure determines the manner in which it is cut. This is especially the case with the diamond, which is always found in the form of an octahedron, more or less perfect in form; and unless the diamond has defects, it is always cut as a brilliant, with an octagonal base, that being the largest regular figure that can be inscribed within the octahedron.

Diamonds that have defects are split by cleavage, and the pieces are cut into rose diamonds, and which form is also adopted for those whole diamonds that are too thin to be cut into brilliants. Other valuable gems are in like manner cut into the largest regular forms they will respectively produce.

With less valuable stones and pastes, the reduction of the material is of less importance, and the form of cutting is rather a matter of choice than otherwise; but in order that they may the more nearly resemble valuable gems, they are usually cut into corresponding forms; this is especially the case with pastes, which are cut on the front in exactly the same manner as the gems they are intended to represent, and the cutting at the back is only modified, so as to cause the play of light to assimilate to that of the gems themselves.

In all cases of cutting gems or pastes into facets, the general contour of the stone is first produced by roughly grinding it into form, much the same as for a rounded stone. Generally the first step is to grind a flat face upon the stone, in order to judge of its quality, and ascertain whether it contains any imperfections, and, if so, the cutting is modified accordingly. If the stone proves to be tolerably perfect, and it is to be cut into facets upon both the front and back, the flat surface first cut is made to constitute the table of the stone, and the edges are corrected to bring it to a regular figure, generally a circle or ellipsis, but sometimes a square, or rectangle, with the corners rounded off, according to the shape that can be produced with the least waste of material. The edge thus ground forms the *girdle*, or extreme margin of the stone by which it is retained in the setting. The part between the girdle and table, called the top of the stone, is then rounded or bevelled off to about the extent that the facets are desired to extend. The back of the stone is afterwards rounded in the same manner to the general shape, leaving a small central plane called the *cullet*, or *cullasse*.

If the stone is to be cut into facets on the front only, the flat face first cut is mostly made to constitute the back of the stone, the edges are corrected for the girdle, and the front is prepared by cutting, first, a flat face for the table, and afterwards rounding or bevelling the top. So far the stones are prepared in the same manner to the general shape, whatsoever form of facetting is to be adopted.

The square cut, or trap cut, is the most simple form of cutting facets, and also serves as the foundation of the facets of the brilliant cut. The method of producing the trap cut will be therefore first described, and this will be followed by some observations on the brilliant cut. In order to avoid confusion, it will be more convenient to limit the majority of the examples to elliptical stones cut with eight principal planes or facets, one on each of the sides of an irregular octagon. Stones are frequently cut with as many as twelve or fourteen sides, but the general method is exactly the same, whatever may be the number of sides.

Fig. 1151 represents in plan, and fig. 1152 in side elevation, a stone cut on the face only with a single row or *height* of eight planes or squares connecting the central table with the girdle. In cutting this form, the stone is cemented upon a stick with the side to constitute the back outwards; this is then ground flat, the edge cut into shape for the girdle, and the back polished; the stone is then re-cemented upon the stick with the front outwards. The stick should be a little smaller in diameter at the end than the size of the stone, which requires to be placed exactly central on the stick, and with the flattened back as nearly as possible at right angles to the axis of the stick, in order that the table may be cut parallel with the back, and also that the squares on the top may be all cut at the same angle.

The cutting on the front of the stone is commenced by grinding the flat table; a uniform bevel is then cut around the top. The bevel is made of about the width of the desired squares, and is called a *water basil*, from its running uninterruptedly around the stone. So far the process is exactly the same as for cutting an elliptical stone with a bevelled edge.

The eight squares, or facets, are then cut upon the bevelled edge. For this purpose the stone is applied to the mill as shown in fig. 1150, the gim peg, *h*, being adjusted for position, until upon trial it is found that, on placing the stone fairly upon the lap

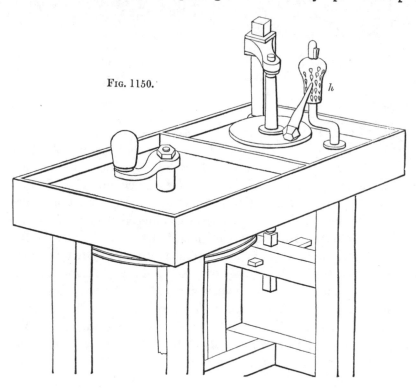

Fig. 1150.

or mill, and inserting the upper end of the stick in one of the notches in the wooden socket, the stick is inclined at the same angle as that at which the water basil was ground. The gim peg is then fixed by the wing nut beneath the bench, and the wooden socket secured by the wedge; the mill is then put in revolution, and the stone is applied, first to cut the two facets on the longest sides opposite to each other, and then those at the two ends are cut as nearly square as practicable, under the guidance of the eye alone; lastly, the four squares at the corners are cut to bring the stone to the octagonal form.

The four planes first cut at right angles serve as the basis of the figure, and some care and practice are required to place them exactly square, but the process is less difficult than might be

Figs. 1151.   1153.

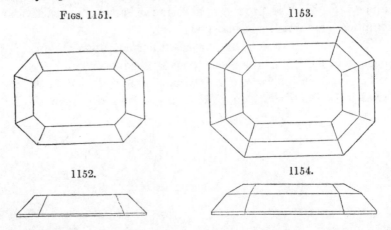

1152.   1154.

anticipated, as in cutting the first pair of opposite planes, it may be readily perceived whether or not they are parallel, and should they not be correctly placed at the first attempt, the stick is slightly twisted in the hand for changing the position of the squares. But little pressure is exerted upon the stone, with the fingers applied above the stick and as near to the stone as convenient. The square position of the pair of planes at the two ends, may in like manner be estimated very nearly by a practised eye, and these foundation squares having been correctly placed, the position of the four squares at the corners is tolerably easy of attainment, and these squares are gradually enlarged until the desired figure is produced. In elliptical stones the corner squares are mostly smaller than the others, in order to avoid the reduction of the material. In cutting a stone with twelve squares on the same height, the four squares at right angles are first cut in the same manner, and the figure is completed by cutting two facets at each of the four angles, instead of one only as for the octagon. Stones with ten or fourteen facets on the one row are rather more difficult to cut by hand, as only the two opposite facets in the middle can be derived from the square figure.

Figs. 1153 and 1154 represent a thicker stone trapped in two heights, or cut with two rows of square facets, one above the other, and placed at different angles with the table of the stone. The row of squares adjoining the girdle is always left somewhat wider than that adjoining the table, partly with the view of compensating for the narrow portion enclosed in the setting.

The stone is prepared in exactly the same manner as for a single height of trapping, except that two water basils of the desired widths of the squares, are cut upon the top of the stone. The row of squares near the girdle is first cut, the cement stick being inserted in the same hole in the gim peg for cutting every square in the same row. The row of squares adjoining the table is then cut in the same manner, except that the stick is inserted in a higher hole in the gim peg, in order to place the squares at a greater angle; and some care is required to cut the upper row exactly opposite the lower.

As previously mentioned, transparent stones, that are of sufficient thickness, are generally cut both on the front and back. In this case about one-third of the entire thickness is given to the front, and about two-thirds to the back, as shown in figs. 1155 and 1156, which represent the side elevation and back plan of a

Figs. 1155.   1156.

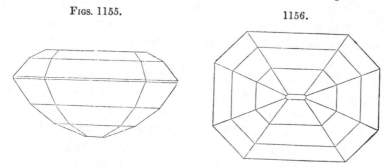

stone trapped in two heights or rows of squares on the front, like fig. 1154, and three heights at the back, a style of cutting frequently adopted for small emeralds and other stones. Those of medium size have generally four heights on the back, and very large emeralds sometimes have three heights of trapping on the face, and from five to eight heights on the back; but with emeralds the trap cut is not often carried to the latter degree of elaboration, unless it be done with the view of keeping the gem as heavy as possible, as the greater the number of heights in the trapping, the more roundness can be given to the general contour of the back, and consequently greater weight to the stone; but if the convexity be too great, it detracts from the lustre of the gem.

In cutting a stone to the form of fig. 1155, it is cemented on a stick, the flat surface of the table is first cut, and the edge is brought to the desired shape of the girdle. Two water basils are then cut around the top, in the same manner as for fig. 1154, but the facets on the front are not cut until the back has been completed; for this purpose the stone is re-cemented upon the stick, and the back is rounded to the general form; a single water basil is then cut around the girdle, to determine the height of the first row of squares, and these squares are next cut, with the aid of the gim peg; the second row of squares are then cut in like manner, but without the preparatory step of cutting the water basil, as the first row of squares serves as a sufficient guide for keeping the squares in the second row uniform; the third row of squares is cut in the same manner, the cement stick being shifted to a higher notch in the gim peg between every row; and, lastly, the stick is held vertical to cut the culasse.

The squares are then polished in the same order, the gim peg being carefully adjusted for height between every row, in order that the stick may be inclined at exactly the same angle as that employed for cutting the squares. As mentioned in the catalogue, a pewter mill supplied with rottenstone and water is employed for polishing stones of about the hardness of carnelian, and a copper mill is generally employed for harder gems. Some lapidaries, however, prefer a bell-metal mill for polishing hard gems, such as the sapphire, as the bell metal, being harder than the copper, the mill is less liable to be worn into ridges.

The stone, when polished on the back, is detached from the stick, and re-cemented with the front outwards. The position of the stone requires to be very carefully adjusted to make it exactly central and square with the stick, or the front of the stone would be liable to be cut oblique to the back. When the stone has been properly adjusted, the squares are cut on the front of the stone exactly as for fig. 1154. The surfaces of the table and squares are then polished, and the stone is detached from the stick by gently warming it over a candle. Lastly, the stone is washed with turpentine to remove any small particles of cement.

The brilliant cut, variously modified, is the form of facetting most generally adopted for the fronts of gems and pastes, and the backs of these stones are mostly trapped, or cut in squares. The principal varieties of the brilliant cut are represented in figs. 1157 to 1168, in which every stone is shown in three views, viz. the plan of the front of the stone, the side view, and the plan of the back. The dotted lines around the upper halves of the front views, are inserted to show more distinctly the manner in which the brilliant cut, consisting of lozenge-shaped facets alternated with triangular facets, is derived from the square or trap cut, by the removal of the angles indicated by the dotted lines.

With the same view of rendering the diagrams more distinct, the outlines of nearly all the girdles are represented of the polygonal forms they would assume, if the facets adjoining the girdles were made strictly angular, so as to terminate in straight lines upon the girdle. In the brilliant cut, however, the girdles are not generally cut to the polygonal forms, but they are made as easy curves, nearly approaching the forms shown in the diagrams, if the extreme angles are supposed to be removed; and in cutting the rows of facets adjoining the girdles, these angles are not quite developed. The rounded form of the girdle is adopted partially with the view of keeping the stone as large as possible, and avoiding the liability of the angles being chipped in cutting the facets, and partially because the rounded girdle is more convenient in setting the stone.

The size of the table, in proportion to that of the girdle, depends in great measure upon the thickness of the stone, compared with its width or *spread*, and the taste of the lapidary, no invariable rule being adopted; but the table is seldom made less than half, or more than two-thirds, the length of the girdle.

The size of the culasse is very small, being only just sufficient to prevent the facets at the back of the stone from meeting in a point, and its width is seldom more than about the thirtieth of an

inch, although in large and long stones it is sometimes as much
as one quarter of an inch in length. The culasse has the effect
of reflecting a small quantity of light into the table, that would
otherwise be lost; but its principal purpose is to prevent the
formation of a weak angle, that would be liable to be easily
broken.

The half brilliant, figs. 1157 to 1159, is the most simple
variety of the brilliant cut, and is very generally employed for

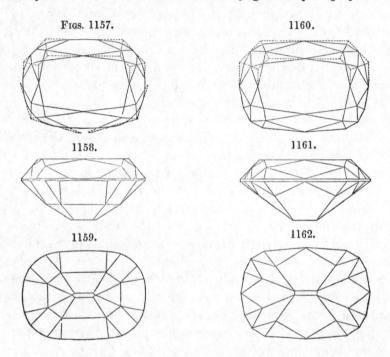

FIGS. 1157.

1160.

1158.

1161.

1159.

1162.

those stones that are too small to admit of numerous facets being
cut upon their surfaces. In cutting a stone to the form of the
half brilliant the front is prepared exactly as for a single height
of trapping, the first step being to cut the table; secondly, the
girdle; and thirdly, the water basil. The stone is then inverted for
cutting the back; in the figure this is shown as consisting of two
rows of squares, or trapping, with eight triangular facets cut
upon the angles of the eight squares adjoining the girdle; these
triangular facets are called *under squares*, and are very generally
employed upon stones that are trapped on the back, partly in
order to diminish the size of the large squares, and increase the
number of facets, and partly to give the stone a more rounded

figure, by removing the prominent angles that would be liable to interfere with the setting.

In cutting the back, the stone is first rounded to the general contour; secondly, the culasse is cut; thirdly, the water basil for the row of squares adjoining the girdle; fourthly, the eight prin- cipal squares are cut on this row; fifthly, the eight squares adjoin- ing the culasse; and lastly, the eight under squares, and the polishing completes the back.

The stone is again inverted upon the cement stick for cutting the facets on the front, and the table is first corrected, eight squares are then cut upon the water basil, exactly as for fig. 1151, as represented by the dotted lines around the upper half of fig. 1157 ; and the surfaces of the eight planes thus produced, constitute the surfaces of the eight principal planes in the finished stone, as shown in the figure. These planes are called *foundation squares*, and are converted into the pentagonal shape shown in the figure, by cutting one row of eight triangular facets around the table, and another row of eight triangular facets around the girdle. The bases of all the upper row of facets around the table, extend from the center of the upper edge of one foundation square, to the center of the upper edge of the adjoining square, and the apex touches the point of the pentagon upon the line of intersection of the two squares ; thus removing the entire angle indicated by the dotted lines in the figure, and altering the position of the original octagon constituting the table of the stone, at the same time that its size is reduced by the removal of its angles. These triangular facets are called *skill facets*, from the difficulty of placing them correctly.

The lower row of eight facets around the girdle is produced by cutting a triangular facet upon every one of the lower angles of the foundation squares, every lower facet is placed exactly opposite the corresponding skill facet, and is extended perpen- dicularly until it reaches the point of the skill facet ; but, in the half brilliant, the lower row of facets is not extended laterally to the middle of the foundation squares, as this would remove too great an angle, and diminish the size of the stone. The lower facets are therefore cut only so wide as can be ventured without interfering with the rounded form of the girdle. The dotted lines on the lower half of fig. 1157 are inserted to show that the lozenge is the primary form of the foundation squares in all the varieties of the brilliant cut, and the pentagonal form of these squares in the half brilliant arises simply from the lower facets being only partially developed.

In all cases of facetting transparent stones, it is very important that the foundation squares on the front should be equal in number, and exactly opposite to the principal squares on the back, and also that the lower facets should be opposite to the under squares, or otherwise the play of light would appear confused, and the brilliancy of the stone would be materially reduced. In order to place the squares opposite, it is quite necessary that both the front and back of the stone should be cut accurately with reference to the shape of the girdle, as the back of the stone requires to be entirely embedded in the cement at the time the front is cut; and the only guide employed by the lapidary for the correct position of the squares, is derived from the general shape of the girdle, and the certainty that the back squares have been correctly placed.

The full brilliant cut represented in figs. 1160 to 1162, may be received as the foundation from which the other varieties of the brilliant cut are derived, and is considered to be the most perfect form of facetting for gems. It is therefore almost invariably employed for all diamonds that are sufficiently thick, and perfect, to admit of its application ; but diamonds, from their crystallisation in the form of the octahedron, generally have a nearly regular octagon for the table and base, instead of the irregular octagon selected for illustration. Diamonds cut into this form are called *brilliants;* and the term brilliant cut, when used alone, is always understood to imply that the front and back of the stone are both facetted, as shown in the figures. Other gems than the diamond, and also pastes, are however often facetted in the same manner on the front only, and the back is cut in some other mode that will permit of a greater number of facets being introduced, generally the trap cut, or the star cut, is employed on the back, and the stone is then said to have a brilliant cut front, and a trapped back, or star-cut back, as the case may be.

In cutting the full brilliant, the front of the stone is prepared by cutting the table, girdle, and water basil, exactly as for fig. 1151 ; and in forming the back, the eight principal squares are first cut just as in trapping a single height, the culasse is then cut, and lastly, the 16 facets around the girdle, called *under facets*, are produced by cutting two triangular facets upon every one of the angles of the eight principal squares, which thus become converted into the irregular pentagons shown in the figures.

In facetting the front, the eight foundation squares, and the eight skill facets around the table, are cut in just the same manner as for the half brilliant; but in removing the lower angles of the foundation squares, two triangular facets are cut at every angle, exactly the same as on the back of the stone. These facets are by some lapidaries called *double skill facets*, from being cut in pairs, and by others *brilliant facets*, because the rays of light are reflected from their surfaces with greater brilliancy than from any other part of the stone.

It will be observed that in the figures the lozenge shape of the foundation squares is irregular, the lower pair of sides being wider than the upper; this form is adopted partly to allow for the small portion enclosed in the setting of the stone, but principally in order to increase the play of light, by making the brilliant facets as large as can be ventured without materially impairing the symmetry of the cutting.

The *split brilliant*, or *trap brilliant*, figs. 1163 to 1165, only differs from the full brilliant, fig. 1161, in the foundation squares being divided horizontally into two triangular facets, forming an obtuse angle when viewed in elevation, as in fig. 1164. In cutting the split brilliant, the face of the stone is prepared by forming two bevels around the margin, which are afterwards converted into squares exactly like the stone trapped in two heights, fig. 1153. The upper height of squares is made narrower than the lower; the skill facets, and the brilliant facets, are cut in the same manner as for a full brilliant, and are both made to terminate on the ridge dividing the foundation squares into triangular facets.

The back of the stone is represented as trapped in three heights of different widths, the narrowest being nearest the culasse. The squares of the trapping are, as usual, placed opposite to the foundation squares on the front, and the row of squares adjoining the girdle has its angles replaced by eight under squares placed opposite to the brilliant facets on the front.

The double brilliant, or Lisbon cut, figs. 1166 to 1168, is a duplication of the brilliant cut, fig. 1161, having two rows of lozenge-shaped squares, and three rows of triangular facets. The

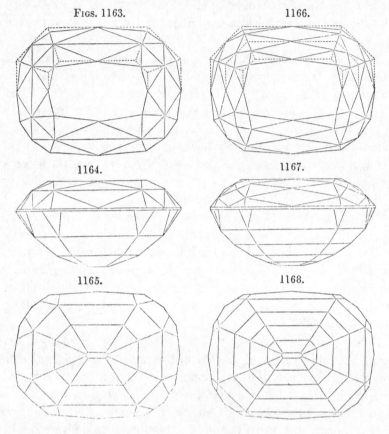

FIGS. 1163.   1166.

1164.   1167.

1165.   1168.

two rows of foundation squares are first cut as for the stone trapped in two heights, fig. 1153; and they are afterwards converted into the lozenge shape, by cutting one row of skill facets around the table, one row of double skill facets upon the angles joining the two rows of squares, and one row of brilliant facets around the girdle. The dotted lines in fig. 1166 show the angles removed by cutting these facets, by which it will be seen that the row of double skill facets in the middle, removes at the one operation the inner angles of both rows of foundation squares.

In some few instances a third row of foundation squares is added, by first cutting the stone in three heights, and then cutting three rows of double skill facets in addition to the row of skill facets around the table; but this degree of elaboration is considered to cause so much confusion in the rays of light, as to entirely neutralise the advantage obtained from the greater number of reflecting surfaces, and is seldom resorted to except for concealing defects in large stones.

The rose cut shown in figs. 1169 to 1173, as previously mentioned, is employed for those diamonds and other transparent

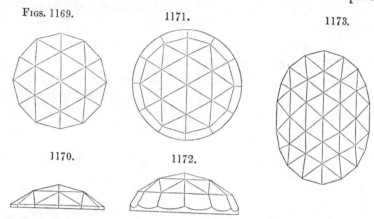

Figs. 1169.   1171.   1173.

1170.   1172.

stones that are too thin to admit of being cut on the back ; and sometimes the rose cut is also employed for opaque stones that would derive no additional lustre from the back cutting. The true rose cut consists of twenty-four triangular facets, cut upon a stone having a circular or dodecagonal base, flat beneath and rounded at the top, as shown in fig. 1170. The central portion of the stone is cut into six equilateral triangular facets, the points of which meet in the center at the summit of the stone, and their bases form a regular hexagon, six other equilateral triangles are joined by their bases to the central facets, and their points rest upon the girdle. The spaces between the outer row of triangles are each cut into two triangular facets, which closely resemble the double skill facets in the brilliant cut.

In cutting the stone, figs. 1169 and 1170, the back is flattened, and the face rounded to the general curve, the central zone of six facets is then cut, commencing with two opposite facets, and when these have been made parallel, and of the required size, the intervals are each cut into two facets, care being taken that all the facets are of equal size. The six principal facets in the outer row are next cut; and lastly, the six intervals between these facets are cut into six pairs of double skill facets, which complete the rose cut, as applied to diamonds, and thin gems generally.

Thicker stones, however, are sometimes cut with an additional row of twelve nearly square facets, arranged around the outer row of triangles, as in figs. 1171 and 1172; every square being equal in width to the base of its adjoining triangle; at other times, instead of squares, the outer row is composed of two rows of triangles.

The rose cut is also frequently applied to elliptical stones, as in fig. 1173; and, as there shown, the central hexagon is elongated, and the triangles are made of irregular forms.

Figs. 1174 to 1176 represent a stone cut in squares, or trapped in one height on both the front and back, which differ from each

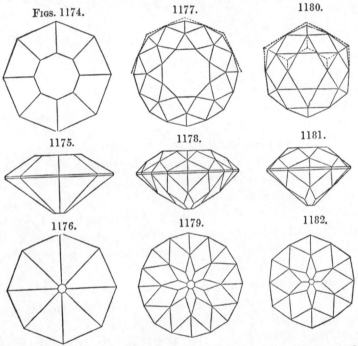

Figs. 1174.   1177.   1180.

1175.   1178.   1181.

1176.   1179.   1182.

other only in the greater thickness of the back, and the culasse being much smaller than the table. This form of cutting is sometimes adopted for small crystals and pastes for cheap jewellery.

Crystals and pastes employed as fictitious diamonds, are generally cut as in figs. 1177 to 1179. The front is cut as a full brilliant of eight principal squares, upon a regular octagonal base like the diamond. The back is first cut with a row of eight squares, somewhat like fig. 1176; a row of double skill facets are then arranged around the girdle, as in fig. 1162 ; and, lastly, a row of eight facets are arranged around the culasse. These facets are cut upon the angles joining the principal back squares, the points are extended until they meet the double skill facets, and the back facets intersect each other near the culasse, giving the appearance of a star, whence this form of facetting for the back is known as the star cut. The row of facets around the culasse materially increases the brilliancy, and causes the play of light more nearly to approach that of the diamond. Figs. 1180 to 1182 represent the same form of cutting applied to a hexagonal stone.

The form of facetting called the × cut, shown in figs. 1183 to 1186, is considered to be a very perfect style of cutting for stones

Figs. 1183. 1185. 1187.

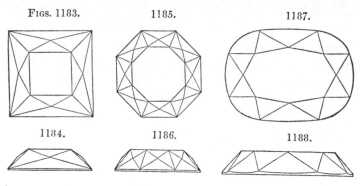

1184. 1186. 1188.

having a square or a regular octagon for their base, as it allows of a considerable number of triangular facets being cut upon the top, and at the same time the table and girdle may be retained of one regular figure. In cutting this form, the front is trapped in two heights, and the squares thus produced are converted into triangles by cutting one pair of triangular facets upon every angle of the square or octagon. As seen in the figures, these facets extend from the table to the girdle, and meet in the center of the sides. The × cut is seldom applied to other than square or octagonal stones, and for these shapes the back is generally facetted with the star cut, but sometimes octagonal stones are trapped at the back.

Figs. 1187 and 1188 represent the *dental cut*, which consists of two rows of triangular facets cut on the top of the stone. The two rows are interposed, so that the bases of one row of triangles form the margin of the table, and the bases of the second row are placed on the line of the girdle, each row extending from the girdle to the table, as seen in the figures, which show the application of this cut to an elliptical stone having eight principal sides. In cutting this form, the front is first trapped in one height with eight squares, and the figure is completed by cutting eight triangular facets around the table, every facet being placed, as usual, upon one of the angles formed by the foundation squares. The back is generally trapped.

All the different forms of facetting are usually cut by practical lapidaries, without any other guide than the gim peg, and cement stick, as shown in fig. 1150. The more difficult cases of cutting valuable gems, arise from the irregular forms of the rough gems, or slight imperfections in their substance, and these difficulties require to be combated rather by judgment and dexterity of hand, than by mechanical guides. This dexterity once acquired, renders the employment of guides less necessary, when the forms of the rough gems are more favourable, especially as the adjustments can be effected more rapidly by the practised fingers, than by mechanical means.

In the comparatively slow process of polishing the facets on diamonds, a very simple form of guide is adopted, as alluded to at page 176, Vol. I.; but this instrument only serves to retain the stone in position, and all the adjustments of angle are effected by hand, in order that the operator may be enabled to place every facet flat upon the skive, without reference to the particular angle at which it was cut.

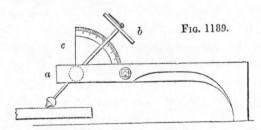

Fig. 1189.

Fig. 1189 shows a modification of this instrument, contrived by a Geneva lapidary, to adapt it to the cutting of facets at definite angles, and published in the *Dictionnaire Technologique*. The instrument, called a *cadrans*, has two jaws, *a*, which are closed like a vice by a screw passing through them, each of the jaws has on the inside a hemispherical cavity, into which is fitted a brass ball; a tube passes through the ball, and carries at its upper end a small flat disk, *b*, having on the upper side several concentric circles divided into equal parts. Every circle has a different number of divisions, which are so arranged as to include all the numbers usually required in cutting facets. The cement stick, carrying the stone to be cut, is made cylindrical, and fits within the tube sufficiently tight to retain its position during the cutting of the stone, and the upper end of the stick is made square to carry a small index point, by which the divisions on the disk are read off.

The vertical angle of the tube is determined by the quadrant *c*, fixed on one side of the jaws, *a*, and the tube is retained at any angle by closing the jaws upon the ball. The center of the quadrant is supposed to be in the center of the ball, and the arc is divided as usual into 90 degrees, the upper division is marked 0, and the lower 70, the remainder of the arc being hidden by the jaw. When the tube is fixed at 0, the cement stick is vertical, and this position serves for cutting the table or the culasse ; on fixing the tube at 20 degrees, all the facets cut in this position will be inclined at that angle, and the number of facets around the stone will be determined by twisting the cement stick in the tube, until the index marks the required division on the disk, *b*.

Fictitious gems are prepared in a variety of ingenious methods, sometimes stones of inferior value are modified in their colours by heat, and substituted for more valuable gems, as in the case of the zircon, which is sometimes rendered colourless by heat, and substituted for the diamond. The colours of carnelian are principally given by heat. In Phillip's Mineralogy, it is stated, that carnelians, when found, are of a blackish olive passing into a grey. " These are first exposed to the sun for some weeks, and then placed in earthen pots, and subjected to heat, which gives them the colours which constitute their value in jewellery."

Carnelian, when imported into England, is generally of a red colour, and when the colour is too light, it is sometimes deepened by putting it in an iron pot, and gradually bringing it to a red heat. Yellow carnelian is by the same means rendered red; but the effect of heat upon white carnelian is to render it more opaque, and advantage is sometimes taken of this circumstance to give white carnelian the appearance of the white onyx. The various colours of agates are, in some cases, more fully developed in the same manner; at other times, the agates are soaked in oil for two or three hours; the oil penetrates the agate, and is afterwards carbonised within the stone by exposing the latter to the fumes of heated sulphuric acid. Nitrate of silver is also sometimes employed for staining agate, and other stones.

Pastes are, however, the most frequent substitutes for precious stones. The foundation of all pastes is a superior colourless glass called *strass*, made from very pure materials, and afterwards coloured by the addition of metallic oxides, in much the same manner that ordinary coloured glass is made, except that the process is more carefully performed throughout. The French are considered to excel in the preparation of pastes, and a variety of recipes for the manufacture of pastes, derived from various French authors, are given in Dr. Ure's " Dictionary of Arts," p. 943, and also in Gill's " Technical Repertory," vol. ii., p. 308.

Metallic foils made of thin sheet copper silvered and burnished, and afterwards coated with transparent colours, mixed with isinglass size, are often employed by jewellers to improve the brilliancy of pastes and inferior stones. The foil is enclosed in the setting, and entirely covers the back of the stone, to which it imparts much of its own brilliancy. When it is desired to modify the colour of the stone, a foil of a lighter or darker tint is used, according to circumstances. Crystals and pastes, set as imitation diamonds, generally have a piece of silvered foil at the back.

Painting is sometimes resorted to for counterfeiting topazes, and other gems; in this case, a colourless stone, such as crystal is employed, and the back of the stone to be enclosed in the setting, is painted with the colour removed from a piece of foil, and another piece of the same foil is placed behind the stone in the setting, to improve the brilliancy. The reflection of the colour from the back of the stone is so uniformly diffused throughout its substance, that, even upon close observation, the unpractised eye fails to detect the absence of colour in the body of the stone. In removing the colour from the foil, the latter is gently warmed over a candle, and, while warm, the colour is worked up with a moistened brush, and immediately applied to the stone, care being taken to cover every portion of the back, particularly the angles formed by the meeting of the facets, as, should the smallest speck remain uncoloured, it would reflect a ray of white light that would altogether mar the effect. The painting of these fictitious gems is sometimes so successfully executed, that only those persons thoroughly conversant with precious stones, are enabled to distinguish between the real gem and the counterfeit, so long as the stone remains in the setting.

Doublets are a more elegant and substantial application of the method of counterfeiting gems by coloured backs, and transparent fronts. In doublets, the front and back are made in two pieces, cemented together on the line of the girdle. The front is made of a colourless stone, and the back of a coloured paste; the two surfaces to be placed in contact, are first ground quite flat and smooth, to fit each other accurately ; they are then cemented together with a very thin layer of clear mastic, and the doublet thus prepared is cut as a single stone.

In real gems, advantage is sometimes taken of the power of a coloured back to give colour to a colourless front. It occasionally happens that a gem may be partly colourless and partly coloured. In this case, instead of dividing the stone, the coloured portion is placed at the back, and, if possible, the stone is so cut that the table shall be parallel to the imaginary line dividing the two portions ; and if the stone has much natural brilliancy, it is not imperative that the coloured portion should extend to the girdle, as a comparatively small piece, properly placed, will serve to colour the entire stone.

A striking illustration of this was recently observed by the writer in the case of a sapphire, the bulk of which was perfectly colourless, and a small part only of a deep blue colour. This gem was about one-sixth of an inch in length, and nearly of the same measure from the table to the culasse, the great proportional depth having been adopted, in order that the colour might be reflected throughout the body of the stone, from the small blue portion, which was scarcely larger than the head of an ordinary pin, and yet in consequence of its being situated exactly upon the culasse, and extending a small distance up the back facets, the blue colour appeared to be uniformly diffused throughout the stone when viewed from the front, although at the time of inspection the stone was not set. When viewed from the back, the body of the stone appeared quite colourless, with a small speck of a dark blue colour on the culasse.

Some management is, however, required to obtain this result, as, if the stone have too much width or spread, the edges will appear colourless, and in extreme cases the blue will only show as a dark central speck. Owing to the various degrees of brilliancy in different stones, and the variation in the size of the coloured portion, no invariable rule can be adopted for the spread of the stone relatively to the depth ; the proportions are therefore obtained by trial, the spread being gradually reduced without interfering with the thickness, until the desired result is obtained.

SECT. III.—LAPIDARY APPARATUS FOR AMATEURS.

LAPIDARY apparatus for amateurs is in some cases made precisely similar to that described in the preceding section, but more generally the laps are driven by a foot wheel and treadle ; the general arrangement of the apparatus then closely resembles the horizontal grinding machine shown in fig. 1039, page 1157, in which the upper surface of the lap is not obstructed by a vertical spindle, as in the lapidary's bench, fig. 1141, and the same spindle is employed for all the different grinding and polishing wheels.

The less difficult process of lapidary work, such as producing a flat or a rounded surface on a pebble, may be executed with facility on the horizontal grinding machine, which is frequently converted into a simple lapidary apparatus by the addition of a slicer and trough to catch the water thrown off the lap. But for the more elaborate processes of lapidary work, such as cutting a stone into thin slices and facetting gems, other additions have been made, in which the principal difficulties of manipulation are removed by the introduction of guides for slitting and facetting, and the apparatus then assumes the more complete forms shown in figs. 1190 and 1192.

Fig. 1190 represents the amateur lapidary apparatus fitted

with the crane, or swinging arm, for presenting the stones to the slicer. The foundation of the apparatus exactly resembles that described in page 1157, except that the rectangular trough, indicated by the dotted lines in fig. 1190, occupies the place of the upper platform in fig. 1139, and the lower platform

Figs. 1190.

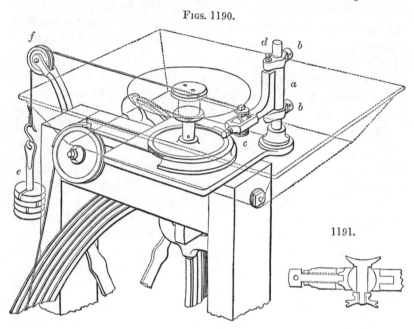

1191.

has an enlargement at its right-hand corner for the support of a strong cylindrical pillar that carries the socket a; this socket slides vertically upon the pillar, and admits of being fixed at any height by means of the binding screws $b\ b$. The swinging arm, c, is supported on the socket by two center screws, one of which is seen at d; these center screws allow of the horizontal motion of the arm, which has near the front a rectangular opening, in which is fitted a ball and socket-joint; and a binding screw at the extremity of the arm serves to retain the ball at any desired angle.

The ball is perforated with a square hole, into which is fitted the square stem of a metal cup, for the reception of the stone to be sliced. The cup and ball are shown separately in fig. 1191; and, as there seen, the stem of the cup passes through the ball, and is fixed by the milled nut beneath. The arm is drawn towards the slicer by the weight e, a line from which passes over the pulley f, fixed on the end of the frame, and is attached to a small stud screwed into the under side of the arm.

In slitting a stone with this apparatus, it is first cemented in a cup of appropriate size, the stone and cup being both heated nearly to the fusing point of the cement. The stone is placed with the intended line of division as nearly horizontal as convenient, and when the cement is set, the cup is inserted in the ball and fixed by the milled nut. The position of the ball is then adjusted until the line of division is exactly horizontal, and the precise height is regulated by sliding the socket upon the vertical pillar. When the adjustments have all been satisfactorily made, the binding screws are tightened, and the weight is attached to the line; this completes the preparations so far as the adjustment of the apparatus is concerned ; and when one cut has been made, if the stone is required to be cut into parallel slices, it is only necessary between every cut to shift the socket a, upwards, a distance equal to the thickness of the intended slice.

Of course the slicer requires to be charged with diamond powder, and lubricated with the oil of brick, as explained at page 1310; and the weight should also be proportioned to the size of the stone. To allow of the ready adjustment of the weight, it is made in detached disks, with central holes that fit upon a cylindrical rod, to which the line is attached. The rod is flattened near its upper end, and every disk has a radial mortise extending from the central hole to the edge. In applying the weight, the mortise is passed over the flattened part of the rod, and the central hole is slipped down the cylindrical portion of the rod, which is too large to pass through the mortise.

In fig. 1192 the apparatus for cutting facets is represented, the upright pillar at the back is here employed to support the platform g, and upon this is mounted the gim peg h, which may be employed for cutting facets in the same manner as that used by practical lapidaries; but the instrument for cutting facets shown at l, is a more exact contrivance, and far better adapted for the purposes of the amateur, as the facets may be cut to any required angle with great exactness, and the operator has only to determine the size of the facets by suspending the process when each facet is sufficiently developed.

The basis of the instrument is exactly the same as those for setting straight and angular turning tools, shown in fig. 1042,

p. 1159, and fig. 1047, p. 1165 ; indeed the same instrument may be made to serve all three purposes when fitted with suitable beds or sockets for the reception of the different objects to be ground. In the instrument for grinding facets the bed g, shown in fig. 1042, is replaced by a frame, which is mounted

Figs. 1192.

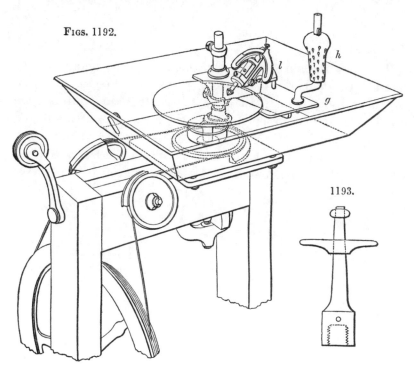

1193.

in the same manner, and is therefore capable of being set to any angle, either vertical or horizontal.

The frame, shown separately on a larger scale in fig. 1194, carries a steel spindle, which is capable of revolving within bearings, and may be fixed at any position by the binding screw, n. A hole bored up the center of the spindle extends nearly through its length, and into this is fitted the cylindrical stem of the cement cup, p, intended for the reception of the stone. The cement cup is retained in the spindle by the small binding screw, q. For determining the position of the spindle, a small pulley, r, is fixed on its front end ; the edge of the pulley is provided with two circles of graduations, the one containing 96 divisions, the other 60 ; and to enable the divisions to be read off with accuracy, an index is fixed on the top of the frame.

The annexed table shows the divisions of the circle that may be obtained from the two circles of 96 and 60, which will be found sufficient for general purposes.

In 2 parts by 48 in 96	In 8 parts by 12 in 96	In 20 parts by 3 in 60
„ 3 „ 32 „ 96	„ 10 „ 6 „ 60	„ 24 „ 4 „ 96
„ 4 „ 24 „ 96	„ 12 „ 8 „ 96	„ 30 „ 2 „ 60
„ 5 „ 12 „ 60	„ 15 „ 4 „ 60	„ 32 „ 3 „ 96
„ 6 „ 16 „ 96	„ 16 „ 6 „ 96	„ 48 „ 2 „ 96

The first column contains the number to be obtained; the second, the number of divisions to be taken in the circle denoted by the third column. In cases where the same intersection could be obtained in both circles, the lowest has been selected for easy reading.

In some cases, instead of the divisions and index, a toothed wheel and click are adopted; but this arrangement gives fewer

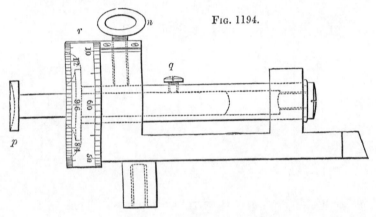

Fig. 1194.

divisions of the circle, as the choice is confined to the intersections in the number of teeth in the wheel. A much greater range is obtained by a worm wheel and tangent screw; but this arrangement is more tedious, and is scarcely called for in cutting facets.

In facetting a stone with the arrangement fig. 1192, the stone is prepared by cutting it to the general contour by hand, in the same manner as practised by lapidaries, the stone being fixed upon an ordinary cement stick, the flat surface for the table is first cut, and then the girdle. The front and back of the stone are afterwards rounded nearly to the required shape, and water basils cut, to denote the width of the principal facets. The stone is then removed from the cement stick, and attached to the cup p, shown in fig. 1194, in the same manner that it was previously attached to the cement stick; but it is here of still greater importance that the stone should be placed exactly in the center of the cup, and quite horizontal; or, otherwise, the facets will be cut at irregular angles.

To assist in determining the position of the stone before it is finally cemented, it will be found convenient, after the cement has been attached to the cup, to press the cold stone into the cement, while the latter is still warm and soft. This serves to form the cement correctly to the shape of the stone, and permits the position of the latter to be more deliberately inspected, and, if necessary, corrected. When the position of the stone is found to be satisfactory, the stone may be warmed over the candle, and the surface of the cement fused just sufficiently to adhere to the stone, which may then be slightly pressed into the cavity; the cement is lastly worked into the angles with the fingers, which may be slightly moistened, to prevent the adhesion of the cement.

The stone is attached to the instrument by sliding the stem of the cement cup p, into the socket, as seen in 1194, and fixing it by the small binding screw q. The projection of the stone from the socket of the instrument should be so adjusted that the socket may be exactly vertical, when the plane, C, fig. 1047, p. 1165, is fixed at 0, on the graduated arc, B, and the face of the stone rests upon the lap, while the feet of the instrument are supported upon the platform. The correct position of the instrument is most readily estimated, by observing that the base piece, A, is parallel to the platform.

With large stones, it will sometimes be found desirable to effect the adjustment by elevating or depressing the platform, instead of adjusting the projection of the cement cup; but with small stones, it will be generally found more convenient to place the platform level with the surface of the lap, under the test of a straight edge, in order that no after-adjustment of the instrument may be required when the laps are exchanged for smoothing and polishing.

The facets are cut in the same order that is adopted in cutting corresponding forms with the gim peg, and which has been already explained in the second section; but the vertical nclination for every row of facets is obtained by adjusting the plane C, shown in fig. 1047, p. 1165, upon the graduated arc B, and the number of facets in every row is determined by the divisions on the pulley of the socket shown in fig. 1194.

Thus, in cutting a stone with a brilliant-cut front, and a star-cut back, like fig. 1178, the plane C is placed at 0, on the arc B, for cutting the culasse. The principal row of eight squares at the back is cut with the plane, C, inclined to about 50, and the socket is fixed successively at the divisions 12, 24, 36, 48, 60, 72, 84, and 96. The row of 16 double skill facets around the girdle is cut with the plane, C, inclined to about 45, and the divisions employed are 3, 9, 15, 21, and so on to 93, in order that the double skill facets may terminate upon the angles of the principal squares. The row of eight facets around the culasse are cut with the plane, C, inclined to about 55, and the socket is fixed at the divisions 6, 18, 30, 42, &c., a facet being cut at every twelfth division, as in the row of primary squares; but, in order that the two rows of facets may be interposed, the intermediate numbers are employed. In cutting the front of the stone, the same series of divisions are employed for determining the numbers of facets, and the vertical angles are, 0, for the table; 50 for the foundation squares; 40 for the skill facets; and 60 for the brilliant facets.

Fig. 1193 represents a supplementary spindle that is screwed on the end of the upright mandrel, and is employed for carrying small mills and balls, which are held by a plain conical fitting, and employed for cutting mouldings and other details, as mentioned at page 1318.

CHAPTER XXXV.

GEM AND GLASS ENGRAVING.

SECT. I.—INTRODUCTION.—SEAL AND GEM ENGRAVING.

Gems, precious stones, glass, and similar hard substances that do not admit of the application of tools with cutting edges, are engraved either in relief, or in intaglio, by the employment of small revolving wheels, charged on their edges with fine abrasive powders, and lubricated with oil or water. The object to be engraved is applied to the lower edges of the wheels with the fingers, unassisted by any mechanism, but the object is twisted about during the process, so as to expose every part of the device successively to the action of the little wheels, which gradually produce small hollows and grooves, that are in section nearly counterparts of the sections of the tools employed in their formation. The wheels are made in a great variety of sizes and shapes, according to the forms they are intended respectively to produce, and with the abrasive powders they constitute the only cutting tools applied in these interesting and delicate processes of abrasion.

For engraving all hard stones, the wheels are made of iron, charged with diamond powder, and generally lubricated with the oil of bricks, and when the engraved surfaces are polished, copper wheels charged with rottenstone and water are employed. For engraving glass, similar but larger tools made of copper, charged with emery and olive oil, are employed, and the polishing is effected with leaden tools charged with pumice stone powder and water. The processes of engraving in gems and glass are very similar, and differ principally in the greater depth and elaboration of the designs in gem engraving, which latter will be first described, and the principal peculiarities of glass engraving will be afterwards alluded to in a separate section.

The most extensive application of engraving on stones, is the sinking in intaglio of armorial bearings on seals, which is called seal engraving, and the engraving in intaglio of more artistic subjects on gems and stones is called gem engraving. When the design is engraved in relief, the process is called cameo cutting, but the apparatus and manipulations are nearly the same in all three branches of the art. The ordinary practice of seal engraving will be, therefore, first described, followed by some observations on the more graceful art of gem engraving, and the practice of cameo cutting will be afterwards adverted to.

The greater portion of the remarks offered on seal engraving have been gathered from the practice of Mr. W. Warner, who has had considerable experience in engraving armorial bearings both in hard and soft stones. The observations on gem engraving and cameo cutting have been derived from Mr. Henry Weigall, whose works in these arts have obtained a celebrity that is a satisfactory guarantee for the excellence of his practice, and to whom the contents of the first two sections of this chapter have been submitted for verification.

The wheels employed in seal engraving are called *tools*, and are made as shown in fig. 1206, with long conical stems that are fitted somewhat like chucks into the hollow mandrel or *quill* of a miniature lathe head, called a seal engraver's engine, the most usual form of which is shown one-fourth of its real size in fig. 1196, this is mounted upon a stout table hollowed out in front somewhat like a jeweller's bench, and either about 2 feet 6 inches or 3 feet 6 inches high, according as the operator may prefer to sit or stand to his work. The engine is driven by a light foot wheel from 18 inches to 2 feet diameter. The tools being of very small diameter, little power is required ; a rapid motion is, however, requisite for some parts of the work, and a steady position of the body is at all times of the first importance; the treadle is, therefore, jointed just beneath the heel of the operator, who is thus enabled to give a rapid motion to the wheel with but little movement of the leg. The entire apparatus should be quite free from tremor, and with this view the bench is made very strong, and, if possible, firmly attached to the building. In some cases the foot wheel is mounted in a frame independent of the bench, in order that any vibration in the wheel or its axis may not be communicated to the tools.

Fig. 1195, shows the section of the engine, which consists of a brass pillar about 6 inches high, having at the base a central

FIGS. 1195. 1196.

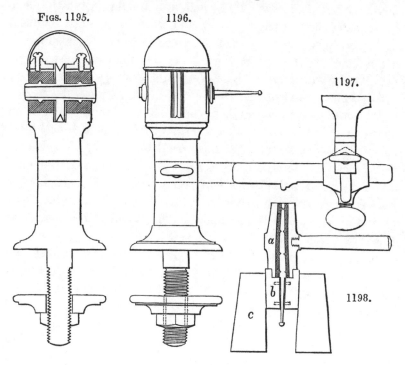

1197.

1198.

bolt, which passes through the top of the bench, and is retained by a nut and washer beneath. The upper part of the pillar has two openings, which cross each other at right angles, and serve for the reception of the pulley and bearings of the quill. The bearings are generally cylindrical, and made of tin or pewter cast upon the quill; each pair of bearings is adjusted to fit the quill by a set screw, passing through a brass cap screwed on the top of the pillar. The quill is of steel, about 2 inches long, and half an inch diameter; it passes entirely through the bearings, all end-play in which is prevented by two small beads upon the quill.

Throughout the length of the quill extends a slightly conical hole, measuring about five-sixteenths of an inch in diameter at the front end, and one quarter of an inch at the back. A small angular groove, about half an inch long, is filed in one side of the

hole, at the front end, for the reception of a corresponding
feather on the tools, which serves to prevent the tools from
slipping round in use, and also to ensure their being always
placed in the same position in the quill. The pulley, which
measures about one inch and a half in diameter, is mostly made
in the same piece with the quill, and when in its place is almost
concealed in the upper part of the pillar. A small hemispherical
cap is fitted on the top of the pillar, to exclude all dust or grit
from the bearings, and it is also very generally used as a rest for
steadying the hand during the process of engraving.

In some cases the quill is made 3 or 4 inches long, and
mounted, more like an ordinary lathe mandrel, in a conical steel
collar at the front, and a back center also of steel. In this case
the conical hole for the tools extends about 2 inches up the quill,
and a central mortise is made at the bottom of the hole, for the
insertion of a lever or wedge, by which the tools are forced out,
or otherwise a collar is cast upon the front end of the tools, and
they are released with a forked lever.

The tools are made of iron wire, prepared from the softest stub
iron, and carefully annealed, to render them as soft as possible.
The conical plug that fits into the quill of the engine, is formed
by casting around the stem of the tool a corresponding cone of
some easily fused metal, as tin, pewter, or lead hardened with a
little antimony. The moulds for casting the conical plugs are
made in various forms, but the general construction will be sufficiently obvious from an inspection of the section shown in
fig. 1198, in which *a* represents the body of the mould in which
the plug is cast ; *b*, the metal socket in which the tool and mould
are fixed to retain them both central ; and *c*, the wooden block
for the support of the whole. The part *a* is made a little longer
than the quill, and is fitted in the middle of its length with a
stem and wooden handle, which give it somewhat the appearance
of a hammer. Throughout its length extends a central conical
hole, the angle of which is exactly a copy of that in the quill,
(both holes being generally formed with the same tools,) and at
the larger end of the hole is filed an angular groove to form a
feather to fit in the corresponding groove in the quill. The end
of the mould *a*, having the groove, has a short cylindrical neck
turned on the outside, and concentric with the hole, and this
neck is fitted into a corresponding recess in the upper part of

the socket *b*. The socket is made in halves, fitted together with steady pins, and has a central hole for the reception of the tools. The exterior of the socket is made rather conical and fits into a corresponding hole in the wooden block *c*.

In preparing the tools after the wire has been annealed, they are first roughly filed into form, the small disks are filed out of the solid, the stem that projects from the end of the quill is made round, rather conical, and a little smaller at the largest part, than the hole in the socket. The shank that is to have the conical plug cast upon it is made square, slightly taper, and with a few notches roughly filed in the angles, in order that it may be firmly held in the casting. The socket *b* is then separated, and the stem of the tool is made to fit the central hole, rather tightly, by winding a slip of paper around it. The socket is then closed, inserted in the wooden block, and pressed tightly down, when the conical form of the exterior of the socket and of the hole, ensure a firm grasp upon the stem of the tool.

The mould *a* is then fitted into the recess in the socket *b*, which ensures the square stem of the tool being central with the conical hole, and the fluid metal is poured in from a small ladle. When the metal is set, the socket is removed from the block and separated, any superfluous metal that may have lodged on the upper end of the mould is filed off, the tool is then pushed out of the mould, and is ready to be inserted in the quill.

It is of primary importance that the tools should run perfectly true in the engine, and therefore after the plugs have been cast, the tools are fixed in the quill, and turned to the required forms, with small gravers applied in the usual manner. The rest for turning the tools is shown in fig. 1197, and much resembles that employed in the turnbench of the watchmaker; when in use the horizontal bar is passed through the mortise in the brass standard, and retained in its position by a binding screw.

The forms and sizes of the tools employed in seal engraving are very numerous, to adapt them to the various parts of the different devices, but the general shape is that of little disks more or less rounded on the edges, which is the part almost exclusively used. Some of the tools for cutting fine lines are made almost as thin on the edge as a knife, others rather thicker and more rounded on the edge, are employed for thicker lines.

For sinking large shields, and similar purposes, the tools are considerably rounded, being in some cases made almost spherical, as a tool with a rounded edge is found to cut more rapidly than one with a more nearly flat edge; and, therefore, a rounded tool is generally used for removing the principal bulk of the material in large works, and a tool with a flatter edge is used for smoothing the surface. For flat surfaces, the tools are of course made with flat edges, and to enable them to be applied to deep works without the stem interfering with their action, the diameter of the front of the tool is generally made somewhat smaller than the back, so as to make the edge rather conical, as seen in fig. 1202.

Figs. 1199 to 1205, represent some of the most usual shapes

FIGS. 1199.   1200.   1201.   1202.   1203.   1204.   1205.

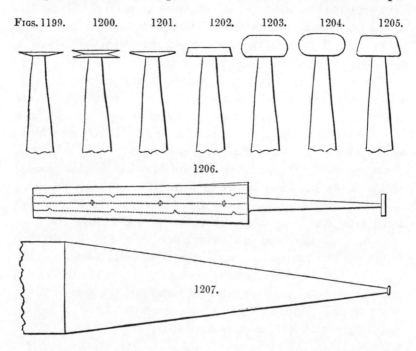

1206.

1207.

of tools, but the sizes are greatly magnified for distinctness, the tools shown in figs. 1199 to 1202, being seldom larger than one-sixth of an inch in diameter, and tools of nearly all the shapes are made very much smaller than that size, some of them being made so small as not to exceed the $\frac{1}{150}$th of an inch in diameter, and can hardly be distinguished by the naked eye from the stem of the tool, which appears to terminate almost in a needle point, although on examination with a powerful magnifier the disks are distinctly developed. The general form of the point of these minute tools is shown in fig. 1207, which represents the disk and part of the stem magnified about fifteen times.

These exceedingly minute tools do not admit of being formed of so small a size by the turning tool alone, they are therefore reduced as small as possible with a fine file, and are afterwards employed for works of a little larger size, until they become sufficiently small to be used for making very minute dots, such as sometimes occur in the markings of the eyes, in figures of men or animals, the full lengths of which do not exceed one quarter of an inch.

All the tools are required to have tolerably smooth surfaces, and to be quite free from ridges or hollows. In use they are liable to be worn into minute hollows, which are called *creases*, and should one of these be formed in the side of a thin tool, such as fig. 1199 or 1201, it would be almost certain to chip off a fragment of the stone, as soon as the crease was embedded in the cut. To prevent the formation of creases in thin tools, the seal engraver makes frequent use of a fine file to smoothen the sides of the tool, and which at the same time serves to prevent the edge of the tool from becoming thickened as it is reduced in diameter by wear.

The tools are charged with fine diamond powder, prepared as described in page 1052, in the mortars shown in figs. 1142 to 1144, p. 1309. Seal engravers generally keep the diamond powder in the mortar in which it was ground ; the powder is mixed into a pasty condition with olive oil, and small quantities are taken out as required. Sometimes the diamond powder, or paste, is kept in small quantities in a little conical cup, and the diamond is supplied to the tool, either by holding the cup to the tool, or a little of the diamond powder is removed with a small spatula, and held to the edge of the tool.

More generally, however, the seal engraver wears on the forefinger of the right hand, a ring made of a strip of tin, to which are soldered two little hollow disks, about half an inch in diameter, one of which contains a very small quantity of the diamond paste, the other, one or two drops of the oil of bricks. The diamond paste is occasionally applied to the extreme edge of the tool while it is revolving slowly, the tool is then moistened with the oil of bricks, and the cutting is proceeded with, until the brick oil is nearly expended, when the tool is again moistened. Should the tool be allowed to become too dry, the diamond would become detached from the tool, and instead of the stone being cut, the tool itself would be abraded, and as the brick oil is very volatile, it requires to be frequently applied. Some artists prefer sperm oil for lubricating the tools, it is less expensive, and has not the unpleasant scent of brick oil, but unless carefully prepared, it is liable to become thick, and impede the action of the tools.

The stones to be engraved are always previously prepared to the general form by the lapidary, and frequently they are set by the jeweller before they are engraved, in either case they are too short to be conveniently held in the fingers, they are therefore mounted on a handle about five inches long, and three-quarters of an inch diameter. If the stone has not been set, it is fixed with lapidary's cement upon a wooden handle, and to prevent the cement from adhering to the fingers, it is sometimes coated with sealing-wax. But if the stone has been previously set, it is inserted in a notch made in a piece of cork, or soft wood, that is frequently inserted in the end of a piece of bamboo of appropriate size. When the stones are hard, and have been previously polished on the surfaces that are to be engraved, the latter are roughened, by rubbing them upon a soft steel plate charged with a little diamond powder and oil; an ordinary plane iron when annealed is often used as the plate. Sometimes the polish is removed from soft stones by rubbing them upon a leaden plate charged with emery, but the steel plate and diamond powder is more generally used, as it serves equally well for hard or soft stones.

The roughened surface of the stone is required partly because the tools penetrate more readily into the rough surface, and are less liable to slip, but principally to enable the outline of the device to be sketched upon the stone with a brass point, which is abraded by the rough surface, and leaves a distinct line. In drawing the design upon the stone, the general outline alone is first carefully sketched, the entire surface enclosed within the outline is then sunk, and the details of the design are afterwards sketched and sunk in succession.

For example, in engraving a shield with quarterings upon a

seal. The outline of the shield is first drawn with the brass point, this is then dotted round with a small tool, such as fig. 1199, having a thin edge, and called a *sharp* or *knife* tool. The dots, which are about the thirtieth of an inch long, and about half that distance asunder, serve to secure the outline, and prepare a path for a thicker tool with a rounded edge, such as fig. 1201, with which the outline is perfected. The bulk of the material, within the outline, is then removed with a thicker and larger tool; having a rounded edge like fig. 1203, the larger tool operates more rapidly, and is also less liable to leave the surfaces irregular, and therefore as large a tool is employed as can be conveniently applied to the purpose. When the body of the shield has been sufficiently lowered, the surface is smoothed with a smaller and flatter tool, like fig. 1202, which cuts smoother, and also allows of being applied closer into the angles. The fine lines for the quarterings are next sketched, and cut with the sharp tool, and the figures or bearings on the quarterings are afterwards sketched, and sunk in succession. If, as frequently happens, two of the quarterings are similar in design, they are sketched and cut together, in order to avoid the frequent change of tools, and also to ensure greater similarity; the same tools being used for corresponding parts of the design. The bolder portions of the bearings are of course cut first, and the smallest details are left to the last. Should the escutcheon have a shield of pretence, this would be sunk after the quartering lines had been cut, and if supporters and garniture were required, the entire outline would be first sketched, and the whole advanced equally, so as to keep the general effect uniform.

The cutting of the fine parallel lines on the field, called colour lines, presents considerable difficulty, as they are very shallow, and to give them a uniform appearance requires much care, and a light but steady hand. To assist in cutting these lines equidistant, a tool is used, having two knife edges, as shown in fig. 1200, and called a colouring tool. The front edge of this tool is used to cut the first line to the required depth, and the second line is at the same time marked out by the back edge; at the next process the second line is cut to the full depth, while the third line is marked in the same manner and so on; the lines being cut in succession from right to left, in order that the operator may be enabled to watch the progress of the tool throughout, and the stone is held in an inclined position, to cause the greater penetration of the front edge of the tool.

The colour lines are sometimes cut before the bearings are sunk, but at other times they are left until nearly all the other details have been completed, the latter course is adopted in order to avoid the risk of injuring the colour lines should the stone happen to slip in cutting the bearings, but the difficulty of cutting the lines, straight and equi-distant, is increased, owing to the want of continuity in the surface, and the tool is liable to cut deeper at the edges of the sunken portions. On this account in the best works the colour lines are usually cut before the bearings, but greatly increased care is then required in cutting the bearings.

When the engraving is quite finished, the flat surface of the stone is finally repolished with rottenstone and water, applied on a pewter lap, exactly after the manner described in the chapter on lapidary work.

During the entire process, the seal engraver watches the progress of the work through a lens of from 1 to 2 inches focus, which is mounted upon an adjustable stand, like that used by watchmakers, and placed immediately over the tool, and the work is occasionally brushed to allow of its inspection; but the seal engraver depends also very much upon the sense of feeling for estimating the position of the work, and upon hearing for judging of the progress of the tool. To enable him to ascertain the depth and general effect of the engraving, he occasionally takes impressions in a black wax, made of bees'-wax and fine charcoal dust, the latter is sifted through muslin and well worked into the wax with the fingers; but the wax is liable to adhere to the fingers, and a more cleanly method is to employ a small piece of blue modelling clay.

For roughing out the work with large tools, as in sinking the body of a large shield, the engine is driven rapidly, and the stone is applied with moderate pressure; in applying the smaller tools the speed employed is slower, and the pressure is less; and for the smallest tools used in cutting the details, the pressure is very slight, and the engine is driven still slower. For greater steadiness in finishing, the seal engraver sometimes puts the foot wheel in rapid revolution, and then, removing his foot from the treadle, stands firmly on both feet while he applies the work, until the tool comes nearly to rest; the foot wheel is then started again, and so on.

From the circular forms of the tools, curved lines and rounded forms, such as are met with in animals, ornaments, and drapery, are more easily executed than designs composed of straight lines, which are cut most readily with tools of as large a diameter as can fairly be applied, but large tools cannot be employed for cutting the corners deeply, and therefore small tools must be used for finishing the corners. To give definition to the engraving, the edges should be left nearly vertical, the amount of bevil required for the relief of the impression, even in deep works, being scarcely perceptible. Fine lines having sharp curves, such as the hair strokes in writing, are very difficult to engrave; they require very small knife-edged tools, and the stone must be applied with great steadiness and delicacy; the bolder lines in German text initials are much more easily managed.

In applying the work to the revolving tool, the stone mounted on the stick is supported and guided in both hands, the stick being held almost vertically below the tool, with the face of the stone upwards, so that both the tool and work are constantly under observation. The stone requires to be held with great firmness, but yet to be applied with exquisite delicacy, especially in cutting the minute details, and considerable practice is required to overcome the difficulties of presenting the stone to the tool with both decision and freedom.

To give steadiness to the arms of the artist, they are supported upon the bench, but the position depends partly upon the form of engine employed, and partly upon the habit of the individual. When the form of engine represented in fig. 1196 is employed, the palm of the left hand is generally rested upon the hemispherical cap of the engine, while the forefinger and thumb embrace the revolving tool, and grasp the upper end of the stick on which the stone is mounted. The thumb and forefinger of the right hand grasp the stick just below those of the left, and the right elbow is supported upon a cushion about 6 inches diameter; this .position gives considerable steadiness to the hands, and allows of a free motion in the fingers, between which the stick is, as it were, suspended; it is, however, rather adapted to small than large stones.

When the engine is made more in the form of a lathe head,

and overhangs the pillar, a different position of the left hand is generally adopted. In this case the left elbow is supported upon a cushion, in the same manner as the right, the two elbows being widely separated, to lower the hands beneath the tool, and give a wide base to the arms. The left hand is rested against the under side of the overhanging frame, and in some cases the right wrist is supported upon a wooden rest, about 6 inches high and 2 inches diameter, having a hemispherical top to allow of the free motion of the wrist in all directions; and the base of the rest is enlarged to about 4 inches diameter, for greater steadiness. The choice of position is not very material, and depends principally upon habit; but those artists who are accustomed to one position cannot conveniently adopt another. The point of greatest importance is, that both hands should be perfectly steady, and capable of being moved in all directions with great freedom. The wooden rest gives great steadiness to the right wrist, but is liable to interfere with the free motion of the hand, it is, therefore, often dispensed with, except for very delicate works.

The general position of the stick is nearly vertical, so as to keep the surface of the stone inclined just sufficiently to prevent the stem of the tool coming in contact with the face of the stone. In dotting the outline, or cutting shallow works with large tools, the stone may be held quite horizontal; but in cutting deep and delicate works, or sharp angles, very small tools must necessarily be employed, and the stone then requires to be considerably inclined, in order to allow the edge of the tool to penetrate to the bottom of the cavity, without risk of the stem being brought in contact with the surface of the work.

In all cases in which the stone can be kept horizontal, the process of gem engraving is comparatively easy, and the principal difficulties that are met with, occur in cutting the curved outlines, and in making a sunk surface quite flat. As previously mentioned, the edges of sunk surfaces should be made nearly perpendicular, to give definition to the impression, and the outlines are cut with a thin tool like fig. 1201, in which the face of the tool is flat, but, to give strength, the back is necessarily made conical.

In those cases in which the flat face of the tool can be applied to the convex side of a curved recess, no material difficulty is experienced in cutting the outline nearly perpendicular, as the stone can be slowly, but continuously, twisted round, to bring every successive part of the curve in a direct line with the flat face of the tool, and should the edge of the outline be irregularly cut at the first attempt, a second cut may be taken with a smaller tool in the same manner, to correct the irregularities of the edge, and during the entire process the tool and work remain constantly under observation.

But it will be readily conceived that the flat face of the tool cannot be so conveniently applied to the concave side of the recess, as the edges would have a continual tendency to encroach upon the curved line, and therefore, in cutting around the concave side of a curve, the conical back of the tool must be made to traverse around the inside of the curve, but the back of the tool being less under observation than the face, it is much more difficult to cut the edge smoothly, and in any attempts to correct the irregularities with a smaller tool, it is necessary to adopt the same course of applying the back of the tool to the concave edge of the work, as it is found that when the edge has been cut with the back of the tool, the face cannot be successfully applied to rectify any minute errors.

The difficulty of making a sunken surface quite flat, arises from the circumstance that the entire face has to be produced with only a very small portion of the edge of the tool, and without any mechanical guidance being derived from the tool itself. For although the edge of a tool, such as fig. 1202, may be turned very nearly flat, still on examination after being used, it will always be found rather convex, owing to the circumstance that the edge has a constant tendency to wear the fastest at the margins, and the rounded edge of the tool has, of course, a continual tendency to cut the surfaces to which it is applied into a series of small hollows, instead of one continuous plane.

In flattening a sunken surface, or, as it is sometimes called, *stippling*, the difficulty is overcome by keeping the stone in continual but steady motion. The stone being quickly traversed with very short strokes beneath the tool, the entire surface is successively passed under the lowest point of the tool, which is only allowed to cut at the highest points of the surface, and these are determined apparently by intuition, so delicate is the sense of feeling acquired by the best gem engravers; but, as may be imagined, this great dexterity of hand is only to be acquired by long and patient practice.

When the stone requires to be much inclined from the perpendicular, to allow small tools to penetrate into the minute details of deep works, the difficulties of gem engraving are materially increased. As previously mentioned, some of the little disks are less than one hundreth of an inch in diameter, while, to afford sufficient stiffness to the tool, the diameter of the stem requires to be about one eighth of an inch at the back, and the front end is made conical for about 1 inch of its length from the disk, as seen in the greatly enlarged section, fig. 1207. To enable these small tools to penetrate even into a flat surface, it is obvious that the stone must be inclined to a greater angle than the cone of the stem, or the latter would rub on the flat surface; but in finishing a deep corner, so as to make it quite square and sharp at the bottom, the stone must be inclined to a much greater angle, and in consequence, instead of the tool cutting perpendicularly downwards, it cuts obliquely, at the same angle as that at which the stick is held, and this tendency of the tool requires to be overcome by the tact of the artist.

In the case of squaring a corner, there is generally sufficient room in the sunken portion to allow the entire disk to be inserted within the cavity, upon the side of which it is principally required to operate, and the surface of the stone may be held nearly vertical. But in cutting fine lines on a deep surface, such as some of the finishing lines in the hair of a deeply sunk head, the lines do not admit of being made much wider than the edge of the tool. Very delicate management is required to sink these lines perpendicular to the general surface, and the stone must be applied to the tool so as to commence the line a little above the exact position for the center of the line, in order that the oblique cut, when made to the appropriate depth, may terminate in the desired position.

In ordinary seal engraving, great accuracy of finish in the details is never attempted, and these difficulties of manipulation are not severely felt, but they are a great obstacle to the practice of the higher department of gem sculpture, which not only requires the artist to possess great talent for the conception of beautiful designs in sculpture, but he must also devote many years to the attainment of sufficient mechanical dexterity, to enable him to realise in detail the conceptions of his mind. The gem engraver also labours under the further disadvantage, that from the minute and delicate character of his works, they can only be properly appreciated by those few persons who have carefully studied the subject.

It is very generally supposed that the ancients greatly excelled the moderns in gem engraving, and that the art has never been carried to the highest perfection in this country. Mr. Henry Weigall, however, states that "this supposition is erroneous, and has probably arisen from the fact of travellers supposing that the collections of gems and impressions that they have made in Italy, are exclusively the works of Italian artists; such, however, is not the case, and I have myself had the satisfaction of pointing out to many such collectors, that the most admired specimens in their collections were the works of English artists. Selections may be made from the works of Wray, Burch, Marchant, and Charles Weigall, which will bear a comparison with the finest works that have been produced in any age or country."

Mr. Henry Weigall could not, of course, speak of his own performances, but the reputation his works have acquired in this and other countries would fully justify the insertion of his name in the above list.

The engraved surfaces of ordinary works, such as armorial bearings, are commonly left from the cutting tools, and are not afterwards polished; but in superior specimens of gem engraving, when it is desired to give the work the highest possible finish, the engraved surfaces are all polished in the most careful manner. For this purpose the surfaces are first smoothed with copper tools, made of the same shapes as the finishing tools used in engraving, and charged in the same manner with diamond powder and oil; but the diamond powder is ground finer than that used in engraving, and the copper tools being softer than those of iron, the particles of diamond become more deeply embedded in the surface of the tools, and therefore leave a much smoother surface. After all the engraved surfaces have been smoothed with copper tools, similar tools made of boxwood, charged with still finer diamond powder, are employed to complete the smoothing. The boxwood tools cut very smoothly, and leave almost a semi-polish, which is completed with copper tools, charged with rottenstone and water.

The process of polishing minute works with much detail is, however, very tedious, as every one of the markings requires to be operated upon separately, and the process demands much skill and attention to prevent the sharpness and delicacy of the engraving from being deteriorated. To economise time in polishing common works, where precision of form in the details is not considered of primary importance, scratch brushes are sometimes employed; these are made of fine copper wire fixed in the end of a tool, and sometimes bent up at right angles to the axis, to make a small wheel brush, which is charged in like manner with rottenstone and water, but the practice is not to be recommended, as it obliterates the delicate forms.

The process of seal engraving is applied to all gems inferior in hardness to the diamond, and even this is said to have been engraved in some rare instances. The sapphire cuts very slowly but smoothly; the ruby cuts slowly, but small pieces are liable to break off in flakes; carnelian and bloodstone are close in their structure, and admit of being cut with very smooth surfaces. Softer stones admit of being cut more rapidly, but do not when finished present such smooth surfaces as the harder and more compact materials. The amethyst is, perhaps, as soft a stone as can be cut very smoothly, nevertheless, glass and even marble are sometimes successfully treated by the seal engraver, but the tools soon become deteriorated, owing to the diamond powder becoming embedded in these soft materials. When the stones consist of layers of different degrees of hardness, increased caution is required to prevent the tool penetrating more deeply at the softer parts. An onyx engraved in intaglio, so that the device is seen from the surface in the colours of the lower stratum, is called a *nicolei*.

The very excellent proof impressions of seals, taken in wax by the seal engravers, are produced in the following manner. The stone is first thoroughly cleaned with a moderately soft brush, it is then warmed over the flame of a candle, the stone being traversed in a circle at a moderate distance above the flame, that it may be heated uniformly. If the stone were held stationary above the flame it would be liable to be cracked, from one portion being heated more rapidly than another. The usual test for the proper degree of heat, is the placing of the seal upon the naked hand, and if the heat is about as great as can be borne by a tolerably sensitive hand without causing pain, it is considered to be suitable. The engraved surface of the seal is then coated with a very thin layer of clean tallow, applied with a small brush, such as a rather soft nail brush, and the tallowed surface is again coated with a thin layer of vermilion, applied with a camel's hair pencil. This completes the preparation of the seal, and when the impression is made, the vermilion becomes attached to the surface of the wax, and materially heightens the beauty of the impression.

The sealing-wax is prepared by holding the stick of wax at a little distance above the flame of the candle, until it is thoroughly softened, but it is only so far heated as is necessary to allow of a sufficient quantity of wax being detached to form the impression, and care is taken to avoid blackening the wax, either by smoke, or allowing it to become ignited. The softened wax is deposited in a small heap upon a piece of stout paper, and when enough to form the impression has been placed on the paper, the fusion of the wax is completed by traversing the under surface of the paper above the flame of the candle, at a sufficient distance to avoid scorching the paper.

When the wax has become thoroughly softened, it is stirred with a small stick, to drive out all the air bubbles, and work it into a uniform mass of a conical shape; the paper is then laid upon the table, and when the surface of the wax has become bright and quiescent, the seal is applied to give the impression. In order that both the seal and wax may be at the requisite temperatures, the preparation of the two is carried on almost simultaneously, and usually the seal is held over the flame of the candle for a few seconds to restore the heat, while the wax is assuming the quiescent state.

In applying the seal to the wax, the seal handle is held between the thumb and the first two fingers, applied as near to the seal as convenient. To give steadiness to the hand, the wrist is rested upon the surface of the table, and the position having been carefully determined, the seal is quickly dabbed upon the wax, with a firm perpendicular stroke, but with only moderate force. Some little practice is necessary to attain sufficient dexterity to give the impression with precision; but the method of

z 2

quickly dabbing the seal upon the wax, yields far more defined impressions than the mode sometimes adopted of applying the seal with quiet but considerable pressure, which not only fails to copy the most delicate of the lines and angles, but the imperfect copy thus produced is also liable to be further deteriorated by the seal sliding on the gradually yielding wax, which then receives a double impression.

In this, as in similar processes, the most sharply defined impressions are produced by employing sufficient momentum to drive the wax at the same instant into all the minute crevices of the seal, exactly as in the clichée casting and type founding, alluded to at page 324, Vol. i.

SECTION II.—CAMEO CUTTING.

CAMEO cutting, or the engraving of gems in relief, is effected with the same apparatus, and by the same general methods as those employed in engraving corresponding forms in intaglio, and both arts are occasionally practised by the same individuals. The principal differences in the manipulations of the seal engraver and the cameo cutter arise from the design being in the former case wrought concave, and in the latter convex. The tools with which the former are produced, being themselves convex, they may in most cases be selected of counterpart curvatures to the concave details required in intaglio engraving ; but the convex forms in cameo cutting, have to be produced with convex tools, which cannot therefore be selected of counterpart forms, but the convex surfaces have to be produced by twisting the stone about at all angles beneath the rounded edge of the tool. For this reason the engraving of gems in relief, is usually considered to be more difficult than engraving in intaglio. On the other hand, however, the deep recesses in cameos are generally more accessible than those in intaglio, and the principal source of difficulty in gem engraving is therefore in some measure avoided.

The stones selected for engraving in cameo, are generally those called onyxes consisting of two layers of different colours forming a strong contrast, as the black and white layers of the agate, or the red and white layers of the carnelian. The design is almost always engraved exclusively in the white layer, and the dark coloured layer forms the back ground, the contrast of the two colours serving to render the design more distinct. Sometimes onyx stones having three or more layers of colours are employed for cameos, these are selected when either from the great amount of relief desired in the engraving, the thickness of the white layer would be insufficient to allow of the entire design being engraved in it, or that it is desired to make the most prominent parts of the design of different colours in order to improve the effect.

Mineralogists generally restrict the name *onyx* to a variety of chalcedony, consisting of alternate layers of brown and opake white, but those artists who work in precious stones usually attach a much more extended signification to the name, and the following interesting particulars from the pen of Mr. H. Weigall will explain the cause of these discrepancies.

" All the stones in different coloured layers employed for cameos, are known to *practical men* by the general name of onyxes; but some confusion has arisen with regard to the nomenclature of stones of this class, in consequence of the imperfect information of those authors who have undertaken to describe them. It is a remarkable fact that no author who has undertaken to describe the onyx, has given this simple, and to all practical persons, intelligible, description of it, namely, a stratified stone occurring in any of the semi-transparent or opaque varieties; thus there is the onyx of the sard, called the sardonyx, that of the carnelian called the carnelian onyx, and so on through the whole variety of stones.

" The name onyx is derived from a Greek word which signifies nail, and the authors before referred to, have evidently been perplexed to make out any resemblance between such an object, and that particular variety of the onyx which they happened to describe. Thus Pliny could see no resemblance to a human nail in the specimen from which he took his description of the onyx (which appears to have been a bad sardonyx), and he therefore thought it must be a horn or hoof, and fancied a resemblance to a horse's hoof. Theophrastus seems to have described a cloudy specimen of the carnelian as the onyx, and he fancies it resembles the pink and white colours sometimes observable on the human nail."

Mr. H. Weigall however suggests that there was an original

propriety in the name, and that it most probably arose from the practice of the ancients in staining their nails, for if the stain were only applied at distant intervals of time, the lower portion of the nail would grow between the applications, and present a band of white at the bottom of the coloured nail, and thus render it a fair type of the onyx stone.

Mr. Weigall has made inquiries of travellers who have visited those Eastern nations where the practice of staining the nails is still continued, and has found this view to be corroborated, as they agree in stating that the nails commonly present two colours exactly resembling an onyx.

The stones to be cut into cameos are prepared by the lapidary, and to avoid wasting the material, each stone is left as large as possible. The cameo cutter has therefore to select a stone as nearly as he can in accordance with his intended design, which must be afterwards modified in some degree to suit the stone.

As a preliminary step to cutting the cameo, it is most important that the artist should have a clear conception both of the design, and the capabilities of the stone. To assist in this, he first makes a sketch of the design on an enlarged scale, and then having considered the degree of relief, that will be adapted to the thickness of the white layer, he makes a model in wax of the exact size of the stone.

With unimportant works this is frequently omitted by practised artists, who depend upon their skill for overcoming any difficulties that may arise, but it is at all times a great assistance in elaborate works, especially to those who have not great practice. The model and stone are carefully compared, and any alterations that may be demanded by the formation of the stone, are first made in the model.

When the stone is in three layers, additional care is required to adapt the design to the stone. It is at all times desirable that the line of division between the colours of the two layers forming the ground and figure should be distinctly defined, but it is sometimes an advantage when the transition between the two colours in the upper layers is more gradual. For instance, in cutting the head of a Medusa, in a carnelian having one layer of white between two of red, if the lines of division between both the layers of red and the white were sharply defined, the features must be cut entirely out of the white layer, and the upper layer of red must be reserved for the snakes, but if the transition between the upper layer of red and the white were gradual, a faint tinge of colour might be left on the cheek with great advantage to the effect, and the skilful engraver of cameos will thus avail himself of every opportunity for heightening the effect that is offered by the formation of the stone. When the stone consists of several layers of colour, considerable scope is afforded for the exercise of the judgment, in selecting a design in which the whole of the colours can be rendered available.

When the design has been accommodated to the stone as nearly as possible, the outline is sketched on the surface, and cut in with a knife-edged tool, and the superabundant portions of the white layer beyond the outline are removed down to the dark layer forming the ground. The general contour of the figure is next formed, and this is followed by the principal details, which are sketched and cut in succession, care being taken to preserve sufficient material at the most prominent parts, and to advance the engraving uniformly, so that the general effect may be compared, from time to time, with that of the wax model.

The surface of the back ground is conveniently flattened with the broad flat surface of a tool such as fig. 1201, and the difficulty of removing the little irregularities on the rounded surfaces of the figure, with the convex edge of a revolving tool, may be entirely avoided by the use of a tool called a *spade*, consisting of a piece of soft iron about 3 or 4 inches long, the end of which is filed at an angle of 45 degrees, and charged with diamond powder. The spade is held in the fingers like a pencil, and rubbed with short strokes, either straight or circular, to reduce the irregularities of the surface. The last delicate touches are executed with very small tools, and the cameo is finally smoothed and polished in the same manner as the best works in intaglio.

The method of *carving* cameos in conch shell, described on pages 1094 to 1097 of this volume, is more expeditious, and presents much less difficulty, than the engraving of cameos on gems, but the shell cameos do not admit of the delicate cutting and elaborate finish usually bestowed on true cameos, and they are also much less durable.

ENGRAVING on glass is executed in much the same manner as seal engraving, and with tools of similar forms, but the designs on glass works are usually of larger sizes than those on gems, and the tools are therefore made of proportionately greater diameter. In order to permit large objects, such as decanters or squares of glass, to be applied to the wheels, the latter are fixed on stems that project from six to ten inches from the front of the lathe head, or as it is generally called, the *tool*.

The wheels employed for engraving are made of copper, and charged with fine flour emery and oil. When the engraved surfaces are required to be polished, similar wheels made of lead, charged with pumice stone powder and water, are used.

The glass engraver's tool shown in fig. 1208, like the engine used by the seal engraver, is mounted upon a stout bench about 2 feet 6 inches high, and driven by a treadle and foot wheel, from 18 to 24 inches diameter. The metal frame that carries the mandrel is supported upon a wooden pillar, called the *stock*, which is generally of such a height as to place the center of the mandrel about 10 inches above the surface of the bench, in order to allow sufficient room for applying the objects to be engraved to the lower edges of the wheels.

For works of ordinary sizes, the mandrel is made about 8 inches long, and is supported at the left hand end in bearings, about 4 inches asunder. The remaining portion of the mandrel projects from the front of the tool, for the purpose of receiving and supporting the spindles of the wheels, which are made, as shown in fig. 1209, with a conical plug cast on a central wire about 10 inches long, and the copper wheels which vary in size, from about one-eighth of an inch to 4 inches diameter, are screwed or rivetted on the ends of the wires.

The overhanging portion of the mandrel has a conical hole, measuring about half an inch diameter, at the larger end, and one quarter of an inch at the smaller end, for the reception of the leaden plug on the spindle of the wheel, which is cast either in the cavity of the mandrel itself, or in a mould of corresponding form, made like that of the seal engraver, shown in fig. 1198, and having in like manner a nick in one side, to form a feather, that fits into a similar nick in the mandrel.

In the tool shown in fig. 1208, a small cylindrical hole extends from the bottom of the conical hole to the back end of the mandrel, to allow of the passage of the spindle, which projects slightly beyond the end of the mandrel, in order that the plug may be loosened, by gently tapping the end of the spindle. More generally, however, the spindle does not extend throughout the length of the mandrel, but a transverse mortise is made

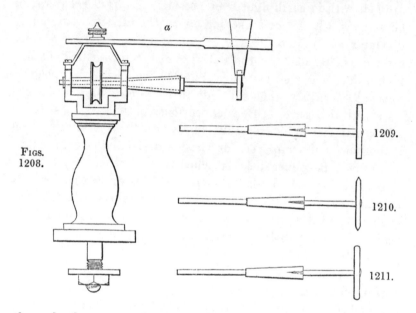

Figs.
1208.

1209.

1210.

1211.

through the mandrel, just behind the front bearing, and the spindle is only made of sufficient length to extend partly across the mortise, in this case the spindle is released by inserting a lever or wedge.

Several other unimportant variations are occasionally made in the construction of the apparatus, which is sometimes made of a much larger size, in order to carry wheels of 8 or 10 inches diameter, but these large wheels are principally required for common works, such as glass shades, and the process then more nearly resembles glass cutting.

The edges of the wheels employed in glass engraving, like those used by the seal engraver, are made in a great variety of forms, but mostly square, angular, or rounded, and the thicknesses of the wheels vary from about one quarter of an inch to a knife edge; but from the large diameter of the wheels mostly used, and the comparative shallowness of the engraving, it is not generally necessary to incline the surface to be engraved, in order to avoid the spindles; and therefore the edges of the wheels used for flat surfaces are made cylindrical, as shown in fig. 1209, instead of being conical as in the corresponding tool for seal engraving, seen in fig. 1202.

For very minute works in glass engraving, however, such as are met with in small figures of animals, architectural views, or landscapes, wheels not exceeding about the fiftieth of an inch in diameter are required. The edges of these small wheels are formed exactly like the tools of the seal engraver, and in like manner are made of carefully annealed iron wire, first roughly filed into form, and then carefully turned down to the required sizes with the graver. But, as previously intimated, glass is too soft a material to be smoothly engraved with iron wheels; iron is therefore only employed for those wheels that are too small to be made as copper disks attached to iron stems.

In charging the wheels for engraving, fine washed flour emery is mixed with olive oil, in a small shallow saucer, which is frequently applied to the lower edges of the revolving tool. The lead wheels for polishing are charged in a similar manner, with pumice stone powder mixed with water.

To prevent the wet powders from being thrown against the person of the artist by the centrifugal force, a light radial arm is attached by a screw to a cap mounted on the mandrel frame, as seen at a. The arm is made of sufficient length to extend a little beyond the edge of the wheel, and has near the end a long slit, cut at a few degrees from the perpendicular, through which is passed a thin strip of metal, or wood, about one inch wide, and tapered at its lower end, which is adjusted for height, so as to rest against the upper edge of the wheel.

Glass engraving is principally applied to the smooth surfaces left by the glass blower, but sometimes for greater elaboration, the works are prepared by the glass cutter, and whether the general surface be greyed, or polished, the engraving is not commenced until the object, such as a decanter or wine glass, is completed in all other respects. The glass engraver first sketches the general outline of the design with a pen and ink, or more generally some fine powder, such as powdered chalk, mixed with a little gum water. The engravings on glass being mostly shallow, do not require to have the outlines deeply cut, as in seal engraving, but the broad surfaces are at once produced, with large tools having flat, or rounded edges, which are applied first to the center of the surface, and this is gradually enlarged until it reaches the outline. The secondary parts of the design are then sketched, and cut in like manner with smaller tools, and as the minute details are approached, smaller and thinner tools are employed, just as in seal engraving.

When the designs are simple, and do not require great exactness, the general outline alone is sketched, and even this is in some cases omitted, when the same design has been frequently repeated, but where great precision is required, all the details are sketched and cut in succession.

In applying the object to the wheels, it is grasped in both hands, and held against the lower edge of the tools, moderate pressure is required to cause the larger tools to penetrate, but the small tools require very little pressure. The arms are steadied by resting each elbow upon a leather cushion, but the large sizes of the works do not allow of the hand being rested against the lathe as in seal engraving. The designs are also larger, and require greater freedom of motion in the hands, the weight of large articles, such as decanters, also increases the difficulty. The execution of small and highly finished designs, therefore, requires great delicacy of touch, and much practice, but notwithstanding these difficulties, very beautiful specimens of the art are sometimes produced.

When the general surface of the object is polished, the engraving is mostly left grey from the emery tools, but when the general surface is greyed, the surfaces of the engraving are polished, in order that it may show by contrast; sometimes, however, the effect is heightened by combining the two methods. Sometimes very pretty effects are produced by employing glass in two colours, in this case the body of the article is made in colourless flint glass, which is afterwards covered with a thin coat of coloured glass, and the design is developed by cutting entirely through the coloured coat so as to leave the pattern colourless. At other times the coloured glass is left to form the design, and the portions around are removed to show a colour-

less panel. In more elaborate works, the design is sometimes
formed entirely in the coloured glass, which in this case is left
thicker, and the effects of light and shade are produced by cutting
nearly through the coloured coat for the highest lights, and leaving the deepest shades of the full thickness of the coloured coat.
When well executed and placed between the eye and the light,
these works present a very soft and finished appearance.

CHAPTER XXXVI.

VARNISHING AND LACKERING.

Sect. I.—Preparation of the Varnishes.

The varnishes are solutions of the various resins, but which are by varnish makers commonly called gums, and those principally employed are amber, animè, copal, lac, sandarac, mastic, damar, and common resin, dissolved in linseed oil, turpentine, wood naphtha, or spirits of wine. The varnishes are all applied to the surfaces of the woods, metals, or other materials, while in the fluid state, like a thin paint, and the solvent is afterwards evaporated, leaving a thin glassy coat of the different resins as a defence from the action of the atmosphere, or from slight friction.

Sometimes the resins are used separately, at other times two or more are combined in the same varnish, and in like manner the solvents are sometimes employed singly, and at other times are combined, according to the qualities required in the varnish.

The durability of the varnishes is of course mainly dependent upon the comparative insolubility of the resins, their hardness, toughness, and permanence of colour. In these respects amber excels all other resins used for varnishes; it resists the action of all ordinary solvents, and can only be dissolved for making varnish by fusion at a high temperature; it is hard and moderately tough, and its colour is but little influenced by the atmosphere; but unless very carefully selected, it is too yellow for delicate works of light colours. Amber is, however, but little used in making varnishes, principally on account of its high price, but partly because the varnish dries slowly, and does not attain its full hardness for many weeks.

Animè is nearly as insoluble and hard as amber, and the best is of a very pale colour; but it is not nearly so tough as amber.

The varnishes made from animè dry quickly, but are very liable to crack, and the colour becomes deeper by exposure to light and air. Anime is, however, extensively used in making oil varnishes, and most of those called copal varnishes contain a considerable proportion of animè, which is substituted principally on account of its quick drying qualities.

Copal is next in durability to amber; when very carefully selected it is almost colourless, and becomes rather lighter by exposure; it is more easily dissolved by heat than either amber or animè, and although softer than these resins, is too hard to be scratched by the nail. Copal is, therefore, a most excellent material for varnish, and numerous attempts have been made to employ it as the basis of a spirit varnish, but hitherto with only partial success. Pure alcohol has little effect on copal; with the addition of a small quantity of camphor, the greater portion of the copal is dissolved, but the camphor impairs the durability of the varnish. Copal may be perfectly dissolved by ether, but this spirit evaporates too rapidly to allow of the varnish being uniformly applied. The essential oils of spruce and lavender have been occasionally employed as solvents of copal, but not with sufficient success to warrant its general adoption in spirit varnishes.

Amber, animè, and copal are therefore usually dissolved for making varnish by fusing the gum, and adding linseed oil heated nearly to the boiling point. They are then amalgamated by stirring and boiling, and the varnish is reduced to the required degree of fluidity by the addition of oil of turpentine. They constitute the more important of what are called oil varnishes, are the most durable of all, possess considerable brilliancy, and are sufficiently hard to bear polishing. They are therefore employed for works of the best quality, that are exposed to the weather or to much friction, as coaches, house decorations, and japanning.

Lac and sandarac are more soluble than the above resins, and are generally dissolved in spirits of wine; but sometimes the pyroligneous spirit, commonly known as vegetable naphtha, is employed as a cheaper substitute. These resins constitute the basis of what are called spirit varnishes, and are employed principally for delicate objects not exposed to the weather, such as cabinet and painted works.

Lac is much harder and more durable than sandarac, and is the basis of most lackers for hardwood and metal, and also of the so called French polish. Of the three varieties, stick lac, seed lac, and shell-lac, the latter is the most free from colour, and the most soluble; it is therefore almost exclusively used in making varnishes and lackers; but the palest shell-lac contains a considerable quantity of colouring matter, that renders it inadmissible for varnishing works of a light colour. In addition, shell-lac also contains a small quantity of wax, and other matters, that are only imperfectly soluble in spirits of wine, and therefore give a cloudy appearance to the varnish, but which is not of great importance in varnishing dark coloured works, and may be in great measure avoided by making the solution without heat, and allowing the more insoluble portions time to be precipitated.

Sandarac is softer and less brilliant than shell-lac, but is much lighter in colour, it is therefore used for making a pale varnish for light coloured woods, and other works for which the dark colour of shell-lac would be unsuited. When hardness is of greater importance than paleness, a portion of shell-lac is added, but when paleness and brilliancy are required, a small quantity of mastic is added. When the varnish is required to be polished, Venice turpentine is added to give sufficient thickness or body.

Mastic is softer than any of the resins previously mentioned, and is dissolved either in spirits of wine or oil of turpentine, the latter is most generally used on account of it cheapness. With either of these solvents mastic makes a varnish of a very pale colour, that is brilliant, works easily, and flows better on the surface to which it is applied than most other varnishes. It is also tolerably flexible, and may be easily removed by friction with the hand; it is therefore much used for varnishing paintings, and other delicate works.

Damar is easily dissolved in oil of turpentine, and when carefully selected is almost colourless; it makes a softer varnish than mastic; the two combined however form an almost colourless varnish, moderately hard and flexible, and well suited for maps and similar purposes.

Common resin is generally dissolved either in turpentine or linseed oil with heat. Varnish made with resin is hard and brittle, but brilliant, and is principally employed to make cheap varnishes for common purposes in house painting, toys, and cabinet work. It is also added to other varnishes in order to improve their brilliancy, but it should be added in small quantities only, as a large proportion of resin renders the varnishes brittle.

Linseed oil is extensively employed as a vehicle for the harder resins, to which it imparts softness and toughness, but causes the varnish to dry slowly, and unless the oil is of the purest and palest quality, well clarified, and carefully combined with the resin, without excess of heat, it materially darkens the colour of the varnish when first made, and it is also liable to become darker by age after it is applied. Linseed oil intended for the best varnishes is clarified by gradually heating it in a copper pot so as to bring it nearly to the boiling point in about two hours; it is then skimmed and simmered for about three hours longer, when dried magnesia, in the proportion of about one quarter of an ounce to every gallon of oil, is gradually introduced by stirring; the oil is then boiled for about another hour, and afterwards suffered to cool very gradually. It is then removed into leaden or tin cisterns, and allowed to stand for at least three months, during which the magnesia combines with the impurities of the oil and carries them to the bottom, and the clarified oil is taken from the top of the cistern as it is required without disturbing the lower portion, and the settlings are reserved for black paint. A pale drying oil may also be made as above, by substituting for the magnesia, white copperas and sugar of lead, in the proportions of two ounces of each to every gallon of oil.

Linseed oil when rendered drying, by boiling and the addition of litharge and red lead, is sometimes used alone as a cheap extempore varnish. In boiling linseed oil, it is heated gradually to bring it to the boiling point in about two hours; it is then skimmed, and well dried litharge and red lead, in the proportion of about three ounces of each to every gallon of oil, are slowly sprinkled in, and the whole is boiled and gently stirred for about three hours, or until it ceases to throw up any scum, or emit much smoke. It is then frequently tested by dipping the end of a feather into it, and when the end of the feather is burnt off, or curls up briskly, the oil is considered to be sufficiently boiled, and is allowed to cool very slowly, during which the principal portion of the driers settle to the bottom. The oil is afterwards deposited in leaden cisterns screened from the sun and air. When the oil is required to be as pale as possible, dried white lead, sugar of lead, and white copperas are employed instead of the litharge and red lead.

Oil of turpentine is employed as a vehicle for most of the resins, the oil varnishes being generally thinned with hot oil of turpentine. Mastic, damar, and common resin are generally made into varnishes by dissolving them in oil of turpentine alone, either cold or with very moderate warmth. Varnishes made with turpentine only, dry quicker than those made with oil, and are paler coloured, but not so tough and durable. Turpentine varnishes hold an intermediate position between oil and spirit varnishes, and are employed principally on account of their cheapness and flexibility. Turpentine varies considerably in quality, and is greatly improved by age; that intended for varnish should be of the best quality, clear and limpid, and be kept for many months, or even years, before it is used; and when employed alone, as for mastic varnish, care should be taken that it is not passed through an oily measure, as is frequently the case in procuring small quantities.

Alcohol, or spirits of wine, is employed for dissolving sandarac and shell lac, to make the white and brown hard spirit varnishes, and lacker for hardwood or brass, and also French polish. The varnishes made with alcohol dry much quicker, harder, and more brilliant than those made with turpentine; but if the spirit contains more than a minute proportion of water, it will scarcely dissolve the resins, and when the varnish is applied, a very slight degree of moisture in the atmosphere will cause the resins to be precipitated from the solution, giving the varnish a dull, cloudy, or milky appearance. It is therefore of the first importance in making spirit varnishes to procure the alcohol as pure as possible.

Ordinary spirits of wine, however, always contains a considerable proportion of water, and is commonly tested for varnish purposes by saturating a slip of writing paper with the spirit, which is then ignited, and if the flame of the spirit communicates to the paper, and the whole is burned, the spirit is considered to be sufficiently good. But if, as frequently happens, the paper should be so far saturated with the water remaining from the evaporation of the spirit as to prevent its burning, the spirit is rejected as unfit for varnish purposes.

Weighing is, however, a far more exact test, the specific gravity of absolutely pure alcohol being nearly ·8, at a tempera-

A A

ture of 60°, it may be easily tested by weighing 10 ounces of distilled water in a glass bottle, marking a line on the bottle to show the exact height of the water, and afterwards filling the bottle with spirit to the same height, and weighing it, when the excess over 8 ounces will show the proportion of water with tolerable accuracy; and should it not exceed 8¼ ounces, it may be considered to be of very good quality, spirit being frequently used for making varnish when its specific gravity is equal to ·85.

Nearly pure alcohol may be obtained from ordinary spirits of wine, by adding about one-third its weight of well-dried carbonate of potash, agitating the bottle, and then allowing it to stand for ten or twelve hours, during which time the potash will absorb much of the water from the spirit and fall to the bottom; the spirit may then be poured off, and fresh alkali added, and the process repeated until the potash remains quite dry, and the alcohol is then to be freed from the small portion of potash which it holds in solution by distillation in a water bath.

A far more convenient method of concentrating spirit of wine for varnish making, is that discovered by Sömmering, founded upon the property of ox bladders, to allow water to pass through and evaporate out of them, but not permit alcohol to transpire, or only in a slight degree. According to Sömmering, as quoted by Ure, " we should take for this purpose the bladder of an ox or calf, soak it for some time in water, then inflate it and free it from the fat and the attached vessels, which is also to be done to the other surface, by turning it inside out. After it is again inflated and dried, we must smear over the outer side twice, and the inner side four times, with a solution of isinglass, by which its texture is made closer, and the concentration of the alcohol goes on better. A bladder so prepared may serve more than a hundred times. It must be charged with the spirits to be concentrated, leaving a small space vacant; it is then to be tightly bound at the mouth, and suspended in a warm situation at a temperature of 122° Fahr., over a sand bath or in the neighbourhood of an oven. Weak spirit loses its water quicker than strong, but in from six to twelve hours the alcohol may be concentrated when a suitable heat is employed. Alcohol may also be strengthened, as Sömmering has ascertained, when the vessel that contains the spirit is bound over with a bladder which does not come into contact with the liquor."

The coating of the bladder with the solution of isinglass appears, however, not to be essential to the success of the method for varnish purposes, as, upon experiment with an unprepared bladder, spirits of wine of s. p. 8·54 was brought in a few hours to s. p. 8·11, showing it to contain about 95 per cent. of pure alcohol.

Naphtha, or the spirit procured by distillation from pyroligneous acid, and commonly known as vegetable or wood naphtha, is frequently employed instead of spirits of wine for making cheap varnishes. It dissolves the resins more readily than ordinary spirit of wine, but the varnish is less brilliant, and the smell of the naphtha is very offensive. It is therefore never employed for the best works.

The preparation of oil varnishes requires the application of considerable heat, and owing to this and the highly inflammable nature of the materials, the process is attended with considerable risk of setting the building on fire. The process should therefore always be conducted in detached buildings constructed expressly for the purpose. Owing partly to the necessity for this precaution, and the circumstance that oil varnishes are greatly improved by being kept in leaden cisterns for some months before they are used, the preparation of oil varnish is carried on almost exclusively as a separate manufacture, the details of which are greatly varied and are mostly kept secret.

In 1833, Mr. J. Wilson Neale, a varnish manufacturer of thirty years' experience, received a gold medal from the Society of Arts for a very complete description of his method of making oil and other varnishes, published in Vol. XLIX. of the Society's Transactions, from which the following directions for the preparation of oil varnishes in small quantities have been extracted :—

" The copper pot employed to make the varnish, is called a *gumpot,* and measures about 2 feet 9 inches in height, and 9½ inches diameter externally. The bottom is hammered out of a single piece of copper, and fashioned like a hat without a brim ; it is about 9 inches deep, and three-eighths of an inch in thickness. The upper part of the pot is formed as a cylinder, of sheet copper, about 2 feet 2 inches in height, and of sufficient diameter to slip about 2 inches over the upper edge of the bottom piece, to which it is firmly rivetted. A wide flange of copper, to support the pot, is also fixed just beneath the lower edge of the cylinder, and a strong iron hoop is fixed a little above the line of the rivets, to serve for the attachment of the horizontal handle, which is made as a nearly straight rod, one inch square, flattened at the end, and 2 feet 8 inches long.

" The *stirrer* is a copper rod about three-quarters of an inch diameter, and 3 feet 6 inches long, flattened at the one end to $1\frac{1}{2}$ inch in breadth for about 8 inches in length, and fitted at the opposite end with a short wooden handle.

" The ladle, which should contain about two quarts, is also of copper beaten out of the solid, and rivetted to a handle of the same metal, 3 feet 6 inches long, and fitted with a wooden handle like the stirrer.

" The copper *jack*, for pouring hot oil into the gum-pot, is made in the form of a pitcher, with a large handle and a wide spout; it contains two gallons. The brass or copper sieve, for straining the varnish, is about 9 inches diameter, and contains sixty meshes to the inch. The copper funnel, for straining the boiling varnish, is large enough to receive the sieve, and should be well made with lapped seams, as solder would be melted with the heat.

" The tin pouring pot, to hold three gallons, is formed exactly like a garden watering-pot, only smaller at the spout, and without any rose. This is never to be used for any purpose except pouring oil of turpentine into the varnish.

" A small broom, termed ' a swish,' used for washing out the gum-pot every time after use, is made from cuttings of cane tied to a small handle like a hearth-broom; the head is 5 inches long, and 5 inches round. This should be washed in turpentine, and kept very clean.

" A three-footed iron trevet, with a circular top, is employed to support the gum-pot. The feet of the trevet are about 16 inches in height, and spread wider at the bottom than the top, which is made of such a size that the pot will fit easily into it, the flange resting on the top.

" An ash-bed should be prepared near the fire, upon which to place the gum-pot when the varnish is ready for mixing, or that the heat is becoming too great. This is prepared by sifting some dry ashes through a fine sieve, to make a smooth layer about $1\frac{1}{2}$ inch thick, and a little larger than the bottom of the gum-pot.

" Place the trevet in a hollow in a field, yard, garden, or out-house, where there can be no danger from fire ; raise a temporary fire-place round the trevet with loose bricks, after the same manner that plumbers make their furnaces ; then make up a good fire with either coke, coal, or wood charcoal, which is far pre-ferable ; let the fire burn to a good strong heat, set on the gum-pot with 3 lb. of gum copal ; observe that if the fire surround the gum-pot any higher inside than the gum, it is in great danger of taking fire. As soon as the gum begins to fuse and steam, put in the copper stirrer, and keep cutting, dividing, and stirring the gum to assist its fusion ; and if it feels lumpy and not fluid, and rises to the middle of the pot, lift it from the fire and set it on the ash-bed, and keep stirring until it goes down (meantime let the fire be kept briskly up) ; then set on the gum-pot again, and keep stirring until the gum appears fluid like oil, which is to be known by lifting up the stirrer so far as to see the blade. Observe, that if the gum does not appear quite fluid as oil, carry it to the ash-bed whenever it rises to the middle of the pot, and stir it down again (keep up a brisk fire), put on the pot and keep stirring until the gum rises above the blade of the stirrer; call out to the assistant, ' be ready !' He is then, with both hands, to lay hold of the copper pouring-jack, charged with (one gallon) clarified oil, and lean the spout about one inch and a half over the edge of the gum-pot. Let him keep himself firm, steady, and collected, and not flinch, spill, or pour the oil, which would perhaps set all on fire. Observe, when the gum rises within five inches of the pot-mouth, call out, ' Pour!' The assistant is then to pour in the oil very slowly until towards the last, the maker stirring during the pouring.

" If the fire at this time is strong and regular, in about eight or ten minutes the gum and oil will concentrate and become quite clear : this is to be tested by taking a piece of broken window glass in the left hand, and with the right lifting up the stirrer and dropping a portion of the varnish on it ; if it appears clear and transparent, the oil and gum are become concentrated or joined together. It is now to be further boiled until it will string between the finger and thumb : this is known by once every minute dropping a portion on the glass and taking a little between the forefinger and thumb : if it is boiled enough it will stick strong, and string out into fine filaments, like bird-lime ;

but when not boiled enough, it is soft, thick, and greasy without being stringy. The moment it is boiled enough, carry it from the fire to the ash-bed where let it remain from fifteen to twenty minutes, or until it is cold enough to be mixed; have at hand a sufficient quantity of oil of turpentine to fill the pouring pot, (2 gallons) begin and pour out with a small stream, gradually increasing it, and if the varnish rises rapidly in the pot, keep stirring it constantly at the surface with the stirrer to break the bubbles, taking care not to let the stirrer touch the bottom of the pot, for if it should, the oil of turpentine would be in part converted into vapour, and the varnish would run over the pot in a moment: therefore during the mixing, keep constantly stirring as well as pouring in at the same time. Have also a copper ladle at hand, and if it should so far rise as to be unmanageable, let the assistant take the ladle and cool it down with it lifting up one ladleful after another, and letting it fall into the pot. As soon as the varnish is mixed, put the varnish sieve in the copper funnel placed in the carrying tin, and strain the varnish immediately; empty it into open mouthed jars, tins, or cisterns, there let it remain to settle, and the longer it remains the better it will become. Recollect when it is taken out, not to disturb or raise up the bottoms.

" Instead of the ash-bed a circle of loose bricks four courses high may be erected to support the gum-pot. The bricks are to be laid so that when the gum-pot is set within it will rest securely by its flange with the bottom about six inches from the ground. Upon this brick-stand set the pot every time there is occasion to carry it from the fire. Near the stand an iron trevet may be placed, upon which to turn the gum-pot every time after it is washed out, as, by so doing, it will always be kept clean and cool gradually, for by cooling rapidly copper oxidises very quickly. Near the trevet have the swish broom and also a large wide tin jack or other vessel to receive the washings. Have also at hand a copper ladle, and a tin bottle with turpentine, for washing with when wanted.

" The moment the maker has emptied the gum-pot, throw into it half a gallon of turpentine, and with the swish immediately wash it from top to bottom, and instantly empty it into the tin jack. Afterwards with a large piece of woollen rag dipped in pumice powder, wash and polish every part of the inside of the pot, performing the same operation on the ladle and stirrer; rince them with the turpentine washings, and at last rince them altogether with clean turpentine, which also put to the washings; wipe dry with a clean soft rag, the pot, ladle, stirrer and funnel, and lay the sieve so as to be completely covered with turpentine which will always keep it from gumming up.

" Eight pounds of Copal takes in general from sixteen to twenty minutes in fusing, from the beginning till it gets clear like oil; but the time depends very much on the heat of the fire and the attention of the operator. During the first twelve minutes while the gum is fusing the assistant must look to the oil, which is to be heated at a separate fire in a copper pot, large enough to contain double the quantity required. The oil should be brought to a smart simmer, for it ought neither to be too hot nor too cold, but in appearance beginning to boil, which the assistant is strictly to observe, and when ready, call to the maker, then immediately each take hold of one handle of the boiling pot and carry it to the ash-bed, the maker instantly returning to the gum-pot, while the assistant ladles the hot oil into the copper pouring jack, bringing it and placing it at the back of the gum-pot until wanted.

A thick piece of old carpet, free from holes, should be kept at hand in case the gum-pot should take fire ; should this happen, let the assistant throw the piece of carpet quickly over the blazing pot, holding it down all round the edges ; and in a few minutes the fire will be smothered.

After the oil has been mixed with the gum, a brisk, strong fire should be kept up, until a scum or froth rises and covers all the surface of the contents, when it will begin to rise rapidly. Observe when it rises about two-thirds the height of the pot, carry it from the fire, and set it on the ash-bed, or brick-stand, stir it down again ; and if driers are to be added, scatter in a few by a little at a time ; keep stirring, and if the frothy head goes down, put the pot on the fire, and introduce *gradually* the remainder of the driers, always carrying the pot to the ash-bed when the froth rises about two-thirds the height of the pot. In general, if the fire be good, all the time a pot requires to boil from the time of the oil being poured in, is about three-and-a-half or four hours ; but *time* is no criterion for a beginner to judge by, as it may vary according to the weather, the quality of the ingredients, or the heat of the fire; therefore, about the third hour of boiling, try it on a bit of glass, and keep boiling it until it feels strong and stringy between the fingers, as before mentioned.

The foregoing directions are, with very little differences, to be observed in making all sorts of copal varnishes, excepting the quantities of oil, gum, &c., a few of which will be now added.

Copal varnish for fine paintings, &c. Fuse 8 lbs. of the very cleanest pale African gum copal, and, when completely run fluid, pour in two gallons of hot oil; let it boil until it will string very strong; and in about fifteen minutes, or while it is yet very hot, pour in three gallons of turpentine, got from the top of a cistern. Perhaps during the mixing a considerable quantity of the turpentine will escape, but the varnish will be so much the brighter, transparent, and fluid; and will work freer, dry quickly, and be very solid and durable when dry. After the varnish has been strained, if it is found too thick, before it is quite cold, heat as much turpentine and mix with it as will bring it to a proper consistence.

Artist's virgin copal. From a select parcel of scraped African gum copal, before it is broke, pick out the very fine transparent pieces, which appear round and pale, like drops of crystal; break these very small; dry them in the sun, or by a very gentle fire. Afterwards, when cool, bruise or pound them into a coarse powder; then procure some broken bottles or flint-glass, and boil the same in soft water and soda, then bruise it into a coarse powder, like the gum; boil it a second time, and strain the water from it, washing it with three or four waters, that it may be perfectly clean and free from grease or any impurity, dry it before the fire, or upon a plate set in an oven. When thoroughly dry, mix 2 lbs. of the powdered glass with 3 lbs. of the powdered copal; after mixing them well, put them into the gum-pot, and fuse the gum; keep stirring all the time; the glass will prevent the gum from adhering together, so that a very moderate fire will cause the gum to fuse. When it appears sufficiently run, have ready three quarts of clarified oil, very hot, to pour in. Afterwards let it boil until it strings freely between the fingers. Begin and mix it rather hotter than if it were body varnish, for, as there is but a small quantity, it will be sooner cold; pour in five quarts of old turpentine, strain it immediately, and pour it into an open jar, or large glass bottle; expose it to the air and light, but keep it both from the sun and moisture until it is of a sufficient age for use. This is the finest copal varnish for fine paintings.

Cabinet varnish. Fuse 7 lbs. of very fine African gum copal, when well dissolved pour in half a gallon of pale clarified oil; and when clear mix with it three gallons of turpentine; afterwards strain it, and put it aside for use. This, if properly boiled, will dry in ten minutes; but if too strongly boiled, will not mix at all with the turpentine; and *sometimes*, when boiled with the turpentine will mix, and yet refuse to amalgamate with any other varnish less boiled than itself; therefore it requires a nicety which is only to be learned from practice. This varnish is very apt to chill all other oil varnishes to which it may be added, and is principally employed as a quick drying varnish for the occasional use of japanners, cabinet and coach painters. Cabinet varnish is, however, more generally made with animè than copal.

Best body copal varnish, used for the body parts of coaches and other objects intended for polishing. Fuse 8 lbs. of fine African gum copal, add 2 gallons of clarified oil; boil it very slowly for four or five hours, until quite stringy, and mix it off with $3\frac{1}{2}$ gallons of turpentine.

The above varnishes being made of the finest copal without driers are the palest and best of the copal varnishes, possessing great fluidity and pliability, but they are rather slow in drying, and retain for months so much softness that they will not polish well, until they give out a moisture and become hard; after which they are very durable. When paleness is not of primary importance a second quality of gum is used, and when the varnish is required to dry quickly, sugar of lead or white copperas are introduced as driers, either singly or combined, in the proportion of from half a pound to one pound to each of the quantities above quoted, but driers are always injurious to the colour, brilliancy and durability of varnishes. When a varnish is required that will dry quick and hard without driers, gum animè is substituted for the copal, but it is less durable and becomes darker by age. Frequently animè varnish is mixed with copal varnish by the maker while both are hot, in different proportions according to the quality required; one pot of animè to two of copal being used for a moderately quick drying body varnish of good quality; and two pots of animè to one of copal for a quicker drying body varnish of common quality.

Carriage varnish is made much the same as common body varnish, except that to 8 lbs. of gum of second quality to about 2¼ gallons of oil, and 5½ gallons of turpentine are used with driers. This varnish is boiled until very stringy, and is used for the wheels and under framework of coaches and other objects not requiring to be polished; it is intermediate in quality between body varnish and the following.

Wainscot varnish consists of 8 lbs. of second quality of gum animè, 3 gallons of clarified oil, ¼ lb. of litharge, ¼ lb. of dried sugar of lead, ¼ lb. of copperas, well boiled until it strings very strong and mixed with 5½ gallons of turpentine. This varnish dries quickly and is principally used for house painting and japanning. When a darker varnish is required as for mahogany a small portion of gold size may be mixed with it.

Pale amber varnish. Fuse 6 lbs. of fine-picked very pale transparent amber, in the gum-pot, and pour in 2 gallons of hot clarified oil. Boil it until it strings very strong. Mix with 4 gallons of turpentine. This will be as fine as body copal, will work very free, and flow well upon any work it is applied to; it dries slowly, but becomes very hard, and is the most durable of all varnishes. It is very excellent to mix in copal varnishes to give them a hard and durable quality. Amber varnish is however but little used on account of its expense.

In making all the above varnishes it should be observed, that the more minutely the gum is fused, the greater the quantity and the stronger the produce. The more regular and longer the boiling of the oil and gum together is continued, the more fluid or free the varnish will extend on whatever it is applied. When the mixture of oil and gum is too suddenly brought to string by too strong a heat, the varnish requires more than its just proportion of turpentine to thin it, whereby its oily and gummy quality is reduced, which renders it less durable; neither will it flow so well in laying on. The greater proportion of oil there is used in varnishes, the less they are liable to crack, because the tougher and softer they are. Increase the proportion of gum in varnishes the thicker the stratum required, and the firmer they will set, and the quicker they will dry.

All body varnishes, or those intended to be polished should have 1¼ lbs. of gum to each gallon of varnish when it is strained off and cold. All carriage or wainscot varnishes, or those not intended to be polished should have full 1 lb. of gum to each gallon. But the quantity of gum required to bring it to its proper consistence, depends very much upon the degree of boiling it has undergone; therefore when the gum and oil have not been strongly boiled the varnish requires less turpentine to thin it, and when boiled stronger than usual a larger proportion of turpentine is required, and if the mixing of the varnish with the turpentine is commenced too soon, and the pot is not sufficiently cool, there may be considerable loss by evaporation.

Copal varnishes should be made at least three months before they are required for use, and the longer they are kept the better they become, but when it is necessary to use the varnishes before they are of sufficient age, they should be left thicker than usual.

In the preparation of spirit and turpentine varnishes, scarcely any apparatus is required; as, generally speaking, the process is almost limited to mixing the resins and solvent together, and agitating the whole until the resin is thoroughly dissolved. Heat is not generally necessary, and although frequently resorted to in order to facilitate the dissolution of the resins, in most instances only a moderate degree of warmth is required, and consequently the preparation of spirit and turpentine varnishes is far more manageable than that of oil varnishes, and entails much less risk of accident.

The resins should be thoroughly free from moisture, and are generally broken into small pieces, in order that they may be dissolved more quickly, and all impurities are carefully picked out; after which the finest and clearest pieces are generally selected and set aside for making small quantities of varnish of a superior quality. Sometimes, with the view of expediting the dissolution of the resins, they are finely powdered before they are added to the solvent; but in this case it is necessary that the agitation should be maintained from the time the resin is added until it is thoroughly dissolved, or otherwise it is liable to agglutinate into one mass that is afterwards very difficult of solution.

In making turpentine varnishes without heat, in quantities of ten or twelve gallons, the resin and turpentine are generally introduced into a large can with a wide mouth, and agitated by stirring with a stout stick ; a number of wooden pegs or nails are mostly driven into the stick near the lower end to increase its effect.

Spirit varnishes are generally made in smaller quantities, and to prevent the evaporation of the spirit, the mouth of the vessel is mostly closed and the vessel itself is agitated. In making quantities of four to eight gallons, the resin and solvent are sometimes introduced into a small cask capable of containing about double the quantity, and mounted to revolve on central bearings at the ends. The cask is made to revolve either with continuous motion by a winch-handle, or with an alternating motion, by means of a cord passed around the barrel, and terminating in a cross handle, which the operator pulls to give motion to the barrel in the one direction, and the momentum of which suffices to coil up the cord ready for the following pull, which causes the barrel to revolve in the opposite direction, and so on continually.

Quantities of varnish, not exceeding two or three gallons, are generally agitated in a tin can, rolled backwards and forwards upon a bench covered with an old carpet, or a sack ; but whatever method is adopted for the agitation, it should be continued without intermission until the resin is sufficiently dissolved, to prevent the risk of its becoming agglutinated, the time required for which depends upon the solubility of the resin, and the strength of the spirit, but is commonly from three to four hours. The further agitation for the thorough solution of the resin may be either continuous or intermittent, according to convenience, but it should not be abandoned until the solution is perfect ; and when it is judged to be complete, the varnish is poured into another vessel for examination, and if any of the resin is not perfectly dissolved, the whole is returned to the vessel for further agitation. When the resin is all dissolved, the varnish is allowed to stand for a few hours, that any impurities may settle to the bottom, and the clear varnish is lastly strained through muslin or lawn into bottles, and allowed to stand for a few days before use.

Very small quantities of varnish are generally made in glass bottles, large enough to contain about one-third more than the quantity introduced, and they are shaken up at frequent intervals ; but although from the small bulk of the resin it cannot agglutinate into so insoluble a mass as when larger quantities are made, still when the agitation is intermitted, several days are frequently required before the resins are entirely dissolved, as the solution depends more upon the amount of agitation than the length of time the resins are submitted to the action of the solvent.

Sometimes, with the view of preventing the agglutination, and facilitating the dissolution of the resins, coarsely pounded glass is introduced with the resin and solvent ; in this case the glass should be thoroughly washed and dried, as mentioned at page 1385, and afterwards sifted, to exclude all the smaller particles, which, from their lightness, would have little effect in preventing the aggregation of the resin, and would be more troublesome to separate from the varnish.

When heat is employed in making spirit varnishes, the lowest temperature should be used that will suffice to dissolve the resins, as otherwise there is risk of losing a considerable portion of the alcohol by evaporation, thereby reducing the strength of the spirit ; the varnish is also liable to be made of a darker colour by excess of heat, and those containing shell lac are less clear and hard when made with heat than when made quite cold, as the heated spirit dissolves the greater portion of the wax contained in the shell lac, and which becomes disseminated throughout the mass ; but when the solution is made without heat, the principal portion of the wax and other impurities remain undissolved at the bottom.

In making large quantities of spirit varnish with heat, a still and worm are sometimes employed, in order to prevent loss by evaporation ; the still is heated by a steam or water-bath, and the resins and solvent are agitated by a stirring-rod passing through a stuffing-box in the head of the still. Quantities of two or three gallons are generally made in a tin can, which is dipped at frequent intervals into hot water, and agitated between every dip by rolling ; but in this case it is necessary to loosen the cork every time it is immersed in the hot water, in order to allow the vapour of the spirit to escape, or otherwise the cork would be driven out with great force, and some of the spirit might be thrown on the fire with risk of serious accident. Glass bottles, although convenient from their transparency, should never be employed for making varnish with heat, as they are liable to break from the alternations of temperature. They are, however, often used for making small quantities, and in this case the safer practice is to heat the water only in a moderate degree, and to allow of the continuous escape of the vapour through a small notch cut lengthways in the cork, and which may be closed by the thumb when the bottle is shaken. There is, however, always some little risk of accident in making spirit varnishes near an open fire, when much heat is employed; and a water or sand-bath, placed on the top of a stove so as to be heated only in a moderate degree, will be generally found to afford sufficient warmth, and is, perhaps, the most safe and convenient arrangement for occasional purposes.

Shell lac never requires more than a very moderate warmth to dissolve it, and the solution is frequently made in stone bottles placed near a fire and shaken occasionally. When it is required to be very clear as for metal lacker, it should be passed through filtering paper, before it is bottled.

It need scarcely be observed, that all the utensils employed in making spirit varnishes should be perfectly clean and dry, as the least moisture or even a damp atmosphere is liable to deteriorate the quality of the varnish.

Best white hard spirit varnish to bear polishing is made by adding 2 lbs. of the best picked gum sandarac to 1 gallon of spirit of wine, they are then shaken up without intermission for about four hours, or until the gum is quite dissolved, 18 ounces of Venice turpentine is then moderately warmed, in a water bath, to make it fluid, and poured into the varnish to give it a body. The whole is then well agitated for about one hour, and afterwards strained and put into bottles, which should be kept well corked to prevent the evaporation of the spirit. After standing about a week the varnish is fit for use. This varnish may be made sufficiently pale to be used on white work when the clearest and palest pieces of the gum are carefully selected. When the work does not require to be polished the proportion of Venice turpentine may be reduced one half.

White hard varnish is also made with 3½ lbs. of gum sandarac to 1 gallon of spirit of wine, and when they are dissolved one pint of pale turpentine varnish is added and the whole are well shaken until thoroughly mixed. Another white hard varnish is made with 2 lbs. of gum sandarac, 1 lb. of gum mastic, and 1 gallon of spirit of wine.

White spirit varnish for violins is made with 2 lbs. of mastic to 1 gallon of spirit of wine, and 1 pint of turpentine varnish. This may be made either in the same manner as the white hard varnish, or the ingredients may all be mixed together in a tin can, placed in a warm situation near a fire and shaken occasionally until dissolved.

Brown hard spirit varnish is made in the same manner as white hard varnish, but shell lac is generally used instead of sandarac. Thus a very excellent brown hard spirit varnish that will bear polishing is made with 2 lbs. of shell lac to 1 gallon of spirit of wine, and after they are amalgamated, 18 ounces of Venice turpentine is warmed and added exactly as described for the best white hard varnish. Another very good brown hard spirit varnish consists of 2 lbs. shell lac, 1 lb. of sandarac, and 2 ounces of mastic, dissolved in 1 gallon of spirits of wine. A lighter coloured varnish is made with 2 lbs. of sandarac, 1 lb. of shell lac, and 1 gallon of spirit. After the resins are dissolved 1 pint of turpentine varnish is added and the whole is well mixed by agitation.

Hardwood lacker is made like the brown hard varnish with 2 lbs. of shell lac to 1 gallon of spirit of wine, but without turpentine. Another hardwood lacker is made with 1 lb. of seed lac and 1 lb. of white rosin dissolved in 1 gallon of spirits of wine.

French polish is made in a great variety of ways, but the simplest, and probably the best, consists of 1½ lbs of shell lac dissolved in 1 gallon of spirits of wine without heat. Copal, sandarac, mastic, and gum arabic, are frequently used in making French polish, partly with the view of making the polish of a lighter colour, and partly to please the fancy of the polisher, and the proportions of the different gums are varied almost infinitely, but with little advantage. A polish that is by some considered to be very good is made with 12 ounces of shell lac, 6 ounces of gum arabic, and 3 ounces of copal to 1 gallon of spirits of wine. When a dark coloured polish is required, ¼ lb. of Benzoin is sometimes added to 1 lb. of shell lac dissolved in

1 gallon of spirits, or 4 ounces of guaiacum are added to 1¼ lbs. of shell lac ; at other times the polish is coloured to the required tint with dragon's blood.

The shell lac alone makes the hardest and most durable polish, and it is a frequent practice to make the polish rather thicker in the first instance than it is required for use, as it may be readily thinned by the addition of spirit.   But if it should be made too thin originally, it would require to be thickened by dissolving a further portion of shell lac.   With the view of avoiding any risk of the polish being made too thin in the first instance, the proportion of shell lac is frequently made 2 lbs. to the gallon of spirit.   Other resins are sometimes added, with the view of making the polish tougher.   Thus sometimes the polish is made with 1½ lbs. of shell lac, 4 ounces of seed lac, 4 ounces of sandarac, and 2 ounces of mastic to the gallon of spirit ; at other times the proportions are 2 lbs. of shell lac and 4 ounces of Thus to the gallon of spirit.

When a lighter coloured lac varnish, or polish, is required than can be made with the palest ordinary shell lac, the bleached lac, sold under the name of white lac, may be employed with advantage.   The varnish made with the white lac is at first almost colourless, but becomes darker by exposure to the light.

Various modes have been adopted for bleaching lac varnish. In 1827 the Society of Arts rewarded Mr. G. Field and Mr. H. Luning for their methods of effecting this object, which are described in Vol. XLV. of the Society's Transactions.   Mr. Field's process is as follows : " Six ounces of shell lac, coarsely pounded, are to be dissolved by gentle heat in a pint of spirits of wine ; to this is to be added a bleaching liquor, made by dissolving purified carbonate of potash in water, and then impregnating it with chlorine gas till the silica precipitates, and the solution becomes slightly coloured.   Of the above bleaching liquor add one or two ounces to the spirituous solution of lac, and stir the whole well together ; effervescence takes place, and when this ceases, add more of the bleaching liquor, and thus proceed till the colour of the mixture has become pale.   A second bleaching liquid is now to be added, made by diluting muriatic acid with thrice its weight of water, and dropping into it pulverized red lead, till the last added portions do not become white.   Of this acid bleaching liquor, small quantities at a time are to be added to the half-bleached lac solution, allowing the effervescence, which takes place on each addition, to cease before a fresh portion is poured in. This is to be continued till the lac, now white, separates from the liquor. The supernatant fluid is now to be poured away, and the lac is to be well washed in repeated waters, and finally wrung as dry as possible in a cloth."

Mr. Luning's process is as follows: " Dissolve 5 ounces of shell lac in a quart of rectified spirits of wine; boil for a few minutes with 10 ounces of well-burnt and recently-heated animal charcoal, when a small quantity of the solution should be drawn off and filtered; if not colourless, a little more charcoal must be added. When all colour is removed press the liquor through silk, as linen absorbs more varnish, and afterwards filter it through fine blotting paper."

Dr. Hare's process, published in the " Franklin Journal," and reprinted in the " Technological Repository," Vol. I, 1827, is as follows: " Dissolve in an iron kettle one part of pearlash in about eight parts of water, add one part of shell or seed lac, and heat the whole to ebullition. When the lac is dissolved cool the solution, and impregnate it with chlorine gas till the lac is all precipitated. The precipitate is white, but the colour deepens by washing and consolidation ; dissolved in alcohol, lac bleached by the process above mentioned yields a varnish which is as free from colour as any copal varnish."

A nearly colourless varnish may also be made by dissolving the lac as in Dr. Hare's process; bleaching it with a filtered solution of chloride of lime, and afterwards dissolving the lime from the precipitate, by the addition of muriatic acid. The precipitate is then to be well washed in several waters, dried, and dissolved in alcohol, which takes up the more soluble portion, forming a very pale but rather thin varnish, to which a small quantity of mastic may be added.

Attempts are frequently made to combine copal with all the spirit varnishes, in order to give them greater toughness and durability, and although copal cannot be entirely dissolved even in pure alcohol, still a moderate portion will be taken up by strong spirit of wine when a temperature of about 120° is employed with frequent agitation of the varnish. In this manner a light coloured varnish may be made with ¾ lb. of shell lac, ¾ lb. of copal to 1 gallon of spirits of wine containing about 95 per cent. of alcohol. The copal should be powdered quite fine, and may either be added to the shell lac and spirit at the commencement, in which case the shell lac should also be powdered, or the shell lac may be first dissolved, and the powdered copal added; but in either case it is only the more soluble portion of the copal that is taken up, and the remainder settles to the bottom in a viscid mass, from which the varnish may be decanted and strained for use. Copal may be added in the same manner to the white hard varnishes, and it is sometimes recommended to fuse the copal and drop it into water before attempting to dissolve it in spirit, but the advantage of adding copal to spirit varnishes is very questionable.

Lacker for brass like French polish is made in a great variety of ways, and as in French polish the simplest and best pale lacker for works that do not require to be coloured, consists of shell lac and spirits of wine only, in the proportions of about ½ lb. of the best pale shell lac to 1 gallon of spirit. Lacker is required to be as clear and bright as possible; it is therefore always made without heat by continuous agitation for five or six hours. The lacker is then allowed to stand until the thicker portions are precipitated, when the clear lacker is poured off, and if it should not be sufficiently clear, it is afterwards filtered through paper into a bottle, which should be kept closely corked and out of the influence of light which would darken the colour of the lacker. This may however be easily prevented by pasting paper round the bottle.

Lackers are frequently required to be coloured either of yellow or red tints. For yellow tints turmeric, cape aloes, saffron or gamboge are employed, and for red tints annotto and dragon's blood are used; the proportions being varied according to the colour required. Thus, for a pale yellow, about 1 ounce of gamboge and 2 ounces of cape aloes are powdered and mixed with 1 lb. of shell lac. For a full yellow, ½ lb. of turmeric and 2 ounces of gamboge, and for a red lacker, ½ lb. of dragon's blood and 1 lb. of annotto. The colour is also modified by that of the lac employed, the best pale or orange shell lac being used for light coloured lackers, and darker coloured shell lac, or seed lac, is used for the darker tints. For pale lackers sandarac is sometimes used with the shell lac. Thus a pale gold-coloured lacker is made with 8 ounces of shell lac, 2 ounces of sandarac, 8 ounces of turmeric, 2 ounces of annotto, and ¼ ounce of dragon's blood to 1 gallon of spirits of wine.

The most convenient method, however, of colouring lackers, is to make a saturated solution in spirits of wine of each of the colouring matters, and to add the solutions in different proportion to the pale lacker according to the tint required, but the whole of the colouring matters are not generally used by the same makers, and solutions of turmeric, gamboge, and dragon's blood, afford sufficient choice for ordinary purposes. The turmeric gives a greenish yellow tint, and with the addition of a little gamboge, is the colouring matter employed in making the so called green lacker used for bronzed works, as noticed at page 1413.

Another mode of making lacker is followed by Mr. A. Ross: 4 ounces of shell lac and ¼ ounce of gamboge are dissolved by agitation without heat in 24 ounces of pure pyro-acetic ether. The solution is allowed to stand until the gummy matters not taken up by the spirit subside, the clear liquor is then decanted, and when required for use is mixed with eight times its quantity of spirits of wine. In this case, the pyro-acetic ether is employed for dissolving the shell lac in order to prevent any but the purely resinous portions being taken up, which is almost certain to occur with ordinary spirits of wine, owing to the presence of water; but if the lacker were made entirely with pyro-acetic ether, the latter would evaporate too rapidly to allow time for the lacker to be equally applied.

Mastic varnish for paintings, and similar purposes, is sometimes made in small quantities with spirits of wine; but more generally oil of turpentine is employed as the solvent, the proportion being about 3 lbs. of mastic to the gallon of turpentine. For the best varnish the mastic is carefully picked and dissolved by agitation without heat, exactly as for the best white hard varnish, and after the mastic varnish has been strained it is poured into a bottle, which is loosely corked and exposed to the sun and air for a few weeks; this causes a precipitation from which the clear varnish may be poured off for use, but the longer the varnish is kept the better it becomes.

Mastic varnish works very freely, but is liable to chill, and the surface frequently remains tacky for some time after the varnish is applied. To prevent the latter evil, it is recommended before dissolving the mastic to bruise it slightly with a muller, and pick out all the pieces that are too soft to break readily, and which may be used for common varnish. To prevent the chilling, which arises from the presence of moisture, Mr. W. Neil recommends a quart of river sand to be boiled with two ounces of pearlash; the sand is afterwards to be washed three or four times with hot water, and strained each time. The sand is afterwards to be dried in an oven, and when it is of a good heat, half a pint of the hot sand is to be poured into each gallon of varnish, and shaken well for five minutes, it is then allowed to settle, and carries down the moisture of the gum and turpentine.

In making common varnish, heat is generally employed to dissolve the mastic, and about one pint of turpentine varnish is added to every gallon of varnish.

Turpentine varnish is made with 4 lbs. of common resin dissolved in 1 gallon of oil of turpentine, it requires no other preparation than sufficient warmth to dissolve the resin; sometimes the resin and turpentine are mixed together in a stone or tin bottle, which is placed near the fire, or in a sand bath over a stove, and shaken occasionally, but varnish makers generally mix the resin and turpentine in the gum-pot, and employ sufficient heat to fuse the resin. This is a more expeditious practice, but is attended with some danger of fire. When a very pale turpentine varnish is required, bleached resin is used, and care is taken not to employ more heat than is necessary in making the varnish. Turpentine varnish is principally used for in-door painted works and common painted furniture, and toys. It is also frequently added to other varnishes to give them greater body, hardness, and brilliancy.

Crystal varnish is a name frequently given to very pale varnishes employed for paper works, such as maps, coloured prints, and drawings. A very good crystal varnish is made with 2 lbs. of mastic and 2 lbs. of damar, dissolved without heat in 1 gallon of turpentine. Another good, but more expensive, crystal varnish is made with equal quantities of Canada balsam and oil of turpentine. In making this varnish it is only necessary to warm the Canada balsam until it is quite fluid, then add the turpentine and shake the mixture for a few minutes until the two are thoroughly incorporated. The varnish may then be placed in a moderately warm situation for a few hours, and will be ready for use on the following day. These crystal varnishes are both nearly colourless, flow freely, and are moderately flexible, so as to bear bending, or rolling, and either of them may be employed to make a tracing paper of middling quality, by applying a thin coat of varnish on one or both sides of any thin transparent paper, such as good tissue or foreign post paper.

Paper varnish, for paper hangings and similar purposes, is made with 4 lbs. of damar to 1 gallon of turpentine. The damar dissolves very readily in the turpentine, either with moderate agitation or a very gentle heat. Sometimes white or bleached resin is used instead of the damar, or the two are combined.

Water varnish.—All the varieties of lac may be dissolved in nearly boiling water by the addition of ammonia, borax, potash, or soda, but these alkalis all have the effect of rendering the colour of the lac much darker. The solutions may, however, be employed as varnishes, which when dried will resist the application of water sufficiently well to bear washing, especially when the proportion of alkali employed is only just sufficient to cause the dissolution of the lac, and which is also desirable in order to keep the varnish as light coloured as possible.—The least colour is given with diluted water of ammonia, in the proportions of about 16 ounces of ordinary water of ammonia to 7 pints of water and 2 lbs. of pale shell lac, to which about 4 ounces of gum arabic may be added. Borax is, however, more generally used, and the proportions are then 2 lbs. of shell lac, 6 ounces of borax, and 4 ounces of gum arabic to 1 gallon of water. When the varnish is required to be as light-coloured as possible, white lac is employed.

Sealing-wax varnish, for coating parts of electrical machines and similar purposes, is made by dissolving 2½ lbs. of good red sealing wax and 1½ lbs. of shell lac in 1 gallon of spirits of wine.

Black varnish may be made with 3 lbs. of black sealing-wax and 1 lb. of shell lac to the gallon of spirit, or fine lamp black may be mixed with brown hard varnish or lacker, according to the thickness required in the varnish. The interior of telescope tubes are frequently blackened with a dull varnish of this kind, made by mixing lamp black with rather thick brass lacker, as little of the lamp black being employed as will serve to deaden the bright colour of the lacker. Mathematical instruments are sometimes blackened with a similar thin varnish, and the surface is afterwards brightened with one or two coats of lacker applied as usual. Ordinary lamp black, however, generally contains greasy impurities and moisture which render it unfit for varnish purposes, and therefore the best kind should be employed, or the lamp black should be purified by ramming it hard into a close vessel, and afterwards subjecting it to a red heat. In the workshop, when small quantities of lamp black are required, it is frequently made for the occasion, by placing a piece of sheet metal over the flame of an oil lamp. A black varnish, sometimes used for metal works, is made by fusing 3 lbs. of Egyptian asphaltum, and when well dissolved, $\frac{1}{2}$ lb. of shell lac and 1 gallon of turpentine are added.

SECTION II.—APPLICATION OF VARNISHES.

In varnishing flat surfaces the varnishes are all applied like paint, with brushes that should be soft, and perfectly clean. For spirit varnishes, camel's hair pencils and brushes are used, the sizes of which vary from one quarter to three-quarters of an inch diameter, according to the size of the work. When the surfaces are very large, flat camel hair brushes are used; but from their comparative thinness, they scarcely contain a sufficient quantity of varnish to preserve the brush uniformly charged in passing over a large surface. Turpentine and oil varnishes require less delicacy, and flat brushes, made of fine soft bristles, are generally used, or sometimes ordinary painting brushes are employed; but they are rather harsh, and, owing to the adhesion of the varnish, the hairs are apt to be loosened, and come out.

The varnishes should all be uniformly applied, in very thin coats, very sparingly upon the edges and angles, where the varnish is liable to accumulate; and a sufficient interval of time should be allowed between every coat for the perfect evaporation of the solvent, whether alchohol, turpentine, or oil. The time required for this depends partly on the kind of varnish employed, and partly on the state of the atmosphere; but, under ordinary circumstances, spirit varnishes generally require from two to three hours between every coat. Turpentine varnishes mostly require six or eight hours, and oil varnishes still longer,—sometimes as much as twenty-four hours. But whatever time may be required, the second layer should never be added until the first is permanently hard; as when one layer is defended from the air by a second, its drying is almost entirely stopped, and it remains soft and adhesive. Every precaution should also be taken to prevent any dust, or loose hairs from the brush, becoming accidentally attached to the varnish; should this occur, they should be immediately removed before the varnish drys, or otherwise they will require to be carefully picked out with the point of a pen-knife, and the surface of the varnish levelled with fine glass-paper, prior to the application of the next coat.

In using spirit varnishes it is at all times of the first importance that particular attention should be bestowed upon carrying on the varnishing in a dry atmosphere; as all solutions of resins in alcohol are precipitated by the addition of water, not only as visible moisture, but even as vapour, which is at all times deposited by the atmosphere at a reduced temperature, in the form of invisible dew, and in this state it precipitates the resin in the thin coat of varnish, and gives the surface a milky, opake, or clouded appearance, when the varnish is said to be chilled; but this effect is frequently produced even on a warm and apparently fine summer day, when the atmosphere happens to be more than usually charged with moisture. This is a frequent stumbling block in varnishing, and is only to be obviated, by carrying on the process in a room sufficiently warmed to keep the moisture suspended in the air, until the solvent has entirely evaporated, and left the resin as a thin glassy coat but little altered, in a chemical point of view, from its primary state of fragment, flake, or grain, and entirely unacted upon by water, upon which circumstance the brilliancy and defensive value of the varnish depends.

Not only should the room be sufficiently heated, but all currents of cold air must be avoided, as cold draughts from the interstices of the door or window, if suffered to pass over the recently varnished surface, are quite sufficient to dull the varnish wherever they extend. When the varnish has been chilled, the brilliancy and clearness may frequently be restored by giving the chilled surface another thin coat of varnish, taking care to avoid the causes of the former failure, and immediately holding the varnished surface at a moderate distance from a fire, so as to warm it sufficiently to partially redissolve the chilled coat; but care is necessary to avoid heating the varnish so much as to raise blisters, which would spoil the surface, and no remedy would remain but to rub off the entire coat of varnish with glass-paper, and recommence the process.

The temperature generally preferred for the varnishing room, is about 72° F.; but a few degrees more or less are not very important. The works to be varnished should be kept in the room for a few hours before varnishing, in order that they may acquire the same temperature as the atmosphere, and the surfaces should be smoothed with fine glass-paper, to remove all traces of moisture or grease, and if it should be necessary to stop any minute holes in the wood before varnishing, it should be done with some of the gums, or with wax, or at all events, nothing containing oil or grease should be employed.

An ordinary preserve-jar is frequently used for containing the varnish, and is sufficiently suitable; but it is desirable to have a wire or string fixed across the top, for reducing the quantity taken up by the brush, which is wiped against the wire every time that it is dipped into the varnish. The quantity of varnish poured into the jar should be sufficient to nearly cover the hairs of the brush, in order to keep it soft. Too small a quantity of varnish is liable to thicken rapidly by evaporation, which should at all times be prevented, as far as possible, by keeping the vessel closely covered when not actually in use. Should the varnish, however, become too thick, it may be readily thinned by the addition of spirits of wine, and for good work it is more desirable to apply an increased number of thin coats than to use the varnish when too thick, as the surface is then almost certain to appear irregular, and full of lines.

In applying spirit varnish, some little tact and expedition are necessary, in order to spread the varnish uniformly over the surface before it becomes too much thickened by evaporation, or it will exhibit a very irregular surface when finished. If the surface does not exceed a few inches square, no material difficulty is experienced, as the whole may be brushed over two or three times before the varnish becomes too thick; but surfaces containing two or three square feet present much greater difficulty, as it is necessary that the varnish should be sufficiently worked with the brush, to exclude all minute air-bubbles, which would spoil the appearance of the work, and can seldom be entirely removed until just before the varnish is becoming too thick to *flow* or spread uniformly after the brush has passed over it.

In first placing the brush on the surface, it should be applied, not close to the edge, which would be liable to give too thick a coat at that part, but at a little distance from the edge, and the strokes of the brush should be directed towards the ends alternately, with steady rapid strokes and only very moderate pressure. If the surface is small, the whole may be passed over at the one operation, and then the brush may be returned to the edge at which it was first commenced, and it may be passed over the surface in the same manner a second or third time, to distribute the varnish uniformly, and work out the air-bubbles. Sometimes, in small surfaces, the second series of strokes is made at right angles with the first, in order to distribute the varnish more equally, and the third is laid on in the same direction as the first; but unless this is done expeditiously and equally, it leaves cross lines, which injure the appearance of the work.

Large surfaces are more difficult, as the varnish thickens too rapidly to allow of the entire surface being covered at one operation; they must therefore either be worked gradually from the one edge to the other, as in laying a tint of water-colour, or the varnish must be applied upon separate portions successively; but it is rather difficult to join the portions without leaving irregular marks. It may, however, be successfully executed by thinning off the edges of the first pieces, and allowing the adjoining portion to overlap also by thinning off the edge with light strokes of the brush, made in the same direction as those on the finished portion; but some care is required to avoid disturbing the former coat while it is still soft and easily acted upon by the fresh varnish. In the same manner, in laying on a second or any subsequent coat of varnish, care must be taken not to continue the application of the brush for a sufficient length of time to disturb the previous coat, which is speedily softened by the fresh varnish, and if the application of the brush were continued too long, it would be disturbed, and give the work an irregular or chilled appearance.

Wood and other porous surfaces absorb a considerable portion of the first coat of varnish, which sinks in deeper at the softer parts, and raises the grain of the wood in a slight degree, a second coat is generally necessary to fill up the pores uniformly, and sometimes even a third is required. The work is then rubbed smooth with fine glass-paper, and if the varnish is not to be polished, two or three coats more generally suffice to finish the work, as the thickness of varnish should not be too great, or it is liable to crack or chip.

With the view of economising the varnish, porous surfaces, such as wood and paper, are frequently sized over, to prevent the varnish from sinking into the surface. For dark coloured works thin size, made from ordinary glue of good quality, is generally used ; but for light coloured surfaces, a lighter coloured size is used, which is prepared by boiling white leather or parchment-cuttings in water for a few hours, or until it forms a thin jelly-like substance, which is used in the tepid state, and sometimes solutions of isinglass or tragacanth are employed in like manner. For wood the choice, except as to colour, is nearly immaterial, the object being only to prevent the absorption of the varnish by a very thin coat of some substance not soluble in the varnish ; but for paper works the parchment size is on the whole preferable, as it is almost colourless, and tolerably flexible. It is better in all cases to use two coats of thin size than one of a thicker consistency, as the size is more uniformly spread in two coats, and there is less risk of any small spots being left untouched, which would show specks in the varnish when completed ; but no greater thickness of size should be employed than is absolutely necessary, or otherwise it would be liable to crack and peel off.

The method of polishing the best varnished works has been already describing in the catalogue of grinding and polishing processes, under the head VARNISHED WORKS, page 1101, from the practice of Messrs. Erats, from whom many of the above particulars were also derived. The routine pursued in the polishing of japanned works is briefly mentioned at page 1069, and similar methods are used with trifling variations, for polishing all other varnished works.

Ornamental painting on varnished works is executed as mentioned in page 1101, after the general surface has received a ground of about six coats of varnish, and been rubbed smooth and level. The colours employed should be of the best quality, ground as fine as possible with turpentine, and mixed to the proper consistence with the same varnish that is employed for the general surface. So far as convenient the transparent colours are to be preferred, and those principally used are dragon's blood, lakes, Prussian blue, chrome yellow, verdigris, white lead, lamp black, and ivory black. Tincture of saffron is also employed for yellow colours, and also for staining the general surface of a yellow tint before it is varnished; the tincture is made by macerating half an ounce of saffron for two or three days in a pint of spirits of wine; and other coloured stains are sometimes prepared and applied in the same manner.

Turpentine and oil varnishes are applied in the same general manner as the spirit varnishes, but as they dry slower, more time may be occupied in laying on the varnish, and therefore large surfaces may be more easily and uniformly covered; but the same precautions with respect to the dryness and warmth of the atmosphere are likewise desirable, when it is wished to produce a brilliant surface.

In conclusion, it may be observed, that generally speaking all coloured works are first painted of the required tints, and a transparent varnish is afterwards laid on to give the required brilliancy, but for delicate ornamental painting two or three coats of varnish are generally laid on and smoothed down after the general ground has been painted, in order to prepare a suitable surface for artistic works.

Japanning on metal, wood, and paper, is executed in much the same manner as similar works in spirit or oil varnishes, except that every coat of colour or varnish is dried by placing the object in an oven or chamber called a stove, and heated by flues to as high a temperature as can safely be employed without injuring the articles, or causing the varnish to blister or run. For ornamental works, the colours ordinarily employed by artists are used; they are ground in linseed oil or turpentine, and are afterwards brought to a proper consistence for working by mixing them with copal or animè varnish. The latter is generally used, as it dries quicker, and is less expensive than the copal varnish.

For black japanned works, the ground is first prepared with a coating of black, made by mixing drop ivory black to a proper consistence with dark coloured animè varnish, as this gives a blacker surface than would be produced by the japan alone. The object is then dried in the stove, three or four coats of japan are afterwards applied, and the work is dried in the stove between every coat. If the surface is required to be polished, as for the best works, five or six coats of japan are necessary to give sufficient body to prevent the japan being rubbed through in the polishing, which is effected as noticed briefly in page 1069.

For brown japanned works, the clear japan alone is used as the ground, or umber is mixed with the japan to give the required tint, and the work is afterwards dried in the oven in the same manner as black japan.

For coloured works, no japan is used, but they are painted with the ordinary painter's colours, ground with linseed oil or turpentine, and mixed with animè varnish; and the work is dried in the oven in the same manner as the black japan.

To protect the colours, and give brilliancy and durability to the surface, the work is afterwards varnished with copal or animè varnish made without driers. Two or three coats of varnish suffice for ordinary works, and five or six for the best works that are polished. Very pale varnish is of course required for light colours.

Ornamental devices are painted on the objects in the usual manner, after the general colour of the ground has been laid on. The colours are dried in the stove, and the work is finally varnished and polished just the same as plain colours, but more carefully.

Metal works require no other preparation than cleaning with turpentine, to free them from grease or oil, unless the latter should happen to be linseed oil, in which case the cleaning is generally dispensed with, and the articles are placed in the stove and heated until the oil is baked quite hard.

Wood that is intended to be used for the best japanned works requires to be thoroughly well dried before it is made up, or otherwise it would be subject to all the evils of shrinking, warping, and splitting when exposed to the heat of the stove. To avoid these evils, the wood, after having been well seasoned in the usual manner by exposure to the air, is sawn out nearly to the required forms, and baked for several days in the japanner's stove, the heat of which is gradually increased, and the wood is afterwards worked up into chairs, tables, trays, and similar articles, which are afterwards again exposed to the heat of the stove, and any cracks or other imperfections that may be thus rendered apparent are carefully stopped with putty or white lead before the japanning is commenced.

Common works in wood, said to be japanned, are, however, not stoved, but only painted, either in varnish or with common oil paint, and afterwards varnished with either animè or turpentine varnish according to quality. In the same manner iron work for common purposes is frequently coated with black paint, brunswick black, or black japan, applied without heat, and either varnished or not, according to circumstances, but all these expedients are greatly inferior to japanning.

In lackering brass and similar metals, the work requires to be perfectly cleaned from all grease or oil, the presence of which would prevent the adhesion of the lacker, and usually the metal is heated nearly to the temperature of boiling water, that the spirit may be rapidly evaporated from the lacker, in order to prevent any risk of its being chilled by the moisture of the atmosphere being condensed on the cold metal. The heat also causes the lacker to attach itself more firmly to the metal, and from the readiness with which it flows, the lacker appears much more brilliant.

The heating of the metal is, however, not imperative, as metal may be lackered in the same manner that spirit varnish is applied to wood, but a dry and warm atmosphere are then essential, or the lackering may be carried on in bright sunshine, but there is greater liability of the adhesion of dust, owing to the lacker drying less rapidly, and on the whole the process is not so successful as when heat is applied.

The lackering of the metals should follow immediately after the polishing processes, which have been already explained at page 1038, or if the lackering must necessarily be delayed, the work should be thoroughly coated with clean oil, or immersed in very pure water, in order to retard the tarnishing, but which will nevertheless occur in water after the lapse of a few hours ; with oil the polish is preserved much longer. Works having ornamented surfaces from which the oil could not be readily cleaned, are sometimes closely wrapped in cloths in order to exclude the air as much as possible, but the sooner brass is lackered after polishing the more brilliant it will appear.

The works polished with oil are carefully wiped before they are heated, first with moslings, and afterwards with whitening, applied either with a rag or a brush, so as thoroughly to remove all traces of grease ; those polished with water merely require to be wiped with a clean cloth, and those finished by the dipping processes are generally dried in saw-dust.

The work is heated prior to lackering in a variety of ways. In manufactories devoted principally to brass works, there is generally a lackering stove, having a broad flat top, upon which the work is laid, completely out of reach of the dust or smoke from the fire. In some few instances a circular row of gas flames is employed, just as in gas stoves, for heating a plate, which is supported on four legs like a table ; this method is very neat and appropriate.

In the absence of either of these a charcoal fire, covered with an iron plate, is commonly used, and another very clean and convenient method is to make the end of a flat bar of iron red hot, and to pinch the bar in the vice, placing the work at some distance from the heated extremity, and gradually advancing it as the bar cools.

Vessels filled with boiling water or steam are sometimes employed ; these are very cleanly and suitable, as there is no risk of excess of heat. Tubes are sometimes heated in the same manner for lackering, by filling them with boiling water, the ends being temporarily stopped with corks. Small pieces not having many holes are sometimes dipped into clean boiling water, the principal portion of which is shaken off when the work is removed, and the remainder speedily evaporates. In lackering the heads of a large number of small screws, they are frequently all inserted in a piece of card, which is heated over a charcoal fire or a gas flame, and the whole are lackered at one process. In thin circular works, the friction of polishing frequently suffices to give the requisite heat, more especially when the milling tool is used.

In whichsoever way the heat is applied, the temperature of boiling water should not be exceeded, as excess of heat is liable to discolour the work by oxidation before it is lackered, for which there is no remedy but repolishing; or if this evil does not occur, the heat may evaporate the spirit so rapidly as not to allow time for laying the lacker on evenly; or it may be sufficient to cause the boiling of the lacker, and in this case the surface will present small dots, caused by the bubbling of the spirit. Should failure arise from either of these causes, the lacker may be removed for another trial, by wiping off the first coat while it is still warm with a rag moistened with spirits of wine, but to remove lacker after it has become hard, it is generally necessary either to apply emery paper, or to boil the work in a ley of pearl-ash and water.

After the work has been heated it is wiped with a piece of clean rag, and it should not afterwards be touched with the fingers, which might communicate some trifling grease or dirt, but the temperature is generally sufficient to prevent the application of the naked hand; advantage is therefore taken of any small hole that may happen to be in the work, and a screw tap, a broach, or an arbor, is inserted to serve as a handle.

For flat works, the lacker is applied in much the same manner as spirit varnishes are applied to flat surfaces, but owing to the employment of heat the lacker sets much more rapidly, and as only a very thin coating of lacker is required, the process is generally completed at one operation. Some care and expedition are therefore necessary to lay the lacker uniformly on the work, but being thinner than spirit varnish it flows more freely, and does not require to be worked to expel air bubbles.

The lackering is generally commenced at one edge of the work, and the strokes of the brush are taken in parallel lines from side to side; the surface generally receives two coats of lacker in immediate succession, and when the works are small, the first coat is always completed before the second coat is commenced, but in large surfaces, the two coats are sometimes carried on simultaneously, the first being a small distance in advance; but this requires to be done expeditiously, or otherwise the extreme edge of each coat will be liable to dry while the other is in progress, and the surface when finished will show streaks wherever this has occurred; it is therefore the better practice to continue the first coat entirely over the whole surface at the one operation, and if necessary the metal may be reheated for the second coat.

The success of the process depends however very much upon the good condition of the brush, and its being kept uniformly moistened with the lacker. Camel hair brushes are always used for lackering, round brushes about one quarter of an inch diameter are employed for small works, and larger round or flat brushes are used for those of greater size. They should always be kept quite clean and soft. When the lacker is in frequent use, it is generally kept in a small bottle, the cork of which is perforated to fit the handle of the brush, which is thus suspended just above the lacker when not in use ; in this manner the brush may be kept in tolerable condition for some time. If however the brush is only used occasionally, it is a better practice to wipe it as dry as possible on a clean rag after use, and immediately wash it in a little clean spirits of wine, which may be added to the lacker to compensate for that lost by evaporation, and the brush may then be laid by for future use. It must also be remembered that the heat of the work speedily thickens the lacker in the brush, which soon becomes stiffened, and leaves streaks on the work. This inconvenience is frequently experienced even in going over a single large surface ; it is therefore a good method in lackering large works to dip the brush in clean spirits of wine, and wipe it, either against the edge of the vessel, or a central wire fixed across its mouth, before taking a fresh supply of lacker. Or if this is thought too troublesome, the brush should at any rate be dipped sufficiently deep in the lacker to cover the hairs, and then be wiped against the cross wire, to reduce the quantity and mingle the fresh lacker with that previously contained in the brush.

The quantity of lacker taken in the brush depends partly upon the experience of the operator ; those who have had much practice are enabled to use the brush tolerably full of lacker, which under proper management flows freely over the surface ; but those who have less experience, will be more likely to succeed when the brush is only moderately moistened, as any irregularities in its application are then less apparent.

Circular works are generally lackered in the lathe, and when the friction of polishing is not sufficient to give the necessary temperature, the arbors, screw chucks or other apparatus necessary for fixing the work in the lathe, are laid in order ready for use, after having been wiped clean with whitening as carefully as the work itself. The work, when sufficiently heated, is rapidly transferred to the lathe, finally wiped with a clean cloth, and lackered with a rather dry brush, which is gradually traversed along the work while the lathe is slowly turned in the direction to lay the hairs straight. The brush should be traversed twice over every part of the work to ensure its being uniformly covered with the lacker; should this not be the case, the surfaces will frequently exhibit prismatic colours. when examined from different points of view.

The lackers, whether pale or coloured, are applied in the same manner to all works either plain or ornamented, but for mechanism the pale lackers are almost exclusively used, and the coloured lackers are principally applied to works of an ornamental character, with the view of giving a richer tint to the metal than it naturally possesses. In some instances the colour is produced entirely by the lacker, as in wood, or leather, which are sometimes covered either with silver leaf or tin foil, and afterwards coated with a gold-coloured lacker. This constitutes a sort of fictitious gilding that is tolerably durable, but disappears on the application of alcohol or naphtha.

Ornamental works in brass, such as house furniture, lamp and gas fittings, whether stamped or cast, are, as mentioned on page 1041, generally brightened and coloured, by dipping and bronzing, which processes will be here briefly described.

After the works have been fitted together, they are annealed by heating them over the open fire to the red heat, and allowing the cooling to extend over one or two hours; but if the works should have been brazed, a longer time is allowed for the cooling. The heat employed in annealing removes any grease or dirt that may have accumulated during the processes of fitting; but annealing is inadmissible with works that have been soft soldered, as the heat would melt the solder, and therefore such works are annealed before they are fitted together, and are afterwards boiled in a ley of pearl ash to remove the grease.

The work is next pickled in a bath of dilute aquafortis, which may be made with two or three parts of water to one of aquafortis; but the old acid that has been used for dipping, and contains a small quantity of copper in solution, is frequently preferred. The work is allowed to remain in the pickle for one or two hours according to the strength of the acid ; but the metal must not be permitted to remain in the pickle for too long a time, or it will be eaten into holes. The entire surface of the work is next scoured quite bright with sand and water, applied with an ordinary scrubbing brush ; the work is then washed and allowed to remain in quite clean water for a few minutes until the dipping bath is ready.

The dipping bath consists of pure nitrous acid, commonly known as dipping aquafortis, a sufficient quantity of which is poured into a glass or earthenware vessel to allow of the work being entirely covered with the acid, so far as the process is required to extend. If the work does not require to be wholly immersed, it is handled with the fingers, but if the entire surface is to be dipped, brass pliers are used, as the insertion of wood or iron instruments would deteriorate the acid.

The bath having been prepared, the work is taken out of the water and dipped into the aquafortis for an instant only ; it is then quickly removed, plunged into clean water and well rinsed to remove the acid, for which purpose two or three vessels containing cold water and one hot water are arranged in order, and the work is transferred from one vessel to another as rapidly as possible, in order to prevent its being discoloured during its passage through the air. The more effectually to remove the acid, some manufacturers add argal to the hot water.

If the work should not appear sufficiently bright, it may be dipped a second time, but the work must be quickly removed from the acid, as it acts very energetically on the metal, and the dipping must not be repeated too frequently, or a bad colour will result, which can only be remedied by cleaning the surface a second time. Immediately after the rinsing, the work is plunged into dry beech or box wood saw-dust and rubbed until quite dry. The work is then burnished at the parts required to be bright, and lackered with as little delay as possible to prevent discoloration.

The green bronze colours, in imitation of the tints that occur on real bronze from long exposure to the atmosphere, are produced chemically on brass and gun-metal, by a variety of acid applications, but in all it is quite essential that the work should be first thoroughly cleaned from grease, and brightened either with the file or emery paper, in order to allow the acid to act uniformly on the surface. Works having ornamented surfaces to which the file or emery paper could not be conveniently applied, are generally boiled in a ley of pearlash, and afterwards scoured with clean sand and water.

Sometimes vinegar alone is used as the bronzing liquid, at other times dilute aquafortis, or a strong solution of sal ammoniac is used; but more frequently sal ammoniac and vinegar are employed together, in the proportions of from one to three ounces of sal ammoniac to a pint of vinegar, according to the taste of the operator, and sometimes a little common salt is added.

A cheap but tedious bronze is made by dissolving half a pound of sal ammoniac in a quart of dilute nitrous acid, say one part of aquafortis to two of water; this takes about two hours before the colour is fully developed. A better and quicker bronze is made with one ounce of corrosive sublimate dissolved in one pint of vinegar; this requires about a quarter of an hour to produce the colour. The best and most rapid bronzing liquid, but the most expensive, is however the nitromuriate of platinum, called chemical bronze; with this liquid the required effect is produced in two or three minutes. The solutions are all employed in the same manner; the work having been thoroughly cleaned, is equally wiped over with the bronzing liquor, and this is allowed to remain until it ceases to act on the metal, which should then appear nearly black. Sometimes to assist the action of the acid the work is slightly warmed, and if necessary a second or third coat of the bronzing liquid is applied. The work is then dusted over with common black lead, and brushed like a stove to give it a good gloss.

With the view of rendering the action of the bronzing liquid as uniform as possible, small articles are sometimes dipped in the acid; for larger articles, the bronzing liquid is sometimes *dabbed* on plentifully with a piece of rag tied to a stick, in order to avoid the appearance of streaks, which sometimes occur when the bronze is applied with straight strokes. In some cases, as soon as the nearly black colour appears to be sufficiently developed, the work is rinsed in clean water to prevent the further action of the acid on the metal, which is afterwards dried and blackleaded. In other cases the bronzing liquid is plentifully covered with black lead, in order to distribute it more equally, and the work is then allowed to remain until nearly dry before it is brushed.

The work is finally lackered in the ordinary manner; but the green lacker, coloured with tumeric, as mentioned in page 1396, is employed to produce the green tint usually seen on bronzed works. The colour of the bronze depends in great measure upon that of the lacker, and should the latter be too green, the colour is modified by the addition of pale lacker in different proportions, according to the tint required. But although the green lacker will communicate a green tint, it is quite essential that a nearly black surface should have been previously produced by the bronzing liquid, and upon which the depth and perfection of the colour primarily depend.

The quality of the metal has also some influence on the colour of the bronze, and on this account it is rather difficult to make the colour uniform when the works consist partly of cast and partly of sheet metal, as the latter does not readily take so dark a tint from the bronzing liquid.

In works partly dipped, and partly bronzed, the latter is the final process.

———————

Hard-wood lacker, or polish, is applied to turned works in the following manner. The work having been turned as clean and smooth as possible, and rubbed with fine glass paper, as mentioned at page 1123, a thin rubber is made of three or four thicknesses of soft linen rag, merely laid over each other, and a few drops of the hard-wood lacker prepared as directed at page 1392, are placed on the center of the rag either by a brush, or by covering the mouth of the bottle with the rag and shaking them together; a single thickness of rag is then put over the lacker, and a drop or two of linseed oil is placed on the center of the rag immediately over the lacker.

The rubber is then applied with light friction over the entire surface of the work while revolving in the lathe, never allowing the hand or the mandrel to remain still for an instant, so as to spread the lacker as evenly as possible, especially at the commencement, and paying particular attention to the internal angles, so as to prevent either deficiency or excess of lacker at those parts. The oil in some degree retards the evaporation of the spirit from the lacker, and allows time for the process; it also presents a smooth surface, and lessens the friction against the tender gum. When the lacker appears dry, a second, third, or even further quantities of lacker are applied in the same manner, working, of course, more particularly upon those parts at all slighted in the earlier steps. After a little practice this will be found a quick and easy process, but when convenient it is always desirable to repeat the process after the expiration of a few days, as the lacker will by that time be partly absorbed, especially in the end grain of the wood, which is more porous, and should therefore receive a larger proportion of lacker in the first application.

For common works, the lacker and oil are frequently both placed on the same surface of rag. In this case the oil is first applied to the rag, and the lacker is then added; but this method, although more rapid, does not produce so even a surface as when the lacker is covered with a single thickness of oiled rag, through which the clearer portions alone percolate gradually.

French polish is applied to flat surfaces in nearly the same general manner as hardwood lacker is applied to turned works. As previously mentioned, the only difference between ordinary French polish and hardwood lacker is, that the former contains rather a larger proportion of spirit, which is adopted principally in order that the French polish may spread more easily, and dry less rapidly upon flat surfaces, which are generally larger than turned works, and, therefore, require more time in polishing, especially as the friction is derived exclusively from the motion of the hand.

The rubbers used in French polishing are made in a variety of methods, according to the fancy of the polisher, and the size is of course proportioned to that of the work, but they seldom exceed three inches diameter. The small cloth or list rubbers mentioned in Article 5, p. 1090, are very generally employed for French polishing, especially in laying on the first coat; and it is mostly preferred that the list should be torn off the cloth, as this makes the edge softer than if it were cut. Sometimes the rubber is covered with a piece of linen rag upon which the lacker is applied; at other times the rag is omitted, and the lower face of the rubber itself is saturated with lacker, in order to soften that which may remain in the rubber from previous use, and the excess is squeezed out before commencing the polishing. These rubbers often serve for several months' use.

At the opposite extreme of durability are the small rubbers, made of wadding, as mentioned in Art. 6, p. 1090, that are thrown away after a few minutes' use; but this is by many considered to be very wasteful, both of wadding and lacker, and they therefore adopt a medium course, and use one wadding rubber for five or six hours. In this case the wadding is first picked to loosen it thoroughly, and any knotted pieces are rejected; the wadding is then thoroughly saturated with the lacker, and squeezed moderately dry, so as to leave a quantity of lacker proportioned to the size of the work. The wadding is then placed in the middle of a piece of soft linen rag, which is gathered up at the back and tied. Sometimes a piece of sponge is used in the same manner; this forms a durable rubber, but of course it requires to be softened every time before use.

The choice of rubber, however, depends principally upon habit, and is nearly immaterial, provided the rubber is moderately soft, and contains a sufficient quantity of lacker to allow of its being gradually supplied to the work as the polishing progresses; but it is at all times necessary that the rubber should be covered with a piece of soft rag, moistened with a few drops of oil, and renewed as often as it becomes so far clogged up as to prevent the lacker passing freely through it, or that any portion of the lacker on the surface has become so hard as to be likely to scratch the half dry and tender polish.

The work having been thoroughly smoothed with fine glass paper, and the dust wiped away with a clean cloth, the polishing is commenced with free, continuous, and uniform circular strokes, applied with very light pressure, and gradually traversed over the whole surface; and the same process is continually repeated, varying the position of the strokes as much as possible, but keeping them about the same size, and taking care that every portion of the surface receives an equal but not excessive quantity of lacker, which is regulated partly by the degree of pressure on the rubber, and partly by squeezing it between the fingers.

The principal points requiring attention are, that the pressure is moderate and uniform, that the circular strokes are taken regularly over the whole surface, and that the rubber is never allowed to remain stationary on the work, or be *lifted* directly from it. Should the pressure be too great, it would be liable to disturb the smooth surface of the tender lacker already applied, and should the pressure or the strokes be irregular, a thicker coat of lacker would be given at some parts than at others. Should the rubber be allowed to remain stationary on the work, it would be liable to adhere to the surface, which would be injured on its removal, and the same injury would be liable to occur if the rubber were lifted directly from the surface, and therefore in removing the rubber it should be slid off at the sides or ends of the work, or if taken from the middle, it should be done with a sweeping stroke, so as to lift the rubber gradually while in motion. Circular strokes are adopted instead of straight strokes, partly because the grain of the wood is filled up quicker and more uniformly, but principally in order to avoid the blemishes which would be almost certain to occur at the end of every stroke taken backwards and forwards, unless the rubber were every time traversed entirely off the end of the work, which is not generally convenient.

The process of polishing is continued until the grain of the wood appears to be thoroughly filled up, and the surface exhibits a uniform appearance, well covered with a thin coat of lacker. It is then allowed to stand for an hour or two to become thoroughly hard, when it is rubbed with very fine glass-paper to smooth down all the irregularities of the grain of the wood, and also of the lacker. The polishing is then repeated, and if it should be found necessary it is again smoothed, and the polishing is persevered in until the surface appears quite smooth, and uniformly covered with a thin and tolerably bright coat of lacker, but which will nevertheless show cloudy marks from the rubber, owing to the presence of the oil, which is finally removed with a few drops of spirits of wine applied on a clean rubber and covered with a clean soft linen rag, with which the work is rubbed with very light strokes, applied first with a circular motion, and when the surface appears nearly dry, straight strokes are taken lengthways of the grain of the wood, and traversed

entirely off the ends of the work; this is continued until the
rubber and work are both quite dry, when the polishing will
be completed.

The polish, however, will be partly absorbed by the wood in
the course of a day or two; and therefore it is desirable to
repeat the process after the lapse of a few days, first slightly
rubbing down the former coat with very fine or nearly worn-out
glass-paper, as it is essential to a smooth and durable surface
that the ultimate body of polish should be as thin as possible.

The intricate parts of carved work that cannot be rubbed
smooth as explained, are varnished with white hard, or brown
hard varnishes, applied with the brush as usual; but the body of
varnish should be as thin as possible, particularly in the angles
and edges of delicate works, or otherwise the character of the
work will be greatly deteriorated. The brown hard varnish is
much harder than the white, and from its lesser transparency it
does not require quite so much care.

In India, a thin liquid balsam, obtained by incision from the
Dipterocarpus terminatus, and one or two other trees, is commonly known under the name wood-oil, and is extensively
employed as a varnish for general purposes, and also for the
Burmese cups and similar ware. For common purposes the varnish is laid on with a brush, as usual; but for the Burmese ware,
the second and subsequent coats of varnish are laid on and
smoothed with the naked hand, both in order to preserve a fine
surface and to enable the workman to discover and reject any
minute particles of dirt.   When first laid on, the varnish appears
of a light brown colour, but rubbing with the hand changes it
to a fine black.   When the articles have been varnished, they
are carefully shut up in a box to exclude the dust, and then
deposited in a deep cold vault for at least three days, which
treatment is said to be essential to the proper hardening of the
varnish.

The Burmese cups of small size are made of thin strips of
bamboo woven together like fine basket-work, and after the first

coat of varnish, the interstices of the basket-work are filled up with a paste, made of wood-oil mixed with different fine powders, such as calcined bones or very fine saw-dust from teak wood. After the paste is smoothed with the hand, the article is again returned to the cold vault, and when it is sufficiently hardened, the surface is smoothed with pumice stone and water; the cups are afterwards varnished three or four times, and finally polished after the same general methods as are adopted in this country for varnished works.

Sometimes the cups are ornamented with raised figures, which are made of the same paste that is used to fill up the interstices of the basket-work; the paste is pressed into tin moulds, and afterwards transferred to the bowls; when dry it becomes hard as solid wood. At other times the cups are ornamented with engraved designs, which are afterwards filled up with different coloured powders mixed with wood-oil, after which the surface is smoothed with wet bran held in the hollow of the hand; the operation is generally repeated to insure the complete filling up of all the lines, and the cups are afterwards varnished and polished as usual.

A very good varnish is prepared by the Moochees with shell-lac and wood-oil, heated and mixed in small quantities. They also prepare a varnish for palanquins by melting sandarach and mixing it with boiled linseed oil rendered drying with litharge, but they do not usually add spirits of turpentine in the manner generally adopted in England for making oil varnishes. To give the appearance of gold to the silver leaf used by the Candapilly Moochees for ornamenting boxes, palanquins, and similar objects, a little aloes is dissolved in the varnish, which is laid over it.

J. Rhode, Esq., of Madras, from whose notes the above particulars were gathered, says, " I know of no better or more durable polish, for teak or furniture woods, than may be prepared by melting three or four pieces of sandarach of the size of a walnut or small egg, and pouring upon it a bottleful of linseed oil rendered drying by litharge or other drier, and after boiling them together for an hour, gradually adding while cooling a teaspoonful of Venice turpentine. If too thick, it may be thinned with spirits of turpentine. It should be rubbed on the furniture, and after a little time, during which it may be exposed to the sun, rubbed off; the rubbing should be repeated daily, and the polish should not be again applied for eight or ten days, after which it may be slightly applied every one or two months. Water does not injure this polish, and any stain or scratch may be rubbed over with the polish, which cannot be done with French polish."

END OF THE THIRD VOLUME.

INDEX.

E E

THE END.

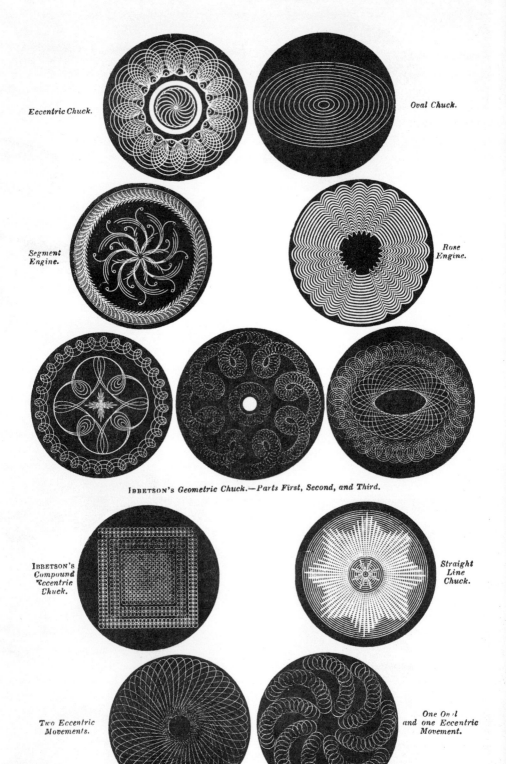

Eccentric Chuck.

Oval Chuck.

Segment Engine.

Rose Engine.

IBBETSON'S *Geometric Chuck.—Parts First, Second, and Third.*

IBBETSON'S Compound Eccentric Chuck.

Straight Line Chuck.

Two Eccentric Movements.

One Oval and one Eccentric Movement.

HOLTZAPFFEL & Co.'s *Compound Oval and Eccentric Chuck.*